AUSTRALIA AND THE PACIFIC ISLANDS

Photographs by

Stan and Kay Breeden

Michael Morcombe

Graham Pizzey

Gordon de'Lisle

Vincent Serventy

Robin Smith

Werner Stoy

Kenneth and Jean Bigwood

M. F. Soper

Derek Duparcq

and others

Maps by Kenneth Thompson

AUS
AND THE

by Allen Keast

Foreword by Alan Moorehead

A Chanticleer Press Edition

The Continents We Live On

TRALIA
PACIFIC ISLANDS

A NATURAL HISTORY

Random House · New York

Second Printing 1967

© 1966 by Random House, Inc.
Foreword © 1966 by Alan Moorehead

Planned and produced by Chanticleer Press, New York

Manufactured by Conzett & Huber in Zurich, Switzerland

Library of Congress Catalog Card Number 66:21843

Contents

Foreword

1.

Australia has never been a fashionable place—I mean fashionable in the sense that large numbers of people have been eager to visit it—nor, until recently, have many people wanted to settle there in the way that they once settled in their millions in America. The country contains no spectacular ruins, no ancient culture, and if you except the Barrier Reef and Ayers Rock no great natural spectacles like the Himalayas or the Niagara Falls.

And yet, as this book will show, it is in some respects the strangest and most interesting of all the continents, and to have seen it as it originally was before the white man arrived, less than 200 years ago, must have been like visiting another planet. One has only to follow the adventures of John Gilbert, one of the earliest and best of naturalists, to feel something of the wonder of the scene that then met the traveller's eye: aboriginal tribes that had had no contact whatever with the outside world, fascinating birds and animals that existed here and nowhere else, a native flora that was unique, and beyond all this a sense of very great antiquity, not of man, but of the earth itself.

There was, however, one great drawback to Australia which instantly impressed itself upon the first explorers: it was difficult if not impossible for a white man to live off the land. The country provided virtually no grain or fruit or vegetables that they cared to eat, and very little meat. The aborigines managed to scrape along on such articles as lizards and wild berries, and on the lower Murray they even had a sophisticated method of cooking an emu: it was roasted in an underground earthen oven with its head protruding, and when steam issued from its beak it was presumed to be done. But the European stomach flinched from such provender. All had to be imported. And so began the immense struggle to subdue the country, to Europeanise it, to convert it into something quite different from what it had been before. It is estimated that within the first 100 years of white occupation one third of the forests of New South Wales were cut down to make way for farms and grazing lands of imported grass upon which sheep, cattle and horses could thrive. In the same period 165 species of exotic plants were introduced (I am quoting from the eminent Australian authority, Sir A. Grenfell Price), and by 1892 even the humble European earthworm had found its way inland as far as the town of Bourke, which is over 400 miles from the coast.

Some of these importations spread with unbelievable virility on this virgin soil. When Governor Phillip came out from England with the First Fleet at the end of the 18th century he called in at Rio de Janeiro, and being in need of scarlet dye for his soldiers' coats, he there picked up some prickly pear plants—it is on these plants that the dye-producing cochineal insect lives. Later on the wild grey rabbit was imported. Prickly pear eventually over-ran sixty million acres of land, and the rabbit, which on mating can produce 13 million descendants every three years, became a national disaster. Both these plagues were brought under control—the prickly pear by the introduction of cactoblastis insects from the Argentine, and the rabbit by the spread of myxomatosis—but other less damaging importations still flourish; innumerable weeds such as box thorn, scotch thistle, and Paterson's Curse, and many such European birds as starlings, sparrows and blackbirds. Among the imported European animals that have also proliferated, some of them in plague proportions, are wild horses, indian buffaloes, wild pigs, dogs and cats, foxes, rats, and *Mus musculus,* the household mouse.

Meanwhile year by year the clearing of the bush continues, either by "pulling"—two tractors joined by a heavy chain wrench the scrub up by the roots—or, where the trees are large, by the simple device of ringbarking; the tree dies and is left standing, but since it no longer has any leaves grass can grow underneath. One can travel for many hours through these skeleton forests, and on the rising ground one sees how the sudden floods of the wet season have cut deep runnels and gorges into the earth. Through the summer there is much dust underfoot, and in high wind it fills the sky like the smoke of a forest fire.

Naturally the wildlife of Australia has fled before this invasion. The animals that were commercially valuable for their fur—the seals, for instance—were all but obliterated very early on, and small creatures lost their habitat. In New South Wales, it is estimated, forty-two per cent. of marsupial fauna is extinct or rare, while eleven species of a total of fifty-two are presumed extinct.

The kangaroo was first hunted with dogs for sport, and I would like to quote here a lively letter which Gilbert wrote on March 27, 1843, to his employer, John Gould, in England. The big male or "boomer," he says, was usually too heavy to escape from the dogs in open country: "Instead of running therefore, he will invariably turn round to face his pursuers, erecting himself to his full height, and, if possible, with his back supported against a tree, and thus awaits the approach and rush of the dogs, endeavouring to strike them with his powerful hind toe or in catching them in his arms, and while thus holding them, inflicts dreadful and often fatal wounds with its foot; old dogs well broken in, and well accustomed to keep a boomer at bay, never attempt to rush in, but by their barking keep the kangaroo stationary till the hunter comes up, who is in general provided with a short, heavy stick, when a blow or two on the head soon brings him down, but even the hunter often runs a risk, for a boomer will frequently, on the approach of a man, leave the dogs and attack him most furiously, and it is no easy matter at times to avoid being severely cut in effecting its death.

"Another common habit is taking to the water, and as the dogs approach, catching them in its arms and holding them beneath until drowned, and if driven into the water too shallow for this mode of drowning, it has been known to catch one dog, and place it beneath its feet, while courageously awaiting the approach of the second . . . it seems to summon up all its sleeping energy for a last struggle, and it would doubtless often come off victor if it had only dogs to contend with, but the moment it sees the approach of a man it appears instinctively to know that he is its most formidable opponent, its lips are twisted and contracted, its eyes become brilliant and almost starting from their sockets with rage, and its ears are in constant motion, accompanied by its peculiar, though not loud tone, a sort of smothered grunt, and half hiss, or hard breathing."

Such encounters are rare today when it is more usual to shoot the animals. The most effective method is to equip a truck with a powerful light and a repeating rifle and to catch the mobs when they are grazing at night. They stand stupefied in the glare of the light and can easily be wounded or killed by a marksman. In this way some millions of kangaroos—no one knows the exact figure—are destroyed, or at any rate maimed, every year. They are hunted partly because they eat the grasses which are wanted for sheep and cattle, and partly for their hides and their flesh, which is frozen and sold as dogs' and cats' meat. Around the eastern coastal areas the animal has now almost died out, and few Australians have ever seen one in a wild state.

Australia's other large wild animal, the salt-water crocodile, has fared even worse. It has been shot and netted to the point of extermination in the tropical northern rivers. Specimens of a smaller species known to the hunter as "stuffers" appear in the tourist shops after they have passed through the taxidermist's hands, and sometimes they are got up with tartan bonnets and clasp little golf sticks in their claws to give them an additional appeal.

So much for the animals. As for the wild aborigines, they vanished from the populated regions long ago, and only a few remain in the centre and the far north.

2.

All this sounds very dismal, but let the traveller—or the reader of these pages—not despair. Australia is an enormous country, a good deal larger than Europe, and there are still only between eleven and twelve million people living there. It is still possible for one to roam far beyond the settled areas and see many of the things Gilbert saw over a century ago. Even in the more heavily populated parts an effort is being made now to preserve the last of the wildlife, and a part at least of its natural habitat. In Victoria, for instance, there is a place named Tower Hill which has been made into a reserve. The land is denuded now, but they have a painting made, I think, by a French artist in the middle of last century, which shows the landscape as it was—miles of rolling hills covered with trees—and to that condition it is now being restored.

The visitor, however, must be warned that Australia is not a country that reveals itself very easily or dramatically, and it is certainly not picturesque. The distances are vast and you have to sweat it out over many dusty, thirsty miles to get to the interesting places. You must wait and listen quietly and accommodate your eyes to apparent nothingness, and then, little by little, an awareness of another world which is ante-diluvian, shy, infinitely subtle and sometimes a little sad, begins to penetrate the mind. Despite its superficial appearance of harshness—harshness of heat and light and outline—it is a gentle country. The aborigines were gentle people, and the kangaroo when it is not attacked is a very gentle animal. There are extraordinarily few predators here. The African ostrich is said to sleep only for a few minutes at a time, such is its fear of enemies. Its sister bird in Australia, the emu, will sleep for hours. The great wedge-tailed eagle is a predator with fanatically glaring eyes and a murderous hooked beak. It has a reputation for taking lambs, and once I watched one gliding in through the gum trees on Kangaroo Island in an attempt to snatch a twelve-pound koala from its perch. Yet I have also seen a young eagle in captivity behave with exquisite delicacy and love towards the man who looked after it. Indeed, it treated him as it might have treated another eagle—it ran that terrifying beak through his hair as gently as a ladies' hairdresser with a comb and it then caressed his cheeks.

Very few Australian creatures, not even the snakes, have any wish to harm you; they would much rather take you on trust. During the last drought, when they were shooting kangaroos by the tens of thousands in southern Queensland, I went for a walk one day along a dried-up river bed. After a while I sat down quietly on a rock to watch the parakeets going by in the evening light, and a young kangaroo slithered down the bank and joined me. He was aware of me but quite unafraid since I did nothing to scare him. There we sat side by side watching the parakeets and listening to the evening noises of the bush, and this might have gone on indefinitely but for the arrival of a willy wagtail. This wretched bird took one startled look at the scene and fluttered squawking around the kangaroo's head. Clearly it was saying, "You fool. Look out. That object there is dangerous." The kangaroo quickly turned its head towards me and then bounded away in panic.

It is the quietness and stillness of the land that is so intriguing once you get used to it. Nowhere else in the world can I remember this intense quality of timelessness, of acceptance of things as they are. In this dry air nothing grows or decays very rapidly, and changes take place with infinite slowness. The aborigines inhabited the continent for perhaps ten thousand years and saw no necessity in all that time to alter their way of life. Most incidents in the bush seem to occur against a background of silence and inanition. The kookaburra perches mutely for hours on the branch of a dead tree; then suddenly he swoops to the ground. When the bird rises in the air he will have a writhing snake in his strong beak and he will let it go so that it will fall and break its back. He may do this several times and then, satisfied that the snake is dead, he will start his meal. Similarly you may have to wait hours on the seashore before you see the oyster-catcher strike. Quick as an arrow he thrusts his flat beak between the unsuspecting limpet and the rock, and then in an instant the shell is levered on to its back. The bird's meal is over in a moment, and then uneventful time closes over the shore again; the waves lap on the beach, the bird once again stands motionless as stone, and nothing happens.

I once took a ten-day crash course on the muttonbirds of the Bass Strait islands, and my instructor was Dr. D. L. Serventy, who is the greatest living authority on that, to me, most interesting of all migratory birds. It was nesting time, and underground in the birds' burrows a teeming life was going on. Yet above ground there was no evidence of this—no noise, no smell, no mess—nothing but miles and miles of Poa tussocks being blown in the wind. An uninformed traveller might have gone by that coast and thought there was nothing there. Each night the sky was filled with the swishing of a million wings as the parents came in from the sea, but it was difficult actually to see them. One was simply conscious of a ghostly rustling in the air and of birds everywhere around one thrusting through the undergrowth on their way to their burrows. It was marvellous to think that the little fluffy grey chicks which were now gobbling down food from their parents' beaks would, in a month or two, be winging their way over Japanese seas and even further north.

Not everything of course happens in silence. There are noises in the bush and some of them are very odd. We have the lyre bird that can imitate any sound you like to make, and the gannet whose cry is said to resemble the noise made by the running out of a rusty anchor chain. And we have Gilbert telling us of the blue-billed duck whose notes have a peculiar "inward tone." The aborigines used to say that it had no voice but made a noise with its heart.

I remember too another time when I was with some friends on Fraser Island, off the coast of southern Queensland. We had gone there to look at the tropical rain forest, which in my experience (I have not been to Brazil) is one of the most spellbinding jungle growths in the world. One does not normally think of Australia in terms of slender eighty-foot palms with lianas trailing down, or of orchids sprouting out of the dank trunks of huge figtrees, or of tropical butterflies making stabs of colour in the hot green gloom below; but it is all there. In the afternoon we emerged into the sunshine again and drove our truck for twenty miles along an ocean beach to a fisherman's hut where we proposed to spend the night. The long swell of the Pacific broke incessantly on the shore and there were many seabirds about, but for the rest nothing disturbed the tranquillity of the evening.

I sat for a long time on the step of the hut, and just as the light was failing I saw the shapes of three wild horses—one white, the others bay—detaching themselves from the trees. They moved in line very quietly and sedately down the beach, stopped when they picked up my smell and caught sight of me sitting there, and then, deciding it was safe, came on again. When they reached the edge of the sea each animal —and I swear wild horses have a special grace—lifted up a foreleg and began elegantly scraping a hole in the sand. Later on I found out why they were doing this—they wanted to drink the brackish water that seeped into the holes as they dug—but just at that moment it was nature transferred into art, and the mind flew away to the Arc du Carrousel in Paris and that other equine group, gold as these horses were gold in the setting sun, on top of St. Mark's in Venice.

3.

One could go on indefinitely recalling scenes just as evocative as this and all entirely different, but I fancy I can better serve the reader by telling him what I should try and do if I were making a trip to Australia and was equipped with stamina and a fair amount of money. I should land in Darwin in the north in July, and proceed at once in a solid vehicle to the swamps of Arnhem Land to observe the tropical and nomadic birds and the wild buffaloes, and perhaps see something of the remaining aborigines. Next I would make for the red centre of the continent, a thousand miles away to the south, not necessarily to the one town there, Alice Springs, but at all events to the desert, preferably Sturt's Stony Desert where the salt pans are white, and the sand ridges are red and the sky is forever blue. Once again to look at the birds—and they really are unbelievable in their plumage, their numbers and their variety—I would camp beside a waterhole in some dry river like the Cooper, and I would expect the day to begin and end with an explosion of colour from the sun.

Then in August, which is still winter, I would make northeast to the coast of tropical Queensland and take a boat out to the coral islands of the Barrier Reef. There would be fresh fish for dinner every night, and perhaps a week might go by before the eye would tire of gazing at that scintillating maze of coral. Then in September with the spring approaching I would head south, pausing in some rain forest on the way, and observing from a low-flying plane that incredible coast where, for hundreds of miles, the bush comes down to rocky headlands and deserted beaches of yellow sand, with the long slow swell of the Pacific forever breaking on the shore. The green water gleams and sparkles as it falls. In New South Wales I would visit a sheep or a cattle station and hope to see a kangaroo or two, and then continue south again to Victoria where, at sanctuaries like Phillip Island and the Mackenzie Reserve outside Melbourne I would be able, as it were, to get a close-up of the wildlife: the koala, the duck-billed platypus, the seals and penguins, and the multi-hued parrots and cockatoos. October would find me moving west, and I would try somehow to get a flight along the 400-foot cliffs of the Great Australian Bight where the icy waves of the Southern Ocean sweep in from the Pole. My trip would come to an end among the wildflowers and the giant karri forests of Western Australia.

That would be an ambitious and perhaps tiring journey but very rewarding. Very few people have ever done it.

Let me add just a brief note about New Zealand and the islands of the South Pacific. Australasia—Oceania—"the lands that lie southeast of Asia," according to my dictionary—never has been a coherent political unity. One almost suspects that the map-makers found it a convenience to get rid of all this vast space by lumping it together, usually at the end of the atlas. Until the Second World War Australians did not consider themselves as Pacific people at all, but rather an extension of the United Kingdom. After the war they felt more closely drawn to America, and now we are beginning to see a new movement: considerable trade has started with China and Japan, people go to the islands for their holidays, and New Guinea has become very much an appendage of Australia. Australasia (or Oceania) is becoming a political reality at last.

In other respects great differences continue to exist, indeed you might almost say that what is lacking in Australia is to be found in New Zealand and the islands. New Zealand, for example, has her volcanoes, her fiords and great mountains, and in the islands there are still traces of a fairly sophisticated culture that existed before the white man came. The Maoris of New Zealand, in contrast with the aborigines of Australia, have managed to achieve co-existence with the whites, and in the warmer islands where there are no hard outlines, no deserts, no vast spaces except the boundless ocean itself, it is still possible to live the soft and sensuous life of popular South Pacific legend. For a northerner it can be a constricting life if he stays too long, but for the visitor it has compulsive charms. The girls with flowers in their hair are still there and so are the dancing and the drums.

So then (to take up my itinerary again) I would advise the traveller to proceed much as this book proceeds: that is to say he should start his journey in Australia and then go on to New Zealand and the islands. In this way he will feel himself moving not only in distance but in time as well—from ancient rocks and the silent past to the green and lively present.

Just how long all the things that are described here in Professor Keast's excellent text are going to stay the same is anybody's guess. There have been tremendous changes in Australasia since Captain Cook first arrived in the Pacific two centuries ago. But enough at least remains unspoiled for the traveller—or indeed for the reader of this book—to feel that he is in touch with the mysterious beginnings of things in a part of the world that is still very little known.

ALAN MOOREHEAD

Acknowledgments

The following specialists were kind enough to check chapters of the book: Dr. Dean Amadon, Chairman, Department of Birds, American Museum of Natural History, New York (Chapter 10); Harold Cogger, Curator of Reptiles, Australian Museum, Sydney (Chapter 12); Prof. H. Barraclough Fell, Museum of Comparative Zoology, Harvard University (Chapters 13 and 14); Dr. J. Linsley Gressitt, Entomologist and Head of Pacific Survey, Bernice P. Bishop Museum, Honolulu (Chapter 10); K. A. Hindwood, Past President, Royal Australasian Ornithologists' Union and Honorary Ornithologist, Australian Museum, Sydney (Chapters 1 and 5); and Arnold R. McGill, Assistant Editor and Past President, Royal Australasian Ornithologists' Union (Chapters 4 and 6); Miss Elizabeth Pope, Curator of Marine Invertebrates, Australian Museum, Sydney (Chapters 7, 11, and part of 3); Dr. Austin Rand, Chairman, Department of Birds, Chicago Natural History Museum (Chapter 12); Dr. D. L. Serventy, Head of Western Division, Wild Life Survey, Commonwealth Scientific and Industrial Research Organization, Perth (Chapters 2, 8, and parts of 3 and 7); M. S. R. Sharland, former Director of National Parks, Tasmania (Chapter 3); Norman Tindale, Honorary Anthropologist and Entomologist, and former Acting Director, South Australian Museum, Adelaide (Chapter 9). I should like to express my sincere thanks to these people. The New Zealand Government Information Service in Wellington and New York was extremely kind, as was the Australian News and Information Bureau in New York.

In addition, various authorities advised on specific points; A. H. Chisholm, Editor, *The Australian Encyclopaedia;* Leonard J. Brass and Hobart van Deusen, Archbold Expeditions of the American Museum of Natural History; Dr. Alfred M. Bailey, Director, Denver Museum; and Dr. Stephen Davies of the Commonwealth Scientific and Industrial Research Organization.

I am also indebted to the many other individuals with whom I have discussed ideas and shared experiences in the field.

I should also like to express my thanks to the two members of the staff of Chanticleer Press with whom I worked in the preparation of the book. The thorough editing of Milton Rugoff was invaluable, as was his facility for clear exposition and finding the right turn of phrase. Ann Guilfoyle, picture editor, had, among many other duties, the task of gathering all the illustrative material. Throughout, she showed the greatest dedication. It was a pleasure to work with both of them.

ALLEN KEAST

Australia: Island Continent

This book is about islands: Australia, the island continent, and the continental remnants, volcanic peaks, and atolls that stud the southern and eastern Pacific. The scenic diversity of this area of tens of thousands of square miles is overwhelming. Australia conjures up visions of kangaroos on endless grassy plains, tall eucalypt forests, quiet rivers where the platypus plays, hot days and white ocean beaches, the Great Barrier Reef, laughing kookaburras and caroling magpies, and red deserts. New Zealand is famous for its deep fjords and snow-covered peaks, Hawaii for its tropical luxuriance and fiery volcanoes, and Tahiti and the Tuomotos for their azure seas and palm-fringed shorelines. Some of the Australo-Pacific landscapes are so ancient geologically that they antedate all animal life, and some of the islands are so recent that they are only now being colonized by plants and animals. This part of the world is bathed in perpetual sun, but only the Melanesian islands are oppressively tropical. Most of the region knows nothing of the harshness of northern winters; the trees keep their leaves all year and few of the birds migrate.

THE AUSTRALASIAN REGION

Australia and the Pacific Islands constitute one of the truly distinct biological regions of the world. The Australian flora and fauna are more different from the Asian than the latter is from the flora and fauna of Africa or the northern continents. This is the result of a long history of geographic isolation, for Australia has been cut off by sea since at least the beginning of the Tertiary geological period, that is, for at least fifty million years. During this time certain forms of life that reached the continent were able to develop and proliferate into all manner of variations: leaping kangaroos, woolly koalas, gliding possums, the wolflike thylacine, lyrebirds, cockatoos and emus, huge goannas and small, snakelike, legless lizards, eucalypts, tea trees, and gnarled banksia trees.

At the same time the sea protected many primitive forms of life, preserving them as "living fossils." Among these are the egg-laying mammals—the platypus and echidna—furred animals that have the reproductive system of a reptile, the lung fish *(Neoceratodus)*, whose ancestors flourished widely in the Devonian geological period, over three hundred million years ago, and New Zealand's curious reptile, the tuatara, a contemporary of the dinosaurs. But, again, through the ages there has been a continuing trickle of life forms down the Indonesian island chain into Australia, forms that could fly or swim, or survive long periods of drifting on logs or tree trunks. To this means of entry Australia owes its bats and rodents, many of its shoreline trees, and its small quota of fangless colubrid snakes. But it is isolation that has given the Australian landscape its distinctive character and kept it free of many of the violent evolutionary surges of other continents. This extends even to man, for the Australian aborigine is a nomadic Stone-Age hunter who knows no agriculture. Until European times he reigned supreme over his Australian domain, thousands of years after his contemporaries in India and Malaysia had been overrun and absorbed by more warlike and culturally advanced peoples.

Considering the string of islands between Australia and Asia, it is at first surprising that the faunas of the two land masses are so distinct. In his detailed study of these islands as long ago as 1850, Alfred Russel Wallace, the great authority on the distribution of animals, made the astounding discovery that the islands as far eastward as Borneo and Java had a typically Asian fauna, whereas the Celebes and Lombok, little more than twenty miles from Borneo and Bali respectively, were populated mostly by Australian types. Thus, on the one hand, there were monkeys, squirrels, deer, rhinoceroses, shrews, cats, barbets, and toucans in the eastern islands and, on the other, cuscuses (an arboreal marsupial), cockatoos, and honeyeaters farther west. The narrow north-south strait that separates Borneo and Java from the Celebes and Lombok, one of the sharpest dividing lines in the fauna of the world, came to be known as Wallace's Line. We now know that Borneo and Java lie on the Asian continental shelf, and so must have been in contact with that continent when, on at least three occasions during the last million years, the great ice ages of the northern hemisphere lowered the sea level of the Pacific by as much as three hundred feet. Celebes, Lombok, and the other islands in eastern Indonesia, by contrast, lie in what has long been a zone of great geological instability. The sea is very deep here, but changes in the earth's crust have from time to time drastically altered the disposition of land. Many islands have come and gone, and some islands are relatively recent.

Again, as living areas, the present-day islands do not provide such a diversity of living conditions as do the larger land areas to the west and east. Later studies have shown that Wallace's Line is not the absolute barrier it was at first believed to be: the change-over from Asian to Australian kinds of life has been found to be progressive along the island chain. Nevertheless, Indonesia has always been the bottleneck that

Rare desert showers produce a carpet of wildflowers within a week or two. In the background Mount Connor rises from the sand plain. (Janet Finch)

restricted, or prevented, the primitive life forms of Australia from being overrun by more advanced ones from the west.

THE AUSTRALIAN CONTINENT

Australia has a land mass of 2,900,000 square miles, almost as large as that of the United States. It is the flattest of all the continents, less than half of it more than one thousand feet above sea level, and only 5 per cent exceeding two thousand feet. The highest peak, Mount Koskiusko, is only 7,308 feet.

The continent falls into three sections physiographically. The Great Western Plateau or Shield, mostly between one thousand and two thousand feet above sea level, covers the western half. This area includes considerable expanses of ancient rock, laid down in the Archaeozoic and Proterozoic periods, long before the first animals appeared on the earth. This rock is as old as any in the world. The Central Eastern Lowlands occupy a broad tract from the Gulf of Carpentaria to the Southern Ocean. This area was under the sea for much of the Cretaceous geological period (estimated at having extended from 120 down to 70 millions of years ago); it seems the continent was then probably severed into western and eastern parts. Much of this segment is less than eight hundred feet above sea level today and the Great Artesian Basin underlies it. Most of the Australian dinosaur fossils have been found in this area. The Eastern Highlands extend in a great arc parallel to the coast from north Queensland to Tasmania and western Victoria. This segment is narrow in the north and up to three hundred miles wide in the south. It is made up of a mixture of ancient Palaeozoic and more recent rocks deposited in a huge geosyncline, or bulge, of the earth's crust. The area of the Eastern Highlands has been subject to successive periods of folding, elevation, warping, and erosion.

A PREVALENCE OF DRYNESS

Dryness dominates the Australian continent. With an annual rainfall of ten inches or less, the vast central area is arid. Measured outward, the rainfall pattern is one of increasingly wet concentric zones. The northeastern, eastern, southeastern and southwestern coastal areas, and Tasmania to the south, are well watered. Here where the tall eucalypt forests grow, the average annual rainfall is from thirty to sixty inches per year. The northwest coast of the continent has a reasonably high rainfall but all the rain falls in the hot summer months so that it is not nearly so effective for plant growth. Agriculturists have classified Australia as one-third arid, that is, unsuitable for any form of land use, and one-third semi-arid, suitable only for pastoral use. This means that only the remainder is sufficiently well watered to support agriculture.

Rainfall dictates the distribution of the various vegetation types. The central sand deserts are alternately covered with extensive tracts of mulga (one of the acacias) and with clumps of spiny spinifex grass. To the south of this area, on the same kind of soil, and extending in a broad belt from east to west, is mallee, consisting of sapling-sized eucalypts with multiple trunks, intermixed with low acacias and spinifex. Grassland dotted with trees singly or in clusters forms a wide arc around the desert to the east and north. Intermediate between the grassland and the coastal forests in the east is savanna woodland, a continuous parklike growth of trees with a grassy substratum. The whole of the northern coastal region of the continent is covered by such woodland. As noted, forests are confined to the coastal regions of the east and south, and cover most of Tasmania. Tropical rain forest, limited to a series of small pockets down the northeast and east, close to the sea, requires high rainfall as well as rich soil. It covers great areas in New Guinea.

ISLAND PLANTS AND ANIMALS

The islands of the Pacific are of three types: continental remnants, volcanic islands, and coral islands, many of which have the characteristically circular atoll shape. Among those that are either certainly, or probably, continental remnants are New Guinea, which is on the same continental shelf as Australia and has repeatedly been joined to it in the past, New Zealand, New Caledonia, Lord Howe Island, the Solomons, the New Hebrides, Fiji, and some of the subantarctic islands such as Campbell Island.

Volcanic islands are scattered widely through the area. They include the Hawaiian chain, the Galapagos, Tahiti and the other Society Islands, the Marquesas, the southern Cook Islands, and Samoa.

Atolls also have a wide distribution. East of Tahiti is the great Tuamotu Archipelago while other groups compose the Gilbert Islands and northern Cook Islands.

As will be shown, island flora and fauna are of great interest in several ways. Insularity has given them distinctness. Primitive kinds of life are able to persist, e. g., the tuatara and the kiwi of New Zealand. But the farther one gets from the larger land masses, the more impoverished the island fauna becomes, since the number of species that can colonize across water is limited. In the absence of competitors, animal groups may change their characteristic ways of life to some extent: for example, in New Zealand, which lacks mammals, many birds have become flightless and some take on roles that might ordinarily be the property of mammals. No such trend is, of course, seen in New Guinea, which, lying close to Australia and being tropical, has a fauna and flora that resembles and is sometimes even richer than that of the continent itself.

This sheltered pandanus-framed watercourse typifies many freshwater streams in the coastal fringes of the Northern Territory. (Gordon de'Lisle)

Gum Trees, Bowerbirds, and Koalas

The Southeastern Forests and Highlands

1 As one approaches eastern Australia by jet aircraft, the tall coastal cliffs are the first part of the continent to appear on the horizon. Then the plane turns south, follows the alternating headlands and yellow beaches, and swings in a wide arc across the crowded metropolis of Sydney with its two million people. The landing is made at an airport on the shores of historic Botany Bay. The bay, a wide, almost circular inlet, its narrow entrance guarded by a pair of bluffs, is in many ways Australia itself. Here, on April 29, 1770, Captain James Cook cast anchor and set in train a series of events that led to the founding, a mere eighteen years later, of Australia.

At Botany Bay, European man had at last reached the fertile east coast of the continent. There was none of the horror experienced by the discoverer of Australia, Dirk Hartog, when he landed on the arid west coast in 1616, or the dismay of a score of subsequent navigators when, en route from the Cape of Good Hope to Java, they were driven to Australia by the fickle trade winds. Cook's task was to discover and map the eastern limits of the "Great Southern Continent," hitherto known only from its western and southern parts. This he did with such skill that most of his charts have not been faulted to this day. And the focal point of his discoveries, the place where he finally landed and rested at the end of his two-month voyage from New Zealand, was Botany Bay.

Botany Bay, so named because of its interesting flora, is of scientific as well as historic importance, for here Australian natural history had its beginnings. Cook's expedition had scientific aims, and the crew included the botanist Daniel Solander and (Sir) Joseph Banks, a famous patron of the sciences. In the eight days that Cook remained in the bay, hundreds of plant specimens were collected, many on the sandy Kurnell Peninsula, adjacent to the southern headland. Included in these were some of the unique plants of the continent: shrubs with huge, oval, yellow flower heads, later named *Banksia* after their discoverer, the flowering branches of gum trees and acacias, the red-flowering vine *Kennedya*, the pink-flowering *Darwinia*, and the gnarled shrub *Isopogon*. These, along with many boxes of insects and other specimens, are still available for study in London. The paintings of striking plants by the artist aboard the H. M. S. *Endeavour* are as fine and accurate as any ever done of those species.

FROM BOTANY BAY TO THE BLUE MOUNTAINS

A good way to appreciate what the forested eastern section of Australia is like is to follow a transect inland from Botany Bay or Sydney across the Hawkesbury plain to the west, and up into the Blue Mountains, that part of the adjacent Great Divide. This trip is also fascinating from the historical viewpoint, for it was the route taken by the first explorers after the settlement in 1788. The old travelers found the going easy until the foothills were reached. Then the mountain scarp with its precipitous cliffs and deep valleys presented a formidable barrier. It was twenty-five years before Blaxland, Lawson, and Wentworth were to reach the top of the range and gaze across rolling plains that extend, seemingly endlessly, to the Indian Ocean two thousand miles to the west.

Botany Bay, wide and shallow, lacks the high hillsides that make the adjoining Sydney Harbor one of the most beautiful and striking inlets of the world. Like the latter, however, it is drowned land, a result of the flooding of the coastline that followed the melting of the glaciers at the end of the ice ages. But the two differ, geologists tell us, in that shallow Botany Bay represents an old coastal plain or valley that was already silted up when "drowned," whereas the rather fjordlike Port Jackson (Sydney Harbor) was a young valley deeply gouged out by a strongly flowing river system.

Botany Bay, around whose foreshores the writer roamed during his boyhood, has mostly a coastal and sand-dune flora, some shallow fresh-water swamps, and sections of mangrove-fringed shoreline. On the higher ground, where the soil becomes richer, there must once have been fine stands of eucalypts like those that today cover the Royal National Park, a few miles to the south.

The Botany Swamps, Sydney's water supply during its early phase, have been partly drained today. But still, in spring, their reedbeds ring with the melodious song of the reed warbler *(Acrocephalus australis)*, the plaintive notes of the little grassbird *(Megalurus gramineus)*, the cluckings of the moor hens *(Gallinula tenebrosa)*, and the quackings of the black duck *(Anas superciliosa)*, white-eyed duck *(Nyroca australis)*, and gray teal *(Anas gibberifrons)*. In the early morning the black swans *(Cygnus atratus)* move majestically over the clear water and the blue-chested, red-legged swamp hen *(Porphyrio melanotus)* defies the traffic by emerging to pluck at grass by the roadside. Adjacent to the swamps, the mudflats of Botany Bay are the summer feeding grounds of thousands of migratory wading birds from the Arctic.

The stunted vegetation that graces the seaward side of Botany Bay and extends for hundreds of miles north and south along the east coast of the continent is commonly known as heathland. It owes its character to the rather

The Three Sisters, Echo Point, Katoomba. In the background is a typical Blue Mountain valley, the Jamieson, with steep sides of multicolored sandstone and dense vegetation at the bottom. (Robin Smith)

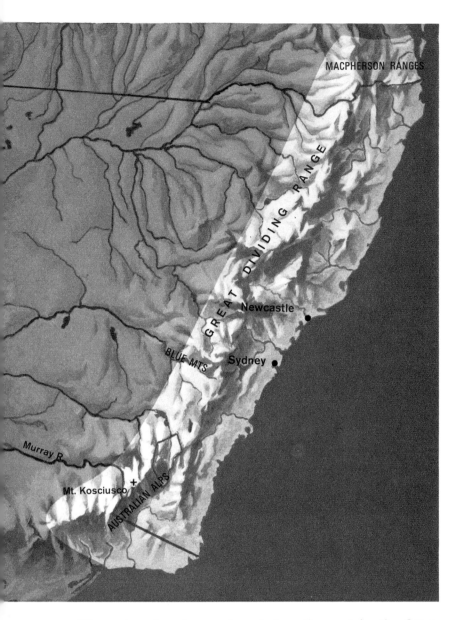

The eastern forest zone, bounded on the west by the Great Divide and on the east by the sea, is one of the most fertile sections of the continent.

grass tree, *Xanthorrhoea,* whose flower spikes project upward for some five to eight feet above a basal mass of grasslike leaves. Grass trees, whose origin goes back many millions of years, are a source of nectar for various kinds of birds, including the little nectar-feeding parrots known as lorikeets. When these trees are burned, a resin results that the aborigines formerly used for affixing the heads of spears to shafts. As interesting as the spectacular grass tree is the insect-eating plant *Drosera,* which is only a few inches tall but has sticky hairs that trap and help digest its prey. It grows along creeks or wherever drainage is impeded.

Several bird species are peculiar to the heathlands. The bleaker and more wind-swept areas are the home of the tawny-crowned honeyeater *(Gliciphila melanops),* a bird whose flutelike notes have a ventriloquial and almost ethereal quality. On the heathlands in spring I have often watched the aerial courtship flights of these birds. I found one nest low down in the middle of a clump of red spiderflowers. The New Holland honeyeater *(Phylidonyris novae-hollandiae)* is invariably more numerous than the tawny-crown, and much more noisy. By contrast, the heathland shelters two rather secretive, little, wrenlike birds, the tiny emu wren *(Stipiturus malachurus),* so called because the filamentary tail feathers resemble the plumes of an emu, and the heath wren *(Hylacola pyrrhopygia),* a splendid mimic.

Nectar feeding is basic to perhaps ninety species of Australian birds. Some of the best nectar-producing eucalypts occur in the rather impoverished soils alongside the sea, with the swamp mahogany and bastard mahogany near Sydney pre-eminent in this respect. The nectar flow varies greatly from year to year; these trees flower in winter, and in a peak year they attract nectar-loving birds from far and near. Some four kinds of little lorikeets, or honey parrots, and up to ten different kinds of honeyeaters come to the trees. On such occasions, the loud medley of song and the brilliant colors of the parrots leave a vivid memory.

THE FORESTS OF EASTERN AUSTRALIA

Leaving for the moment the path of the explorers, let us take a broader look at the forests of Australia. To start with, forest is relatively rare in Australia: it covers only 2 per cent of the country, compared with 38 per cent in Canada, 59 per cent in Japan, and 20 per cent in New Zealand. It forms a narrow belt, mainly between the mountains and the sea, in the east and south of the continent. There are patches of it in northern Queensland, but the continuous belt stretches from the Bunya Mountains in southern Queensland to the Grampians in western Victoria. There are outliers in the Mount Lofty Ranges of the Adelaide area and in the southwest corner of the continent. Much of Tasmania is forested. Despite its limited extent, however, the forested segment of Australia shelters many of the more interesting and striking forms of life.

The dominant tree of the Australian forest is the gum tree

impoverished soil, which is stony, sandy, and too porous to hold water for long. But the number of plant species found there is great, and in September the wild flowers are a pleasure to behold. Common plants collected by Banks and Solander were the small shrub *Callistemon,* which prefers damp places and has large red blossoms called bottlebrushes. Of the several banksias, *Banksia ericifolia* is the most spectacular, and it is always alive with the nectar-feeding New Holland honeyeater, which makes the air ring with its melodious notes. Closer to the ground are dense masses of pink *Boronia (B. latifolia)* and native rose *(B. serrulata).* Alternating with the splashes of pink are the yellow pea flowers, such as *Dillwynia,* various species of *Grevillea,* with flowers that are red, pink, gray, or white, depending on the species.

There are also various heaths, especially *Epacris microphylla,* with its spikes of tiny white flowers. A plant that adds a somewhat bizarre touch to the landscape is the spectacular

The koala (Phascolarctos cinereus), *Australia's most attractive small animal, eats only the foliage of gum trees. Until protected they were slaughtered in the hundreds of thousands for their pelts. (Stan and Kay Breeden)*

or eucalypt, of which there are no less than five hundred species. Only some of these species are true forest trees, but many of the more striking types belong to this region. Under forest conditions few species of these evergreens are less than fifty feet in height. They have straight trunks and are crowned by a rather sparse or open canopy confined to the upper parts. In many species the older trees have a gnarled and somewhat battered appearance, due in part to natural growth patterns but also to branches that have broken off and left rounded knobs. When trunks and branches are hollow they are used for roosting by possums and for nesting by birds. The foliage of the gum tree appears to be a rather drab blue- or gray-green, especially when compared with the vivid light green of the trees of the northern hemisphere. The leaves are long, narrow, and shiny, and tend to hang with their broad faces away from the hot sun. When new leaves appear they may be either pale green or reddish, but they soon assume the hue of the mature leaf.

Gum trees are somewhat erratic in their flowering, but once in blossom they rank with the beautiful flowering trees of the world. Most have white blossoms, but in the southwest of the continent there are red-, orange-, and yellow-flowering species in unusual abundance. A flowering gum tree is the gathering place for hosts of nectar-seeking birds and insects; a human observer cannot help noting the heavy sweetness of the pollen in the air and the vitality of the movements of the creatures in the tree.

The Californian, South African, or Middle Easterner, accustomed to the small tracts of gum trees planted by man in his country, can hardly appreciate the diversity and magnificence of the forest eucalypts of eastern Australia. In the more southern parts, Gippsland and the Otways, and in Tasmania, are tall stands of mountain ash *(Eucalyptus regnans)*, magnificent, white-trunked trees that rise up to three hundred feet and may be several feet across at the base. Mountain ash vie with the California redwoods for the honor of being the world's tallest trees. In the deep coastal valleys of New South Wales the huge blue gums *(E. deanei and E. saligna)* grow; one of the most spectacular of the remaining stands of these is found in the Grose River Valley in the Blue Mountains. A favorite trail of hikers is the precipitous track over Govett's Leap near Blackheath and through the dense undergrowth of the valley floor to the Blue Gum Forest. Fortunately this haven is likely to remain inviolate for a long time since it is a sanctuary, the terrain is too rugged for loggers, and the narrowness of the valley is a natural protection against bush fires.

Botanists call the eucalypt forests of Australia sclerophyll (literally, hard leaf) forests to distinguish them from rain forests. The leaves of these trees are long and slender and have a thick cuticle, and are thus able to withstand dryness and strong sunlight. The trees do not shed these leaves even during the worst droughts. Rain-forest trees, by contrast, commonly have large, broad leaves, with a maximum surface area for chlorophyll synthesis. Drought is unknown in rain forests, but should conditions become excessively dry, such leaves would shrivel and die.

Easily recognizable eucalypts are the shaggy stringybarks, whose fibrous bark can be pulled off in shreds, and the ironbarks, whose bark is hard and ridged. The bark of many gums comes off, seasonally, in flakes, but an axe is needed to remove that of the ironbark. Another interesting species is the scribbly gum, a small tree that inhabits areas of impoverished soil. Its smooth yellow or gray bark is etched with curious zigzag markings made by bark insects.

A distinctive tree in the sandstone country near Sydney is a large, spreading species with smooth pink bark, gnarled branches, and great knobby protuberances on the upper parts of the trunk. This tree, which is not a eucalypt but a close relative, the angophora *(Angophora costata)*, stands out in the various coastal parks.

Though eucalypts dominate the Australian sclerophyll forests, casuarinas, or she-oaks, with knobby trunks and drooping, needlelike foliage are prominent, especially along rivers. Turpentines are common here and there. Acacias, or wattles, are numerous, but most of the forest species are small; since, however, there are autumn, winter, spring, and summer flowering species, their abundant pale yellow blooms do much to enliven the forests. In fact, so striking is the late-winter flowering of the wattles that on the first of August Wattle Day is celebrated in the schools of New South Wales.

The shrubby sublayer in sclerophyll forest is one of its main distinguishing characteristics. By contrast, the continuous canopy of rain forest precludes the growth of shrubs, and woodland is characterized by a grassy substratum. The forest shrubs are at their most colorful in spring. Then the waratah *(Telopea)*, with its five-inch-wide flower head of brilliant crimson, justifies its choice as the state flower of New South Wales, and the banksias, the wattles, the multicolored grevilleas, the pink boronias and aeriostemons, and the yellow peas like *Dillwynia, Pultenaea,* and *Gompholobium* splash the lower levels of the forest with brilliant color.

THE KOALA

The Australian sclerophyll forests have a very distinctive animal life. In fact, some zoologists have divided the continent into three faunal provinces or zoogeographic subregions. A special name, the Bassian subregion, distinguishes the forested section, the others being the dry interior of the continent (Eyrean subregion) and the tropical north (Torresian subregion).

Many of the forms of life confined to the Bassian province have obviously had a long period of evolution there. Thus, among the furred animals, we have the greater glider *(Schoinobates volans)*, a dark brown phalanger with a three-foot wingspan that enables it to volplane for distances of up to 150 yards. There is the gray or forester kangaroo *(Macropus giganteus)*. Pretty, spotted, marsupial carnivores called native cats *(Dasyurus quoll)* and tiger cats *(Dasyurops maculatus)* hunt their prey after dark around rocks and the forest floor. Here too are tiny so-called marsupial mice, such as *Antechinus flavipes*. Long-snouted bandicoots "fossick" and dig for subterranean grubs. And in the trees are dainty, prehensile-tailed leaf-eaters like the ring-tailed possum *(Pseudocheirus)*. No forest inhabitant, however, is so well known and popular

Belmore Falls near Robertson, N.S.W., drops from a eucalyptus-covered plateau into a gully floored with moss-covered rocks, ferns and clumps of temperate rain forest trees. (Robin Smith)

as the marsupial bear—the koala *(Phascolarctos cinereus).*

The koala is a short—about two-and-a-half feet long—round-bodied, tree-dwelling animal, with large ears and long, woolly fur. Its softness, sleepy eyes, and tranquil disposition have made it a universal favorite, so that many reserves have been set aside for it; any game park having a few koalas is assured of good attendance. Alas, it was not always so. Common throughout Australian forests in the early days of settlement, it was slaughtered in the hundreds of thousands for its fur (an animal that just sits on a branch and stares is easy game), or it died off in epidemics until it was all but exterminated. Thus, from a population that permitted the taking of two million pelts as recently as 1924, and six hundred thousand in 1927, its numbers have fallen to perhaps several thousand. We do not know exactly how many koalas there are today, but heartening news came from a recent survey by the New South Wales Fauna Protection Panel that many small pockets of koalas exist in widely scattered localities. One of these, interestingly enough, is in the Palm Beach–Avalon area, an outer suburb of Sydney.

The koala has one of the most specialized diets of any animal in the world—the leaves of less than a dozen species of eucalypts. This is why, in contrast to kangaroos, black swans, and some of the other Australian animal celebrities, koalas are not found in zoos outside their native land. The koala is literally bound to the gum trees of Australia.

With its long claws and granulated palm- and sole-pads, the koala is well-fitted for climbing. Its whole life is spent in the trees, feeding on tender shoots when hungry, dozing in the branches when sleepy. *Koala* is an Australian aboriginal term and is said to mean "no drink," a reference to the creature's ability to get along without surface water. Nevertheless, captive koalas have been observed drinking water. They descend to the ground to get from one tree to another and there are even reports that they have been seen swimming.

Koalas eat an estimated two-and-a-half pounds of leaves per day, processing them with the aid of an appendix from six to eight feet long! They breed at about three years of age, and thereafter apparently on alternate years. Only a single young one is born. Koalas commonly live to twelve and occasionally to as much as twenty years. In former times the aborigines esteemed them as food, but otherwise their only enemies were probably an occasional eagle and large owls.

In eastern New South Wales, koalas mate between November and February. The tiny embryo leaves the womb when it is about thirty-two to thirty-five days old, and makes its way upward, as do the young of other marsupials, to the mother's pouch. Once inside the pouch it fastens itself to a teat. It takes a few months before fur appears and the eyes open. Then, at about the age of six months, between June and August, the youngster will make its first appearance, leaving the pouch to test out its claws and feet on the branches round about. It is then six to seven inches long, and so appealing that ladies seeing it in a zoo must be almost forcibly restrained from climbing into the cage to pat it. For the following three to four weeks the baby spends less and less time in the pouch, finally leaving it in August or September. Its wanderings become more extensive, but when lonely or tired it climbs up on mother's back. In zoos, where several females with young are often kept in the same enclosure, a cub sometimes goes to the wrong mother. Still, the disposition of the koala is such that neither mother nor young seems disturbed unless, as I

once saw happen, two young try to clamber onto the same parent. No hostility was evident, only what appeared to be a surprised bewilderment on the part of the mother when her knees suddenly buckled.

Koalas are not often seen in the wild today, but there are probably more of them than meet the eye, especially in the remote forest areas. The first wild koala I saw was in the Macpherson Range in southern Queensland. Despite the fact that it was suffering from a huge tick on its side, its capture and the removal of the offending parasite was no easy task. Where koalas are still found near human communities they can occasionally be seen slowly crossing roads, to the complete confusion of motor traffic. On roads near Burleigh, in southern Queensland, signs reading "Koalas Cross Here" may be seen, interesting counterparts of Africa's "Elephants Have Right of Way" and of "Danger, Deer Crossing" in the United States.

FOREST BIRDS AT HOME

The forests of eastern Australia are particularly rich in birds. Calculations made by Keith Hindwood and Arnold McGill for a segment of some 1,650 square miles, from the coast to the Hawkesbury River and from Broken Bay in the north to Bulli in the south, showed that a total of 377 species of land and sea birds have been recorded. Of these, only about forty-five are oceanic birds. A skilled observer could list between 230 and 260 different kinds in a year. Recently, one winter day in May, the writer and a friend, visiting various kinds of forest as well as grasslands and marshes, recorded 101 species.

Many forest birds have a superficial resemblance to species of other lands, but a North American or European observer would certainly not recognize many in familiar families. The largest group limited to Australia and the Pacific is the honeyeaters (Meliphagidae), so called because nearly all indulge in nectar feeding. Mostly slim-bodied birds with fairly long tails, the size ranges from that of a pigeon down to that of a sunbird or large hummingbird. One feature they have in common is a brush-tipped tongue for sweeping up nectar and pollen from the flowers. Honeyeaters are possibly the main pollinators of *Eucalyptus, Banksia,* and various other Australian trees.

Most honeyeaters are brownish in color and often have a few yellow or white feathers behind the eye; a few species are red, or black-and-white, or mainly yellow. All have bright, melodious calls, but few are good songsters. Nearly all build cup-shaped nests and lay white or pinkish eggs spotted with red. The species occupy a variety of habitats. Some inhabit mainly shrubby undergrowth. Others do their insect hunting among the outer foliage of the trees, or along trunks and branches. Several species have flycatcher-like feeding habits, making sorties into the air from a lookout perch. A few hover before nectar-laden flowers in the manner of hummingbirds or sunbirds. A couple of species, such as the painted honeyeater *(Grantiella picta),* have changed over almost completely to feeding on berries. Many are nomadic, their seasonal

The rufous fantail (Rhipidura rufifrons), *a dainty little flycatcher that each October migrates south to nest in pockets of rain forest along the east coast. (Norman Chaffer)*

Female forester, or gray kangaroo (Macropus giganteus), *with young. The "joey" dives into the pouch head-first, then twists around so that it can look out, while its legs hang over the rim.* (Christa Armstrong: Rapho-Guillumette)

movements synchronized with the flowering of trees in different places.

One of the most familiar birds, both in bush and garden, is the blue wren *(Malurus cyaneus),* a small species with an upturned tail; the male is blue-and-black and the female is brown. Thornbills *(Acanthiza)* are little warblerlike insect-eaters that feed either among leaves or on the ground. Shrike thrushes *(Colluricincla harmonica)* are larger, blue-gray in color, and brownish on the wings. They take the larger insects

from the bark and ground. Shrike tits *(Falcunculus frontatus),* black-and-yellow in color, pull strips of bark from the trees to get at the insects hiding underneath. Dollarbirds *(Eurystomus orientalis),* so called because of the large white patch on the wing, wood swallows *(Artamus cyanopterus),* and swallows *(Hirundo neoxena)* hawk the open air for insects. They are joined, in summer, by two kinds of swifts *(Hirundapus caudacutus* and *Apus pacificus),* which breed on the coasts of China and Japan. Kingfishers are there, too. The little blue-backed, orange-breasted azure kingfisher *(Alcyone azurea)* sits patiently over a stream waiting for a tasty morsel to drift past. His big brown relative, the kookaburra *(Dacelo novae-guineae),* is by contrast purely a forest species, feeding on large insects, snakes and lizards, and baby birds. The cheery laughter of the kookaburra is one of the most delightful sounds of the Australian bush, groups of three or four birds combining at dawn or dusk to produce a chorus. Magpies *(Gymnorhina tibicen)* and butcherbirds *(Cracticus destructor)* enliven the spring mornings with their beautiful caroling: surely they are among the finest songsters in the world. And evenings in the bush are marked by the solemn "boobook" call of the small boobook owl *(Ninox boobook).*

THE VERSATILE BOWERBIRD

A few miles south of Sydney is the Royal National Park, a tract of 36,000 acres of rich forest. Here and there in the deeper gullies the rich, chocolate-colored "Narrabeen shale," laid down under lake conditions almost 200 million years ago, is exposed at the surface and supports little patches of temperate rain forest. Here grows the lilypilly *(Acmena smithii),* a dark green tree with beautiful pinkish to purplish berries (much sought after by the pied currawong and satin bowerbird), the coachwood *(Ceratopelatum),* sassafras *(Doryphora),* fig, and other trees. Here, too, one can find arboreal orchids, vines that hang like tendrils from the upper branches, and, along the edges, a dense growth of magnificent tree ferns. The rain forest has a small group of "special" birds: rufous fantails *(Rhipidura rufifrons)* and blackfaced flycatchers *(Monarcha melanopsis)* come migrating from the north to breed in October, along with the large, ground-feeding wonga pigeon *(Leucosarcia melanoleuca),* the Lewin honeyeater *(Meliphaga lewini),* and others. Lyrebirds *(Menura novae-hollandiae),* so abundant in the national park that the cold winter days ring with their magnificent calls, find this forest a wonderful place to scratch for their crustaceans and insect food.

Of the various bird groups peculiar to Australia and New Guinea none is more interesting than the bowerbirds. The males of the species build a bower, a playground in which they sing and dance during the breeding season. Sydney's Royal National Park is the home of one of the most striking of these, the satin bowerbird *(Ptilonorhynchus violaceus),* and it is here that some of the most important studies of the behavior of the group have been carried out. One can often find a bower by walking quietly along the roadside or path through the forest and listening for the curious churring and wheezing calls of the male as he displays. Just above the fringe of the rain forest is a good place for bowers, but other males prefer the higher, drier hillsides.

The male satin bowerbird is a shiny blue-black in color and the female is drab olive-green. The eye of both is rich blue. The body size is about that of the domesticated pigeon. The bower consists of two parallel walls of sticks about eighteen inches long and a foot high, and is constructed in a clearing a few feet across on the floor of the forest. It will probably be recognized by the great accumulation of "playthings" surrounding it: the blue tail feathers of the crimson rosella, bleached yellowish snail shells, dried strands of grass, and small yellow flowers, which are renewed daily. The bird is an inveterate collector, and civilization makes available to it all manner of artificial items. One bower I saw here contained twenty-three pieces of blue glass, five pieces of blue cloth, eleven pieces of blue plastic toys, seven blue bottletops, and two predominantly blue cigarette packets.

But the building of a display structure and gathering of "beautiful" objects is by no means the limit of the bowerbird's horizons. The bird has developed the fascinating practice of "painting" the stick walls of its bower. It chews up small pieces of charcoal left over from a forest fire or decayed wood and, using a small wad of bark at the tip of the bill to make it flow properly, wipes the mess up and down the sticks. This is one of the rare cases of a bird using a tool. We do not know what the purpose of the blackening is.

The bower-building activity of the bowerbird is most unusual. Naturalists long thought that the bird had an aesthetic sense and that the bower had no true biological function. But such ornithologists as A. J. Marshall and E. T. Gilliard have offered the theory that the bower building is a subversion of an extinct nest-building instinct, pointing out that the male bowerbird takes no part in the construction of the nest, incubation of the eggs, or tending of the young. These functions are the role of the female. Certainly, the bower has a territorial function, for two males never build their bowers close together and, occasionally, adjacent males exhibit jealousy by raiding and destroying each other's bowers. Also, the bower acts as a point of attraction for the female who, at the appropriate season, is lured by the curious calls of the male and by the bizarre postures he strikes. Copulation occurs when she enters the bower. There is still no explanation of the curious fact that the display objects are of two basic colors, blue and yellow, but it is noteworthy that these are the colors of the species itself. We also do not know what advantages the species gains from this strange departure from normal behavior. Certain biologists believe that bowerbirds, like birds of paradise, are polygamous, and that natural selection has functioned to produce patterns of behavior that encourage the females to visit the males rather than the reverse.

THE REMARKABLE PLATYPUS

As the early settlers moved westward across the plain beyond Sydney and approached the foothills of the Blue Mountains they suddenly came upon a splendid river. It was the Hawkesbury, one of a series of streams that rise along the Great Divide and follow a fairly swift course to the sea. There are many of these in eastern Australia: the Snowy, which drains the Australian Alps; the Shoalhaven, which enters the sea about a hundred miles south of Sydney; the Hawkesbury; the Hunter, at whose mouth the city of Newcastle has been built; and others. Some of these streams follow a headlong course straight down to the sea, but others run for some distance parallel with the Divide and the coast before turning east.

Siesta time in koala-land. (Australian News and Information Bureau)

The Hawkesbury is such a stream and geologists have long been fascinated by its complex path. One of its major components, the Wollondilly, flows north for a hundred miles; then, after being joined by the Cox, which plunges out of the mountains, it enters a narrow, steep-sided chasm, a secondary bed obviously cut through a section of the mountains that became elevated across its former path. Thereafter, as the Hawkesbury, the stream turns northward again for thirty miles before swinging east to the sea. The Hawkesbury system is, accordingly, an ancient one that antedates the periods of geological uplift.

Naturalists see the Hawkesbury as a delightful stream. There are several large swamps on its flood plain, and periodically, when the river overflows, these fill up. These marshes support the jacana or lily-trotter *(Irediparra gallinacea),* a bird that uses its toes, which are longer than its body, for walking over aquatic vegetation; the jacana is a tropical species that reaches its southern range limits here. Large numbers of black swans aggregate on these marshes seasonally. From time to time one sees the great jabiru *(Xenorhynchus asiaticus)* here, Australia's native stork. White ibises *(Threskiornis molucca)* and royal spoonbills *(Platalea regia),* Pacific and white-faced herons *(Notophoyx pacifica* and *N. novae-hollandiae)* wade in the shallows. It is a delight also to sit under the graceful she-oaks on the bank of the main river itself and watch the wild-animal traffic up and down stream, the twistings and glidings of the bee eaters or rainbowbirds *(Merops ornatus)* as they hawk for insects, flocks of ducks sweeping over the water, the snakebird *(Anhinga novae-hollandiae)* and cormorants *(Phalacrocorax melanoleucos* and *P. sulcirostris)* diving for food, and perch or mullet breaking the surface. Dusk is perhaps the most fascinating time of all, for then the spoonbills and ibis come in to roost in the tall trees along the stream, and there is much clamoring and quarreling as the best perching places are disputed.

It was on such an occasion that I caught my first glimpse of the platypus *(Ornithorhynchus anatinus),* the curious duck-billed, web-footed mammal that is one of the wonder creatures of Australia. Platypuses are crepuscular: that is, they become active at dusk. A swimming platypus may be identified by the telltale stream of bubbles it leaves behind. On this occasion I saw one emerge from the shadows of the bank and swim upstream, then drift past with the current, its small form barely discernible in the near-black water.

The platypus first became known to the settlers along the Hawkesbury River about 1797. In due course skins reached Europe, but they were treated with almost complete disbelief, for who ever heard of a furred animal with a bill and the webbed feet of a duck! It was not until Edward Hume, in 1802, dissected specimens that the platypus was accepted as a real creature. He found that the structure of the female organs was "unlike anything hitherto met with in 'quadrupeds,'" and a new class of animals was created for the creature. Interest in the platypus quickened. The dissections of the French naturalist Geoffrey Saint-Hilaire caused him to suggest that the animal was an egg-layer, unheard of among mammals. Jean de Lamark, an early evolutionist, agreed, but also stressed that unlike a reptile it had a four-chambered heart and diaphragm, both mammalian characteristics. As no mammary glands were present Lamarck decided it could not be a true mammal and hence created the category Prototheria (meaning prototype mammal) for it. Finally, in 1824, the German anatomist, Johann Meckel, found that platypuses were true milk-givers but that, in lieu of nipples, a multitude of tiny milk pores was scattered over part of the abdomen. It is now believed that the baby induces the mother's milk flow by nuzzling and then licks the droplets off the fur, making this an interesting early stage in the evolution of the mammary gland.

But arguments continued on all sides about whether or not the platypus laid eggs. Finally, half a century later, a young English zoologist, W. H. Caldwell, went to the Burnett River in southern Queensland and at the beginning of the breeding season of 1884 shot an adult female. There, inside the body was a sizable egg with a large yolk, and the egg was enclosed in a leathery membrane like that of a lizard. Triumphantly he cabled a meeting of the British Association for the Advancement of Science: "Monotremes oviparous, ovum meroblastic." In everyday language this meant that the controversial platy-

pus was an egglayer and that its eggs resembled those of reptiles and birds in having a large amount of yolk.

The platypus is an inhabitant of the rivers and lakes of eastern Australia from Cape York and the Leichhardt River to Tasmania and southeastern South Australia. Inland from the coast it is common in the Murray and Murrumbidgee river areas. Its food, which it obtains by nuzzling the river bottom with its sensitive, leathery, ducklike bill, is crayfish and worms. It surfaces to swallow the food and to take in air. By day the platypus remains in its burrow in the bank, entering it through an opening generally six to twelve inches above the waterline. The longest tunnels are constructed by breeding females and range from twenty to sixty feet.

Platypuses may sometimes be observed at dusk, provided the observer remains very still. If it is the beginning of the breeding season, which lasts from September to October, the observer may be lucky enough to see a pair engaged in one of their characteristic courting activities, swimming around in circles with the male clinging to the tail of the female. It is difficult to make out details of the swimming movements in darkened water, but study of the platypus in a glass tank shows that the animal swims by means of its webbed feet, while the flattened, beaverlike tail trails behind. The animal closes its small eyes when it dives and it catches its prey by touch only. The location of the nostrils at the tip of the bill enables the platypus to elevate them just above the water when it surfaces to breathe.

Knowledge of the life of the platypus is largely due to the studies of two men, Harry Burrell and David Fleay. Fleay was able to persuade the animals to breed in captivity. In Victoria he found that mating took place between mid-September and mid-October. The nest of eucalypt leaves at the end of the breeding burrow was constructed toward the end of October. When the female retired to lay, she plugged the mouth of the burrow with mud in two or three places, apparently to preserve the humidity of the chamber and protect the eggs from shrinkage. There are one to three white eggs, about three-quarters of an inch long. The female keeps them warm by curling around them. The incubation period was from seven to ten days long.

Young platypuses are blind and virtually helpless for some eleven weeks. The one studied did not enter the water until it was seventeen weeks old and about thirteen-and-one-half inches long.

THE BLUE MOUNTAINS

The Blue Mountains, so named by early colonists because of their misty blue color, rise precipitously beyond the Hawkesbury River. No more than a fine bluish line on the horizon when viewed from the western suburbs of Sydney, closer up they are seen as a continuous ridge, with high knolls and protuberances alternating with deeply notched V-shaped water gaps. There is a mysterious air about the dark green of their heavily timbered sides.

A group of great-gray kangaroos (Macropus giganteus) *drink at a drying bush waterhole. Largest of living marsupials, they can leap 20 to 25 feet. (Graham Pizzey)*

A platypus (Ornithorhynchus anatinus) *swimming. The nostrils at the top of the bill enable the animal to breathe and still remain largely submerged. (Norman Laird)*

When the early settlers first attempted to penetrate the Blue Mountains they followed the steep-sided valleys, facing well-nigh impenetrable undergrowth, stinging nettles, rock slides, and insect and leech attacks, to come to a full stop at the vertical cliffs of the valley head. Only when Blaxland, Lawson, and Wentworth tried keeping to the ridges did European man finally conquer these mountains.

Modern roads and railways, too, follow the ridges. The gradient is steep. But as the traveler moves upward through the somewhat sparse timber on the more exposed slopes he is rewarded by a series of magnificent panoramas of the Sydney plain behind him. Presently, the gullies falling away on either side become increasingly deep and precipitous, until one can no longer see their bottoms. But the whitish, yellowish, and reddish tones to the sandstone precipices are not only very beautiful but quite interesting—they reveal bedding plains tilted and bowed by the deep internal compressions that originally elevated the plateau.

At the high points of the range, where the altitude reaches four to five thousand feet, the scenery is truly grand. From places like Echo Point near Katoomba and Govett's Leap near Blackheath, chasms six hundred and more feet deep fall away on either side. Stark precipices of multicolored sandstone, bare but for a few shrubs and spindly trees clinging to their

sides, extend away toward the horizon. Here and there headlands jut out over the valley and, in places, deep gaps reveal another valley converging with the main one. White, glistening, pencil lines on the cliffs indicate the presence of waterfalls; there is a steady drainage of water from the plateau tops into the valleys. And here and there a group of residual rocks that have withstood the weathering of wind and water stand out from the valley sides or bottom like sentinels. One of the best known of such features is the trio of vertical rocks at Echo Point known as the Three Sisters.

The valley bottoms are shrouded in dense foliage. A visitor must descend one of the steep cliff trails, a hazardous and exhausting experience, to appreciate the magnificence of the trees and the density and luxuriance of the undergrowth below. But even from high on the plateau top it is possible to learn much about the birds living in the valley. The whip-crack call of the coachwhip bird *(Psophodes olivaceus)* comes echoing up the rock walls. The melancholy "caaaaaww" of the raven *(Corvus coronoides)* is interspersed with the "woooooom" of the wonga pigeon, the melodious chatter of a flock of crimson rosellas *(Platycercus elegans),* the ringing calls of the lyrebird *(Menura novae-hollandiae),* and the "chop chop" notes of the yellow robin *(Eopsaltria australis).* A knowledge of the habits of these birds in other places enables one to conjure up an image of what the vegetation of the valley floor must be like.

Presently, as the observer sits on the cliff edge, a small brown, robinlike bird will fly up over the top, alight on a rock nearby, and utter a series of harsh scolding notes. It is the rock warbler *(Origma solitaria),* a specialized rock dweller that occurs only in the sandstone and limestone areas of central coastal New South Wales. Its nest is unique, a dome-shaped structure with a "tail," suspended by cobwebs from the roof of a cave.

The Blue Mountains are composed mainly of sandstone, the so-called Hawkesbury sandstone, which was laid down in a salty estuary in Triassic times, perhaps 190 million years ago. But here and there volcanic residuals, such as Mounts Wilson and Tomah, rise above the plateau. The eastern scarp, as noted, is steep, but to the west the slope is gradual, affording broad, grassy valleys like the beautiful farming lands of the Megalong and Capertee. Hidden in a forested valley, slightly to the west of the main "backbone" of the range, are the spectacular Jenolan Caves. These, with their magnificent stalactites, stalagmites, drapes, curtains, and mounds of glistening white stone are among the most remarkable limestone caves in Australia.

THE ROCK ETCHINGS OF A LOST PEOPLE

When the *Endeavour* anchored in Botany Bay, Cook's voyagers were fascinated by the Australian aborigines or Australoids. The fertile east coasts had quite a population of these hunting and fishing folk, and throughout the travelers' sojourn in the bay several dugout canoes containing one or two fishermen were always visible. The natives, they found, were timid and, though on one or two occasions spears were thrown by way of a demonstration, no direct contact was made with these Stone Age men.

The aborigines of eastern Australia are no longer a distinct entity; their descendants have long since been absorbed into the white man's urban communities. Only one reminder of former times remains, the Australoid rock etchings in the sandstone of the coastal plateau tops and the Blue Mountains. The vicinity of Sydney is particularly rich in these, and new groups are being discovered constantly. Since the aborigines practiced no agriculture and were dependent on yams, fish, and mammals, they were an integral part of the ecological or biological community of their time. The motifs in the etchings are a constant reminder of this.

Frederick D. McCarthy, formerly Curator of Anthropology at the Australian Museum, made a special study of rock etchings and cave paintings and their ritualistic significance. Over six hundred galleries have now been found within fifty miles of Sydney. Some depict gigantic anthropomorphic figures representing the great creator and other spirit beings; others show hunting heroes with their boomerangs, shields, and head ornaments. Footprints tell the story of hunts. Outlines of the important food animals—wallabies, kangaroos, emus, anteaters, possums, flying foxes, whales, and fish—abound. It is now too late to ascertain the precise function of many of the symbols and figures, but we do know that in some parts of Australia the animal outlines were touched up periodically in the belief that this led to a greater abundance of game or greater success in hunting.

The etchings, made by a series of punctures half an inch or so in diameter that were then connected by grooves, are exposed to the weather and are slowly being worn away. Even more vulnerable are the cave paintings of white clay, black charcoal, and red and yellow ochres. Best preserved of these are the stenciled outlines of hands, which the artist made by squirting chewed clay over his own outstretched fingers. There is now widespread interest in the aboriginal rock galleries; efforts are being made to get a complete record of them and, where possible, protect them for the future.

THE COASTS: DUNES, CLIFFS, AND SANDPIPERS

A characteristic feature of the eastern coast of New South Wales is the broken shoreline made up of alternating cliffs and long sandy beaches. Within these stretches there are many bays and estuaries, most of them shallow and giving way on the inland side to brackish lagoons or marshes. Many of the inlets have sandbars so that they connect with the sea only during heavy rains or exceptionally high tides. These bars are the result of current and wind action, the latter coming particularly from the south and southwest.

Cook observed extensive sand dunes on the south side of Botany Bay. Similar dunes are prominent in other areas; a tremendous group of them, possibly the largest on any seashore, form extensive sand islands off the south Queensland coast. Most important of these is Stradbroke Island, thirty-five miles long, and Moreton Island, twenty-five miles long. Here wind has piled the sand up to form peaks eight hundred to nine hundred feet high. Most of these east coast sand dunes are now "senile," that is, they have stopped growing and are partly covered with shrubs, grasses, and stunted trees.

If there had been an ornithologist in Cook's party he would have left as enthusiastic an account of the bird life as of the plants of Botany Bay. But the journals contain very little about birds. It has likewise been left to later generations to appreciate the diversity of the life in the intertidal zones of the rocks, beaches, and bays. The abundance of crabs, shrimps, starfishes, brittle stars, sea urchins, flatworms, polychaete worms, jellyfish, clams, mussels, whelks, and other marine snails, is surprising. Certainly aboriginal man reaped a rich harvest from this source, hunting it on foot and by canoe. The great piles of bleached shells in places testify to their being the feasting places of generation after generation.

A walk along the clifftops, with the strong breeze blowing in one's face and the Pacific surging and churning beneath one, is a most exhilarating experience. Gulls *(Larus novaehollandiae)* are in constant attendance, an occasional kestrel *(Falco cenchroides)* sails on the upcurrents, and now and again a peregrine falcon *(Falco peregrinus)* may sweep past. If it is low tide the exposed platforms below will have little groups of migratory waders, gulls, the odd reef heron *(Demigretta sacra),* and perhaps a pair of sooty oyster catchers *(Haematopus fuliginosus).* Occasionally one glimpses an albatross, giant petrel *(Macronectes giganteus),* or gannet *(Sula bassana)* out to sea.

Sea birds are abundant off the coasts of eastern and southern Australia, many of them winter visitors from the Antarctic. Most spectacular of all is the great wandering albatross *(Diomedia exulans),* the world's largest flying bird, with a wingspan of up to ten feet six inches. A favorite gathering place of these

birds is at a sewer outlet near Malabar, a suburb a few miles south of Sydney. Since these birds can take to the air only when a stiff breeze is blowing, enthusiasts venture out to net and leg-band them. The results of this banding have been spectacular, some having subsequently been recovered at breeding colonies in the Falkland Islands, while others banded in the Falklands have been recovered at Malabar. Australian gannets, very similar in appearance to the European and North American species, are another striking feature along this coast. These birds also venture into Sydney and other harbors, and they can be readily distinguished by their diving habits, the feeding birds plummeting headfirst into the water from heights of fifty feet and more. Their main food are the mackerel, pilchards, and other pelagic fishes that form large shoals. There are five gannetries in Australian waters, all in the far south. The only truly accessible one is that on Cat Island, the others being on islands that rise precipitously from the sea. This is just as well, since the Cat Island colony has been subjected to repeated raids by fishermen, who use the young birds as crayfish bait.

SEA BIRD ISLANDS OF NEW SOUTH WALES

About nine different species of sea birds manage to nest along the coast of New South Wales despite the relative paucity of suitable islands. Most interesting of these is a small petrel, gray above and white below, known as the Cabbagetree Island or white-winged petrel *(Pterodroma leucoptera)*. This is a race, *leucoptera leucoptera,* of a species that has a fairly wide range farther east in the Pacific. The race breeds on only one island, Cabbagetree Island (so named because of its many cabbagetree palms) off Port Stephens, the total colony containing perhaps two hundred birds. The little petrels have shallow shelters in the rocks and beneath the palms and dense pisonia trees, leaving them in late summer and returning to them in September. Because they are strictly nocturnal, only the experienced ornithologist knows of their presence. The enemies of the timid petrels are the sticky pisonia seeds, which sometimes gum up the feathers of the birds so that they cannot fly; the occasional bush fires; and their own low reproductive rate— they lay only one egg per year.

The most interesting island group, and the one best known to the writer, is the Five Islands, a sanctuary off Port Kembla south of Sydney. Like the other coastal islands, these represent old hilltops isolated by a rising sea. They range in size from a hundred or so acres down to small rocky domes of an acre or two. Rank grasses and small shrubs grow on the sandy crowns of all the islands. One island (called Toothbrush Island because of its shape), consisting of a low rocky reef with an elevated shrubby plateau at one end, is the nesting place of

Left above: Male satin bowerbird (Ptilonorhynchus violaceus) *courts a female at his bower. The playgrounds of these birds on the forest floor are decorated with brightly colored objects, including bits of glass. (Norman Chaffer)   Far left: Female ring-tailed possum* (Pseudocheirus laniginosus), *her two young on her back, emerges from her stick nest in a tree. (Allen Keast)   Left: Male mistletoe bird* (Dicaeum hirundinaceum), *3½ inches long, with a mistletoe berry, which the bird will peel and swallow. (Michael Morcombe)*

white-faced storm petrels *(Pelegadroma marina)*, which have their burrows beneath the pig's face *(Mesembryanthemum)*, and little penguins *(Eudyptula minor)*. The latter occupy caves. Melancholy are the flutings and squawks of the penguins as they make their way ashore and up the slopes at night. As I learned to my discomfort, they are afflicted with small fleas; one stormy night when I camped on Toothbrush Island it became necessary to take shelter in a rocky cave, and I had to eject the occupants, an adult and two nearly grown penguins. But the penguins had their revenge. The sand contained a liberal population of fleas, and these made rapid course for the nearest warm object. Penguin fleas do not seem to bite man, but their peregrinations over me gave me an uncomfortable and sleepless night. The rocky reef is the annual nesting place of a pair of sooty oyster catchers, and the feeding area of flocks of small sandpipers from the Arctic.

The largest of the Five Islands, Jenkins Island, has a colony of perhaps five thousand silver gulls *(Larus novae-hollandiae)*, the small, white, red-billed gull so characteristic of Australia, and a few hundred breeding crested terns *(Sterna bergii)*. In any year the terns occupy the higher parts of the island, crowding in groups as a measure of defense against the egg-eating proclivities of the gulls. Wedge-tailed shearwaters *(Puffinus pacificus)* and a few short-tailed shearwaters *(P. tenuirostris)* also nest on the island, but they are nocturnal and the visitor does not become aware of their presence until he accidentally breaks through the sandy soil and finds himself knee-deep in a burrow.

ARCTIC VISITORS

Every year, up to thirty species of waders, dotterels, plovers, sandpipers, godwits, whimbrels, and the big sea curlew, come south from their breeding grounds in Siberia and Alaska to spend the Australian summer on the estuaries, beaches, and sand flats of Australia. Botany Bay is a favorite gathering place, and the list of types occurring here from week to week is as large as can be found anywhere.

The first flocks of the northern waders appear in September and thereafter the number and diversity of species quickly increase. A sand flat that had only a few gulls and cormorants one week becomes dotted with hundreds, if not thousands, of small brown forms running hither and thither, heads bobbing and tails tipping as they feast on the tiny worms and other life left behind by the falling tide. The flocks are of all sizes, some containing hundreds of individuals, others only a handful. Some tend to be "pure" flocks made up of a single species like the sharp-tailed sandpiper *(Erolia acuminata)* or the little stint *(E. ruficollis);* others contain a conglomeration of varying shapes and sizes. The smaller species are high-strung, dashing into the air when alarmed. As they rise, their path is a zigzag. Then they sweep the clouds with their swiftly beating wings, one minute silhouetted against the blue of the sky, the next a jumble of ill-defined shapes against the ruffled water. Just as precipitously, they drop back onto the sand and resume their impatient feeding.

These visitors from the Arctic make the longest flights of any that come to Australia. Why none of them ever stops to breed in the southern hemisphere is a riddle no one can answer. When the birds arrive they are already losing their breeding colors and assuming a dull brown that camouflages

A water dragon, a 15-inch lizard that lives on the banks of rivers and creeks, and takes to the water when threatened. (Stan and Kay Breeden)

them well. For the rest of the summer they follow a fairly fixed routine, feeding as the tide falls, resting just above the high-water mark or in one of the adjacent swamps or fields in between. With the coming of autumn they don resplendent colors once again. Golden plovers *(Pluvialis dominica)* have their backs flecked with gold and their breast black. Mongolian dotterels *(Charadrius mongolus)* become brick-red underneath, while the long-legged, long-billed godwits *(Limosa lapponica)* acquire rust-red breasts. With the approach of the migratory season an obvious psychological change comes over the flocks. The birds become restless and nervous, and one cannot approach them closely. The ornithologist seeking birds new to him faces unexpected problems, but, in compensation, autumn is a time when the flocks of birds change almost daily, as new species arrive from the south.

The destination of these birds after they leave Australia is the northern tundra, where the earth is being exposed by the retreating snow. Their home is the land of the polar bear, musk ox, and caribou. June will see them hiding their eggs among the fast-growing grasses and sedges, feeding on the abundant flies and other insect life that summer brings to the Arctic.

THE MOUNTAIN BACKBONE

Australia is unique among the continents in that there are no high mountains, no permanent snowfields, no glaciers, and no active volcanos. The highest peak, Mount Koskiusko, is only 7,308 feet high. Australia is the flattest of the continents: it has been estimated that less than 5 per cent of its land area is more than two thousand feet above sea level.

Yet the higher mountains of Australia are of the greatest importance. The Great Divide, or Great Dividing Range, which extends from north to south parallel with the east coast for two thousand miles, is a vast rainfall trap. It provides a wide range of conditions and is responsible for much of the biological diversity of the Australian continent. The eastern mountains also provide some of the continent's most spectacular scenery.

This physiographic feature, the major one on the continent, varies between 1,000 and 6,000 feet in height. Thus, in Queensland, sections 3,000 to 4,000 feet in height are separated by an extensive low area that permits inland forms of animal life to reach the coast. In northern New South Wales the volcanic peaks of Bajimba and Capoompeta are 5,000 and 5,100 feet in height respectively. The Blue Mountain Plateau is 3,000 to 3,500 feet high. The Koskiusko Plateau is 6,000 to 7,000 feet and the high country of eastern Victoria, the Victorian Alps, are 5,000 to 5,500 feet above sea level. Farther west, there is a low gap immediately north of Melbourne (1,100 feet), and the Grampians in western Victoria are about 2,000 feet in their highest parts. Throughout its course the Divide breaks up the drainage pattern into a series of coastal rivers flowing swiftly eastward or southward, and into longer inland rivers. On its eastern face are waterfalls, cataracts, and tumbling creeks. But the westward-flowing rivers, meandering as they do over hundreds of miles of flat plains country, are sluggish, and most of them flow only intermittently.

The alternative uses of the words divide and range should be explained. The use of "range" stems from the early settlers, who likened the precipitous eastern face to the great mountain ranges of the other continents. Geological surveys, however, soon showed that it was not comparable, the western escarpment sloping gently. Nor does it have a series of peaks like a true mountain range. The structure is essentially an uplifted plateau that has been deeply slashed by rivers and streams. Geologists prefer the term Great Divide, thus emphasizing how it separates the drainage into eastward and westward patterns.

AN ERODED LANDSCAPE

Geologically, the Great Divide is a complex combination of many types of rock, some very ancient, others more recent in origin, all uplifted, twisted and eroded. Among the older rocks are granites laid down in Paleozoic times, and fossil-bearing limestones and other rocks stemming from the Silurian and Devonian periods, 350 to 400 million years ago. Of intermediate age are the coal-bearing Permo-Carboniferous strata, 200 to 300 million years old, and the estuarine sandstones of the Triassic. The newest rocks are the caps of basalt, left behind by the long volcanic phase that extended from perhaps forty million years ago down to one million years ago. Some of the higher points, the so-called monadnocks, composed of erosion-resisting granites and basalts, are the vestiges of what were hills before the elevation of the Great Divide.

The history of this striking feature is most interesting. The evidence is that two periods of uplift were involved, one toward the close of the Miocene period, perhaps twenty million years ago, and one in the late Pliocene, about two million years ago. It is evident throughout that an older elevated surface worn down by erosion has been secondarily uplifted so that streams were rejuvenated and cut new paths for themselves. The Koskiusko plateau reached its present extent during the second period of uplift.

THE AUSTRALIAN AND VICTORIAN ALPS

The Australian Alps, as the Koskiusko plateau and its adjacent highlands are called, straddle the border of New South Wales and Victoria in the east. It is said that during the relatively short winter there is more snow-covered country here than in Switzerland. The winter snow line ranges mostly from 5,500 feet down to 5,000, but goes to 4,500 feet in Victoria and still lower in Tasmania. The area of country covered by snow in winter is about 2,000 square miles on the mainland and 2,500 on the island. Snow falls from May to October, but the amount varies greatly from year to year. Skiers count only on the period from July to September for deep snow and ideal skiing conditions.

The climate of the high country is much what one would expect in so exposed a region. Winds may blow with gale or even hurricane force for short periods, mainly from the northwest or southwest. In winter these winds whip the snow up into banks and seem to cut right through clothes, making skiing impossible. In these winds, too, an ordinary summer rainstorm becomes merciless. Diurnal fluctuations in temperature may reach fifty degrees in the intermediate seasons, with the days warm but the winds making the night cold and unpleasant.

The annual precipitation in the alpine tract—about half of it rain—ranges from 70 to 120 inches, and from 30 to 80 inches in the subalpine area below. Average mean monthly temperatures in summer are 55 to 60 degrees in the upper parts and 50 to 55 in the lower, and respectively 30 to 35 and 35 to 40 in winter. For six months of the year the minimum temperatures do not fall below the freezing point.

The Australian high country differs from that of the northern continents in that it lacks conifers. Instead, a eucalypt, the snow gum *(Eucalyptus coriacea),* has become specialized for life in the snows. It covers large sections of the slopes and tops of the mountains between four thousand and six thousand feet. It is a stunted and twisted tree, but it has a smooth trunk that is beautifully streaked with reds, browns, and creams when the bark is peeling. When wetted by melting snow it glistens and gleams in the sunlight. Like other eucalypts, the snow gum is an evergreen. Thus a skier in Australia weaves his downhill path through gum trees, not hemlocks and spruces—another expression of the peculiarly Australian landscape.

RUGGED GRANDEUR AND ALPINE MEADOWS

The Australian Alps were discovered by the Polish explorer, Count de Strzelecki, in 1839. The knobs of erosion-resistant granite that stand out above the rest of the plateau include four points that exceed seven thousand feet in height: Mounts Koskiusko, Townsend, Twynam, and Ramshead. Strzelecki named what he believed to be the highest peak after the Polish patriot Koskiusko, and wrote of it: "Conspicuously elevated above all the heights hitherto noticed, and swollen by many rugged protuberances, the snowy and craggy syenitic cone of Mount Koskiusko is seen cresting the Australian Alps." Later surveys, however, showed that the peak named Townsend was higher; obligingly, the authorities interchanged the names.

The Snowy Mountains or Australian Alps are actually a plateau within another plateau, the Great Divide proper. Thus, on his way to the summit Strzelecki passed through a subalpine zone, from three to five thousand feet up, heavily timbered with such trees as the mountain ash, candlebark, and giant stringybark. Between the peaks the broad alpine meadows and sphagnum bogs form a vast drainage basin. The major river draining the heights is the Snowy, with its innumerable little creeks, fed by the steadily melting snows,

A marsupial-mouse (Sminthopsis murina), *a delicately-built little insect-eater, with a wide distribution in southern Australia.* (Stan and Kay Breeden)

converging to form raging torrents at the plateau's edge. Near Jindabyne, at three thousand feet, the main river, deeply entrenched, has a flow of eight thousand gallons per second and resembles a boiling cauldron. In its lower reaches the Snowy emerges onto the coastal plain in northeastern Victoria and enters the sea near Orbost.

The most spectacular feature of the western side of the Koskiusko plateau is a gorge almost 4,500 feet deep, into which the upland waters pour to form the Swampy Plain River, a tributary of the westward-flowing Murray, Australia's largest river.

At the southern end of the bow-shaped highlands are the high peaks of Victoria, topped by Mounts Feathertop, Bogong, and Hotham, all over six thousand feet. Mount Bogong is well known because of high plains and extensive alpine meadows like those of the Koskiusko region. These peaks are composed of granite, weathered into hummocks and rounded knolls but jagged at the margins. Shallow gullies radiate outward

from the central mass. Hotham and Feathertop are slate, but their summits are capped by sheets of hard basalt, the remains of former lava flows. This gives them relatively smooth summits and slopes. Another peak, Mount Buffalo, a flattened granite mass with steep sides, provides magnificent vistas. Vertical joints have created granite monoliths suggesting Gothic architecture. There are sharp and jagged ridges, as well as alpine meadows, with streams tumbling down joint lines, past heaps of great boulders, and over precipices to the flatter country below.

OLD GLACIERS AND GLACIAL LAKES

The Koskiusko plateau shows considerable evidences of former glaciation: glacial moraines, widened valleys, polished rocks, and erratics, that is, etched boulders transported by the moving ice sheet far from their place of origin. Geologists believe that the southern hemisphere, like the northern, had four glacial periods in about the last million years. In Australia the area covered by ice was very small, the continent being relatively close to the equator. In fact, only in the high mountains is there evidence of an ice sheet. During the first of these glaciations, the Malanna, ice apparently covered an area of four hundred square miles and extended from about twelve miles south of Mount Koskiusko to about twenty miles north, overflowing down the eastern slopes for several miles. It was probably about two hundred feet thick. At this time ice covered almost half of Tasmania.

Little trace can be found of the second and third glaciations in Australia since evidence has been covered by the last glaciation. The latter, which is believed to have ended ten to fifteen thousand years ago, apparently did not form a large ice sheet but was restricted to individual glaciers formed at the heads of the valleys. These cut many amphitheater-like basins called cirques. One of these, at the source of the Snowy, was about thirteen miles long at its maximum.

One delightful aspect of this country is a series of small lakes. These nestle high among the granitic boulders, and have shorelines of tumbled rocks or vivid green grass and sphagnum moss. Just east of Charlotte Pass near Koskiusko's slopes is the beautiful Blue Lake. It lies in a rock basin left by the melting ice. Hedley's Tarn, a smaller lake nearby, is held back by an old moraine. Lake Cottapatamba, Australia's highest lake (6,700 feet), is framed by granite slopes and drifted snow.

SUMMER IN ALPINE MEADOWS

With the retreat of the snow up the slopes the alpine meadowlands are soon ablaze with flowers. White snow daisies *(Clemesia longifolia)* come out in their millions. Golden everlastings *(Helichrysum)* form wide swaths. Yellow groundsels *(Senecio)* clothe the hillsides. Here and there one sees alpine

Golden wattles grace early springtime in the Australian bush. Next to the gums the acacias, with 600 species, are the most characteristic trees of Australia. (Adelie Hurley: Rapho-Guillumette)

bluebells, the tiny yellow stars of *Stackhousia,* clumps of the delicate pink *Pimelea,* white snow anemones, yellow buttercups, alpine heath, violets, sun orchids, hopbush, and dwarf grevilleas. Also here is the curious "mountain parsley" *(Aciphylla),* white flowered and with spiny leaves rather like those of a miniature fan-shaped palm frond. Trigger plants *(Stylidium),* with their erect stems of numerous bright pink flowers, are common. The botanical diversity of the snowlands is such that fifty species of flowering plants can be recorded in a few hours.

Studies of the origins and relationships of the various alpine plants occurring at an altitude of six thousand feet have shown that the flora is a composite of elements derived over a vast period of time from different places. Many of the high alpine plants show the same adaptations to severe conditions as do those of similar habitats on other continents, to wit, the tendency to be dwarf-size, to cling to rocks, and to occur perennially, dying back to the roots and sprouting again every spring. Some resist fierce winds and ice by forming tussocks or becoming hard-leafed and spiny. Of course, any that remain aboveground must be extremely hardy to resist being buried by snow for long periods.

One of the plants of the high country, the trigger plant *(Stylidium),* is most interesting in its method of pollination. *Stylidium* is very abundant in the snow country, but it is not basically alpine: ninety of the hundred-odd Australian species occur only at sea level in Western Australia. It also occurs in New Zealand, South America, and Asia. Protruding from the center of the four petals of the pink flower is a long, bent column bearing the male and female organs at its tip. This column is sensitive and when touched by an insect it flips over, dabbing its pollen on the insect. Fertilization results when the insect brushes against the ripened column of another flower. One of the most important pollinators of *Stylidium* is a small bee, *Exoneura.* The column regains its sensitivity in about fifteen minutes and is ready to dab another insect.

ALPINE GRASSHOPPERS, FROGS AND LIZARDS

One of the most striking animals of the Australian snow country is the mountain grasshopper *(Acripeza reticulata),* which swarms in countless millions on the meadows of snow grass. It is a master of color change, going from blue to fawn brown, depending on the light and its "emotional" condition. The males perch on top of the *Olearia* and *Leucopogon* plants to emit their harsh, rattling chirp, stridulating most vigorously at dusk and before sunrise. Another interesting insect, the alpine cicada *(Tettigarcta crinita),* is among the world's most primitive cicadas, mothlike in form, with the forewings opaque and brown, and the body hairy. Unlike other cicadas,

both sexes have sound-producing organs. It is strictly nocturnal, hiding beneath the bark by day and avoiding light. The pupae emerge in January and February and make their way up the trunks of the snow gums to transform into adults. The Koskiusko species has a close relative in Tasmania, *T. tomentosa.*

The alpine meadows and streams of the highlands are the home of two very beautiful frogs. The black-and-yellow-banded, inch-long corroboree frog *(Pseudophryne corroboree)* is an inhabitant of the sphagnum bogs. It takes its name from the ceremonial dance of the Australian aborigines, in which the dancers paint their bodies in bizarre patterns. The first of these frogs was found by an American zoologist, J. A. Moore, in a bottle at the Australian Museum. The specimen, which had been received at the museum a few years before, was so unlike any known Australian frog that the authorities believed it to be a hoax, the pet of some overseas traveler. Moore's studies showed that, despite its colors, it was a member of an Australian frog group. Other specimens have since been obtained from the Koskiusko area. The other characteristic frog of the alpine country is a vivid green and brown race of the small tree frog, *Hyla ewingii (alpina).* It is common along the streams, whereas the corroboree frog keeps to the sphagnum moss. Both frogs breed in summer and hibernate beneath the snow in winter. The creeks are inhabited by crayfish, too,

Left: The kookaburra (Dacelo novae-guineae), *whose joyous laughter, uttered mainly at dawn, dusk, and just before a storm, is very characteristic of the Australian bush. (Stan and Kay Breeden) Right: The snows of Mount Kosciusko have retreated well up the slopes by December and January, leaving the high meadows carpeted with flowers such as the beautiful Kosciusko anemone buttercup* (Ranunculus anemoneus). *(A. B. Costin)*

The rugged summit slopes of Mount Kosciusko in summer. The snow gum occurs only from a height of four thousand feet to the tree-line at six thousand. (A. B. Costin)

many aquatic insects, and a small fish, *Galaxias findlayi,* that apparently migrates to lower levels before winter.

Several of the more interesting reptiles of the snow country also appear in Tasmania. Among them is the blotched blue-tongued lizard *(Tiliqua nigrolutea),* a large-bodied, sluggish creature that hides beneath boulders and grass tussocks. The little dragon lizard *(Amphibolurus diemenensis)* is often seen on the trunks of the snow gums. Skinks are numerous, including a small form known as *Leiolopisma ocellata.* The deadly Australian copperhead snake *(Denisonia superba)* is seldom seen, taking good care to escape before an observer approaches. Interchange of animals and plants between Koskiusko and Tasmania is presumed to have taken place during the glacial periods. Because of the withdrawal of water from the oceans, Bass Strait must at that time have been dry, and suitably low temperatures probably prevailed through the intervening country. With the warming up of the climate, the groups that like cold temperatures survived on the mainland by retreating to the mountaintops.

EMUS AND WOMBATS

Several birds move into the high country with the retreat of the snows. Most numerous of these is probably the little pipit

(Anthus novae-zeelandiae), a larklike brown bird that runs over the stones and grass, feeds on insects and seeds, and nests beneath a protective tussock. Swallows *(Hirundo neoxena)* hawk through the air, finding an ample food source in the small flies and other insects above the meadows. Kestrels, too, are found here, hovering above the granite outcrops. The omnipresent ravens are also characteristic of the high country.

In summer, little groups of emus may be seen grazing here and there on the alpine uplands. The emu, which shares the Australian coat of arms with the kangaroo, is one of the most widespread of Australian birds. Formerly it inhabited both grasslands and woodlands, but today there are few left in coastal areas and we characteristically think of it as a denizen of the interior. *Dromaius novae-hollandiae* stands three-and-a-half feet to four feet high at the shoulder, and when the head is in the alert position it reaches five-and-a-half feet. It weighs seventy to eighty pounds, and sometimes up to 120 pounds. The body color is a drab gray-brown, and like the other flightless ratites, or running birds, it has much reduced wings and strong and powerful legs. Speeds of up to thirty-five miles per hour can be attained in level country. The emu is the world's second largest bird; only the African ostrich is bigger.

I always get a thrill when I see a party of emus stalking majestically across the plain or through the timber. On one such occasion I decided to test the oft-repeated tale that if one stands still and gently waves a handkerchief, emus, always curious, will come quite close. This was near the Warrumbungle Ranges in northwestern New South Wales. It worked perfectly, and the birds came to within about one hundred feet before taking it upon themselves to turn tail and race away again. In central Australia the aborigines prefer emu meat to any other. When out on collecting expeditions, I found that native companions who were unimpressed by the sight of a kangaroo virtually jumped up and down with excitement when an emu hove into view. Emus must drink frequently; on one occasion when I was camped by Ayers Rock in central Australia a party of these ungainly birds came to drink at the waterhole at the foot of the cliff each morning.

The female emu tends to be slightly larger than the male. The species is characteristically a winter breeder, in some areas laying eggs as early as April. The nest is a trampled mass of grass und leaves, and is generally placed under a tree or beside a bush. Eight to ten greenish-black eggs form the clutch. The duties of incubation always fall to the male, as is the case among all the flightless birds. The young hatch in about sixty days. They are striped brown and white and difficult to see as they crouch in the grass. Emus eat wild fruits such as quandong *(Fusanus)*, sour plum *(Owenia)*, young grasses, and insects. At one time they were accused of spreading the introduced prickly pear, a notorious plant pest. Emus break fences and, like the kangaroo, are charged with competing with sheep for pasture. The Australian natives speared the birds when they came to drink, or drugged them by poisoning waterholes with the leaves of the pituri *(Duboisia)*.

The wombat *(Phascolomys hirsutus)* is a broad-headed, heavy-bodied, burrowing marsupial that has small eyes, short legs, and the proportions of a marmot or groundhog. The body color is brown to black, and the hair coarse. A large individual will be three-and-a-half feet in length and weigh eighty pounds. Since the wombat likes hilly areas, the Koskiusko plateau seems to be ideal habitat for it. Its large, low-arched burrows are a feature of some of the uplands. These burrows, from fifteen to one hundred feet long, have a nest of bark or grass at the end. Burrowing is said to be accomplished by the animals lying on its side and scooping out the soil with the strong shovel-like nails. Near the burrow is a shallow excavation where the animals like to sun-bathe. The wombat's diet

The trees of the high snow country are a cold-adapted species of eucalypt, the snow gum (Eucalyptus coriacea). *(Charles P. Mountford)*

is grass, roots, and fungi, cropped with the aid of its continuously growing, rodentlike incisor teeth.

In the Koskiusko region I have seen young wombats out in the winter snow. They prefer to remain underground during the cold weather, however. Wombats make pleasant, good-natured pets, even though their strength enables them to burrow under, and break through, fences.

35

Wildflowers and Parrots in an Ancient Landscape

The Southwest Corner

The wildflowers of southwestern Australia are unsurpassed elsewhere on the continent. September finds the countryside ablaze with color. Hillsides are splashed with golden wattle. Blue *Leschenaultia* and the bluebell *Orthrosanthus* form carpets. *Epacris* and other shrubby heath plants have turned to white and pink. The wild pea bushes are blotched with brown and yellow. Little trailing vines, the white *Clematis* and the purple *Hardenbergia,* festoon fallen logs and drape over banks. Here and there on the forest floor are clumps of the curious kangaroo paws *(Anigozanthos),* their flowers red-and-green and black-and-green, and as bizarre in shape as in color. Up above, the gnarled old banksias have adorned themselves with large yellow-and-orange flower heads. Many of the gums are alive with flocks of honey-eating birds, calling joyously as they jostle the blossoms.

In early spring, southwestern Australia is a wonderland of warm cloudless days, bright colors, and singing birds. It is no wonder that tourists converge on Perth from all over Australia at this time.

THE RICHEST FLORA

But the beauty of the flowers of the southwest is only part of the story. To the botanist this isolated segment of forest, woodland, and heathland, hedged in by desert, is the most fascinating part of the continent. For one thing, the flora is amazingly rich and varied, numbering about six thousand species. It has been said that there is no richer flora anywhere outside of the tropics. The second interesting feature is that some 80 per cent of the plant species occur nowhere else. Thirdly, the true, or basically, Australian plant groups reach by far their greatest diversity here. Thirty-seven of the fifty-odd species of *Banksia* are found only in this region, as are

106 of the 120 species of *Melaleuca* (tea trees), 112 of the 180 *Grevillea,* 71 of the 100 *Hakea,* and 26 of the 30 species of *Isopogon.* All 52 species of *Dryandra* and all 15 of *Beaufortia* are confined to the area. The abundance of these groups has led one authority to refer to the southwest as the cradle of Australian flora.

The richness and uniqueness of this flora has long been known. In 1860 the famous biogeographer Alfred Russel Wallace puzzled over it: "Southwest Australia is far less extensive than the southeastern division—less varied in soil and climate, with no lofty mountains, and much sand desert; yet, strange to say, it contains an equally rich flora and far greater proportion of peculiar species and genera of plants." One hundred years later botanists are no further advanced in explaining the diverse plant life of southwestern Australia.

THE NULLARBOR PLAIN

My first trip to southwestern Australia was overland by train from the east. The journey, which takes about two days, provides an interesting example of what the more arid parts of the Australian continent are like since it stretches across the full width of the Nullarbor Plain. The Nullarbor, sandy, clayey, or stony, is practically devoid of trees and over much of it the only vegetation is sparse and usually withered shrubs. The harshness of the desert is due, of course, to the low rainfall (less than ten inches per annum) and the porosity of the sand. In the case of the Nullarbor, however, water loss into the ground is even more acute, for the underlying rock is limestone. There is little time for the plants to gain any benefit from rain before the water sinks out of reach.

The Nullarbor Plain marks the southern end of the Great Western Plateau, or Shield—the vast elevated expanse of sand and rock that covers the western half of Australia. The plateau, averaging eight hundred to twelve hundred feet high, is formed in part of some of the world's most ancient rocks. Outcrops that form hills near Albany, the adjacent sea cliffs, and the wave-swept Recherche Archipelago to the south, are dated as Archaeozoic. In the 1,500,000,000 years since these granitic and metamorphic rocks were formed, life appeared and developed on the planet. The limestones of the Nullarbor are much more recent, having been laid down when the sea invaded the area in Miocene times, a mere twenty million years ago. The subsequent elevation of land, faulting, and drop in sea level is responsible for the almost unbroken line of cliffs, from two to four hundred feet high, that fringe the Great Australian Bight for almost six hundred miles.

The western limits of the plateau can be clearly seen on the narrow coastal plain just east of Perth. The Darling scarp, resulting from a series of faults, rises quite precipitously beyond the plain and the fault line itself extends to the vicinity of Geraldton, two hundred miles to the north, where it is fifty miles inland.

The Murchison River, flowing through arid inland country to reach the sea near Geraldton, is only a string of pools in the dry season. Gnarled gum trees fringe the stream. (Michael Morcombe)

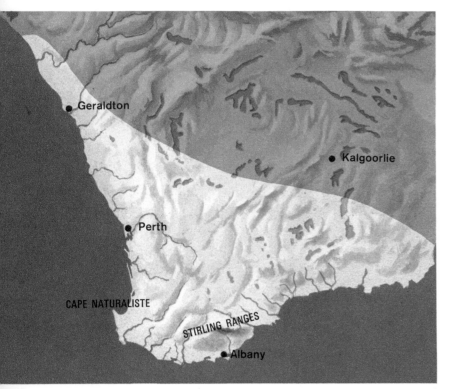

Southwestern Australia, the fertile corner bounded by arid country to the north and west has one of the richest floras, of any area outside of the tropics.

FROM DESERT TO FOREST

Biologists think of southwestern Australia, with its distinctive plants and animals, as delimited by the ten-inch line of average annual rainfall. As pointed out by Dr. D. L. Serventy, Western Australian biogeographer and ornithologist, this is associated with a clear-cut vegetation change, the gums replacing the spindly desert mulga *(Acacia aneura)* as the dominant tree. This "mulga-eucalypt" line forms an arch around the southwest corner. The average train traveler, however, knows that conditions for life are improving when overnight after approaching Zanthus a eucalypt woodland appears. This continues with intersecting belts of sand heath until about Southern Cross, where arable farming begins and wheat paddocks appear. Then, in a hundred miles or so, the trees become noticeably more numerous and the country greener. Forest appears and the grasses give way to shrubs.

The climate and vegetation of southwestern Australia are clearly zonal. A broad belt of twenty to thirty inches of rainfall supports savanna grassland, with eucalypts such as the salmon gum, the gimlet, and the tuart. In a dumbbell-shaped area, where the rainfall is thirty to forty inches per annum, grow forests of jarrah *(Eucalyptus marginata),* one of the famous timber trees of Western Australia. Jarrahs grow to a height of about 150 feet and have shaggy bark. They prefer somewhat hilly terrain, where the soil is porous and contains small reddish stones called laterite. Tongues of sand heath, composed of shrubs up to ten feet high, intrude into the jarrah areas, extending down the coastal plain from the north. It is here that most of the more interesting plants occur.

Southwestern Australia has what is known as a Mediterranean climate, meaning that most of the rain falls in the winter month and that temperatures are mild. On rare occasions, mornings will leave a slither of ice on ponds, and, with the sea modifying extremes, summer temperatures average only sixty-five to seventy degrees Fahrenheit. Rainfall reaches a peak in the far corner of this segment, where the land bulges into the ocean in the form of a heel. Here, between capes Naturaliste and Leeuwin, the annual rainfall averages sixty inches. The plants have responded to such benevolence by producing one of the most spectacular forests found anywhere—the karri *(Eucalyptus diversicolor)* forests. The karris rise on straight white trunks to heights of three hundred feet above a rich understory of shrubbery. They remind the eastern Australian very much of the mountain ashes of Victoria and Tasmania. A man cannot help but be awed by the majesty of these trees as his eyes follow the receding trunks up to their canopy against the sky. The birds feeding among the foliage high above are but black specks, though their calls come echoing down to remind the observer that the tops have their own share of vibrant life. One giant karri near Pemberton supports a ladder and a fire tower, the only place where man can ascend and momentarily share this treetop world. In former times loggers, prizing this valuable hardwood, systematically combed the whole southwest in search of choice trees. The tracts of forest, already limited, shrank drastically. Today a license is necessary to fell a karri tree.

IN THE PORONGORUPS AND STIRLING RANGES

Southeast of Perth near Albany, lie two very interesting massifs, the Porongorups and the Stirlings, the nearest approach to ranges in this part of the continent. The former, about eight miles long, are striking because of the regular way in which their granite has weathered along joint planes to form huge angular blocks. They rise to a height of two thousand feet and include areas of vertical wall a few hundred feet in height. They afford the right conditions for forest and it was here, in a delightful area of striking scenery, creeks, tall trees, and spring wildflowers that I spent several weeks in September 1957, studying the birds. The southwestern forests, isolated as they are by arid country, have proved to be one of the most interesting parts of the continent for many species there have developed marked differences from their eastern counterparts. Among these are a few, such as the red-capped parrot *(Purpureicephalus spurius)* and the white-breasted robin *(Eopsaltria georgiana),* that are so distinctive that their relationship is revealed only by a study of their behavior.

One approaches the Porongorups along gravel roads from the main Perth–Albany railway line. It is a joy after the long Nullarbor Plain to find oneself among rapidly changing scenery again, and fascinating to discern the differences between western plants and animals and those of the east. A forester kangaroo hops across the road and its gray fur has a somewhat more reddish tone than one would expect. A delightful scent comes from a low shrub: it is a boronia, but the flowers are brown with yellow undersides, very different from the large, pink, scentless species of New South Wales. The small *Caladenia* orchids of the forest floor are yellow instead of white. There are several gnarled old *Banksia* trees in the area but the flower shapes and colors are unfamiliar. Here and there are a number of interesting strangers—the bizarre kangaroo paws, the brilliant blue *Leschenaultia,* and the low shrub called *Dryandra.* The *Clematis* vine climbing over some

Grass trees (Xanthorrhoea preissi) *are among the botanical curiosities of Australia. (W. H. Hodge)*

of the smaller trees is, however, covered with white flowers just as in the eastern forests, and there is little difference in purple *Hardenbergia.*

The bird life is, for the most part, familiar both in appearance and song. One recognizes willie wagtails, jacky winters, gray thrushes, gray fantails, ravens, mistletoe birds and several kinds of honeyeaters. But there are no bowerbirds or lyrebirds, and no dainty azure kingfishers sit along the wooded streams. One looks in vain for dollarbirds hawking in the air and misses the garbled chattering of the noisy friarbird and good-natured laughter of the kookaburra, although the latter has now been introduced to parts of the southwest. I found that the forest here had only about 70 per cent of the species that occur in the east.

SOME COLORFUL BIRDS

Soon we encounter unfamiliar species. The wren twittering from the undergrowth suddenly reveals itself to be the splendid wren *(Malurus splendens),* a brilliant ball of blue, far more vivid than the blue wren *(M. cyaneus)* of the East. The treecreeper *(Climacteris rufa)* is dull rust-red, not brown. The silvereye *(Zosterops lateralis gouldi)* has a green, not a gray back, the common black cockatoo a white instead of a yellow tail, and the yellow robin a gray instead of a yellow breast. Not only has prolonged evolution in isolation produced color variations, but behavior differences as well. The common spinebill honeyeater *(Acanthorhynchus superciliosus)* is a noticeably shyer bird than its eastern counterpart. There are also differences in the habitat preferred by certain birds. Among the little treetop-frequenting pardalotes, the spotted species *(Pardalotus punctatus),* the common forest species in the east, is quite rare, being replaced largely by the striated pardalote *(P. substriatus),* but, interestingly, the eastern counterpart of the latter is a woodland, not a forest, dweller.

By far the most fascinating bird of the area is the red-capped, or king, parrot *(Purpureicephalus spurius),* a gaudily-plumaged creature with green back and wings, red cap, pea-green face, and purple underparts. Its beak is curious, the

upper mandible being very long and fine. Ornithologists do not know its nearest relative but some believe it to be a New Caledonian species. The red-cap is by no means a shy bird and is often shot when it is seen attacking apples in orchards. The function of the elongated upper mandible, unique among Australian parrots, was the subject of much speculation until Angus Robinson, a Western Australian ornithologist, compared seed capsules of the red gum or marri *(Eucalyptus calophylla)* that had been attacked by this bird and other parrots and found that the red-cap was able to hook the nut neatly from the cup of the capsule. By contrast, the twenty-eight parrot *(Barnardius semitorquatus),* so called because of its curious call note, had to chew the capsule to get the nut while the black cockatoo *(Calyptorhynchus baudini),* which has a very heavy bill, shattered it completely. Interested in determining why a bill similar to that of the red-cap had not been developed by a parrot in eastern Australia, the writer compared the relative sizes of the seed capsules of the common eastern and southwestern eucalypts and found that the latter tended to be bigger. The inference, accordingly, is that the bill of the red-capped parrot is an adaptation for handling outsized seed capsules.

One of my most interesting experiences in the Porongorups was meeting a grayish bird known as the white-breasted robin *(Eopsaltria georgiana).* Australia has many kinds of robins but only in Tasmania, in the mangroves of the far north, and in southwestern Australia do gray species occur. This species had long been regarded as being related to the northern bird but the possibility remained that it was actually derived from one of the colored robins, in particular the yellow robin of the east. My first encounter with the bird came as I was descending a trail into a dense thicket of spindly saplings in a dry creekbed: suddenly I came upon a small gray bird clinging to the shaded side of a tree trunk. Immediately it dropped to the ground and glided out of sight, and I began stalking it over piles of fallen leaves and between the trees. It proved a tantalizing quarry, keeping just ahead but periodically uttering soft scolding notes. Then the bird, obviously a white-breasted robin, apparently decided that I was just not worth worrying about. It was joined by a second bird and together they "fossicked" within a few feet of me. I now saw that here, reproduced in this plain-colored bird, were the familiar characteristics—hopping and feeding on the ground, hunting in pairs, clinging to trees, uttering chattering notes, and curiosity and fearlessness—of my old friend, the yellow robin of eastern Australia. This then was obviously where the white-breasted robin's relationships lay, not with the pied, red or other gray robins.

THE WAY OF AN EAGLE

The view from the granite crown of the Porongorups southward to Albany and the sea, and over the tops of the forest to the plains of the east, is a spectacle not soon forgotten. In few other parts of Australia is one so conscious of being above

The numbat or marsupial anteater (Myrmecobius fasciatus), *a small marsupial, lives largely on white ants. (Vincent Serventy)*

The quokka (Setonix brachyurus), *one of Australia's small wallabies known as pademelons, forms runways through course grass and hops along them with considerable speed. (Vincent Serventy)*

everything else. One imagines that the horizon is Antarctica, thousands of miles to the south, and it seems that only the heat haze prevents the spectator from seeing the endless sands of the central Australian desert. The granite crown is a very exposed place. Winds whistle up the slopes, drowning out the sounds of birds and tossing the shrubbery in a frenzied dance. High overhead a wedge-tailed eagle *(Aquila audax)* hangs on outstretched wings eight feet across. When facing into the wind he is almost motionless; then, turning, he sweeps past with a great rush. Presently, he alights, wobbling, on an adjacent dome, eying suspiciously the human intruder in his remote domain. The blackish-brown coloring of this bird identifies him as more than seven years old. For a few minutes he rests, then springs into the air again and, wings flapping, flies out over the treetops. Using the wind to gain altitude, within minutes he is once more high overhead, soaring in great wide spirals.

PITCHER PLANT AND CHRISTMAS TREE

The two greatest botanical curiosities of southwestern Australia, the pitcher plant and the Christmas tree, may both be seen in this area. The pitcher plant *(Cephalotus follicularis)* is insectivorous, subsisting on creatures it traps in a juglike formation consisting of modified leaves. The Christmas tree *(Nuytsia floribunda),* whose beautiful orange-red flowers may be seen in December, is actually a mistletoe that has evolved into a tree. It grows to a height of forty feet or more. It is a parasite when young, drawing its nourishment from the roots of other trees. The ecology of the adult tree, however, is by no means understood.

Pitcher plants occur in the moist coastal forests and submarshy country west of Albany. Since they are only an inch or so high they can be found only by resolute hunting. The color of the plant is green with pink and purple tones and scarlet edges. The jug, into which is exuded a sticky and somewhat smelly fluid attractive to insects, has a hinged lid to keep out the rain. Insects entering the pitcher find themselves adhering to the walls, and even if one does manage to make its way upward it finds the rim lined with a palisade of incurved spikes that ends all chance of escape. When the insect finally falls back into the powerful digestive fluid at the bottom, it is dissolved and absorbed. Though quite unrelated to the tropical pitcher plants, *Nepenthes,* it shows a striking resemblance to them. Examples of plants nourishing themselves on the bodies of animals are by no means rare. Sundews *(Drosera)* are prominent in Australia, as on other continents.

QUOKKAS, HONEY POSSUMS AND NUMBATS

The mammals of the southwestern forests and woodlands closely resemble those of the east, though there are several distinctive types. One sees a large kangaroo and several smaller wallabies. Brush-tailed and ring-tailed possums occur, though none of the gliders reach here. There is the honey possum *(Tarsipes spenserae),* a unique little mouse-sized phalanger with a long snout. There are no koalas, though they must once have occurred here since fossils of them are found in the Margaret Caves and elsewhere. Along with these fossils, interestingly enough, there are fossils of the thylacine and Tasmanian devil, large carnivorous marsupials that now occur only in Tasmania. The western native cat *(Dasyorinus geoffroyi)* is rather different from the eastern species, as is a rare, and possibly extinct, little marsupial mouse known as *Parantechinus.* As elsewhere, bandicoots roam the forests. The peculiar little marsupial anteater or numbat *(Myrmecobius fasciatus)* is undoubtedly the most interesting mammal. It formerly had a wide range through the southern interior of the continent, but today survives only in southwestern Australia, in a relatively restricted tract where the York gum grows.

Left: The splendid wren (Malurus splendens), *one of the most brilliantly colored of the fourteen Australian wrens, is not uncommon in the southwest. (Michael Morcombe)   Right: Karri trees* (Eucalyptus diversicolor) *near Pemberton. These forest giants may reach a height of nearly three hundred feet. (Albert Tasker)*

The willie wagtail (Rhipidura leucophrys), *common in city and country, has a melodious call interpreted as sounding like "sweet-pretty-little-creature." (J. Clark)*

The quokka *(Setonix)* has become one of the best known of the mammals of Australia because it has been the subject of detailed studies by zoologists of the University of Western Australia. The project started when it became known that this small wallaby, which is now virtually extinct on the mainland, occurred in large numbers on Rottnest Island off

Fremantle. Offshore islands are the last haven of a number of Australian marsupials since there they are not threatened by introduced carnivores, forest fires, and hunters.

The quokka inhabits dense thickets, hiding by day and emerging at night to graze. A true herbivore, it has independently evolved a rumen, a special chamber for bacterial digestion, in the manner of the sheep and the cow. In contrast to the sheep, it is able to thrive in areas deficient in cobalt. In summer, however, when there is no rain and the vegetation is of poor quality, many quokkas die of starvation. Another interesting finding was that the quokka has achieved delayed implantation; after the young is born and moves to the pouch the female mates again, but the fertilized ovum does not take up its position in the uterus until the young one stops suckling. Thus, should the older young be lost, another is ready to take its place, an invaluable adaptation. Young quokkas are normally born at the end of summer and leave the pouch in September or October. They are independent of their parents when a year old, and mate in their second year.

Another interesting marsupial is the nectar-feeding honey possum. Its lips have flanges that can form a tube, up which the nectar is drawn by the long, brush-tipped tongue. Such a structure, reminiscent of the adaptations of the honey-feeding birds, is unique among marsupials. A tubular proboscis of similar type has, however, been evolved independently in two groups of bats, the tropical American *Choeronycteris* and the Asio-Australian *Macroglossus*. The honey possum is a very active little mammal and can sometimes be seen by flashlight running over and around the upper limbs of the flowering banksias and systematically examining each floret. Captive animals will eat small insects as well as sweetened fluid. When fed sops of bread sweetened with sugar they insert their long tongues into the mass so that the bread becomes completely honeycombed. They survive longest, however, when fed the large nectar-laden flowers of *Banksia, Dryandra,* and *Hakea.*

The numbat is a terrestrial marsupial about the size of a large rat, but with a bushy tail about seven inches long. Its coloring and pattern make it among the most beautiful of all marsupials. The back is reddish-brown interspersed with white hairs, the rump is dark with white bars, and a white stripe runs through the eye. Its face is pointed and the long tongue can be protruded several inches. As in other animals that specialize in feeding on termites and ants, the numbat's teeth are like small pegs. Recent field studies by zoologist John Calaby have revealed that, unlike most marsupials, the numbat is diurnal. It inhabits areas of fallen logs and, in searching for food, sniffs the ground as it walks along. Its main food, the termite, is abundant in the subsurface soil; when it locates termites it sits on its hind feet and digs rapidly, stopping to lick up the insects as they are exposed. The young are born between January and March, four being the usual number. There is no pouch, so the young cling tightly to the teats and undersurface of the mother's fur. The chief causes of the reduction of the numbats are the clearing of the land, bush fires that destroy their log homes and, to some extent, the introduced foxes and cats.

A curious rock face in the dry country near Hyden, 250 miles east of Perth. (Australian News and Information Bureau)

REPTILES, FROGS AND FRESH-WATER FISH

The abundance of small skinks and lizards soon make one aware of the richness of the reptile life in southwestern Australia. As in the east, there are many species of small snakes. Three larger, dangerous ones occur, the tiger snake *(Notechis scutatus),* the brown snake *(Demansia nuchalis)* and the mulga snake *(Pseudechis australis),* which grow to five feet in length and have a potent venom. Two curious lizards occur: one, the stumpy-tail or double-headed lizard *(Trachysaurus rugosa),* so called because it looks alike at both ends, is thick bodied, has very large scales and grows to a length of eighteen inches. The second, the spiny or mountain devil lizard *(Moloch horridus),* which is discussed in Chapter 9, is a fantastic-looking little creature for it is completely covered with spines and has red, brown and yellow blotches. It is an inhabitant of the central desert and reaches only the fringe of the southwest corner.

Only one family of reptiles is peculiar to Australia—the legless lizards or pygopods (Pygopodidae). They resemble snakes, having lost all trace of limbs save for a pair of tiny skin flaps, one on each side of the anus. The tail region is greatly lengthened and the creatures wriggle along like snakes, taking refuge under fallen leaves and rocks. They are brown or gray in color and are usually no more than six to eight inches in length, though one species grows to about a foot. When handled they shed their tails in typical lizard fashion.

The frog fauna of southwestern Australia is a mixture of species peculiar to the region and others that are closely related to eastern forms. The large burrowing frogs called *Heleioporus* are widespread, with different species inhabiting high, medium, and low rainfall areas. One small frog, *Metacrinia nichollsi,* has met the threat of desiccation by living in termite mounds. Another type, the little-known *Myobatrachus gouldii,* which is found well away from water, is believed to retain the eggs inside its body until they have hatched, thus avoiding the necessity of finding a pond at spawning time.

The fresh-water fish of the southwest are restricted to eight species, as might be expected from the scarcity of rivers there. The few distinctive types either are perchlike, such as *Bostockia* and *Nannatherina,* or, like *Galaxias,* resemble tiny trout.

ANTS AND SNAILS

Australia has many primitive insects and one of the most interesting is an ant found in 1934 in a patch of sandy heath country near Esperance. The American entomologist Dr. William L. Brown has described it: "The most primitive member of the subfamily Myrmeciinae, which includes the most primitive known of the living fossil ants." The ant is apparently quite rare as subsequent expeditions to the area, including

The red-flowering gum (Eucalyptus ficifolia) *of southwestern Australia is now widely grown as an ornamental tree. Most gums have white flowers. (Australian News and Information Bureau)*

one led by Dr. Brown himself, have failed to find it. It is still not so rare as the scorpion fly, *Austromerope poultoni;* only one specimen of this species has been taken, and nothing like it has been found elsewhere in Australia. Closely related forms do occur in North America and Chile.

The land snails of the southwest form a distinctive group, the genus *Bothriembryon,* characterized by a rather elongate spiral shell. Some thirty species have been described, though the total number is probably closer to a dozen. They are confined to the southwest, though one has reached Eyre Peninsula in South Australia, and another the Macdonnell Ranges.

THE HISTORY OF AN ANCIENT AREA

It is worth considering for a moment the possible reasons for the plants of southwestern Australia and some animal forms being so different from those of the rest of the continent. It would be appropriate to raise some speculations about why this is so. There is reliable geological evidence that during the Cretaceous geological era, that is, from about 130 million to about 58 million years ago, Australia was separated into an eastern and a western section by a broad arm of the sea extending from the Gulf of Carpentaria. The continent was

Far left: Red-capped parrot (Purpureicephalus spurius) *a spectacular species found in forested southwest Australia, flies from its nesting hollow. Left: Purple-crowned lorikeets* (Glossopsitta porphyrocephala) *at nest. Only seven inches long, these nectar feeders are the smallest parrots in the southwest. (Both by Michael Morcombe)*

therefore not a single land mass but two large islands. Later the two halves united, though for a good part of the subsequent Tertiary period, much of the present Nullarbor Plain was covered by water; it was during this time that the familiar limestones of that area were deposited. The Great Australian Bight was formerly a much deeper inlet. Farther east, in South Australia, a vast inland lake, Lake Dieri, extended from north to south and embraced both lakes Eyre and Torrens, until comparatively recent times.

Obviously the plants and animals of the southeastern and southwestern parts of Australia have been separated by water during much of their evolution. Today there are equally significant barriers in the soil type and aridity. The limestones of the Nullarbor Plain weather to alkaline soil, unsuitable for the growth of most of the western plants, which are accustomed to living in areas of sandy acid soil. Botanists refer to this as an edaphic (soil-type) barrier. Added to this, the rainfall here is a scant ten inches per year, and when the rain does fall it quickly drains away through the porous limestone.

Notwithstanding the differences in plants, there are many similarities in the animal life of the two parts of the continent. Among birds and mammals able to cross inhospitable barriers, the correspondence is very close. Nevertheless, even these forms are loath to leave their customary living places, and biologists postulate that at one time there must have been a measure of continuity in the vegetation around the head of the Great Australian Bight, permitting an interchange of species between east and west. They speculate that there was a south-north movement of the climatic belts in Australia from time to time, just as, in the northern hemisphere, the glaciers first advanced toward the Equator and then retreated north again. Since Australia is in a warmer region, rainfall would have changed more than temperatures, and if the region of aridity centered between the limits of rainfall areas had moved north, a richer kind of vegetation could have extended along the southern seaboard. Animals would have colonized this new habitat both from east and west, while plant types with special soil requirements could not have done so.

One other circumstance that challenges explanation is that the southwest of Australia has so many more plant species than other regions. We are at a loss to account for this beyond noting that a similarly rich flora occurs at the southern tip of Africa. It is possible that plants that evolved in many other areas over vast periods of time have become compressed into these two refuges by steadily worsening climates elsewhere.

Black-faced cormorants (Phalacrocorax fuscescens) *off the southwest Australian coast. Other cormorants are mainly inhabitants of estuaries and rivers. (Vincent Serventy)*

Verdant Island of the South

Tasmania

3 Imagine an island which for most of the year has the greenness of England, a rugged and wave-swept coastline, tall forests, running streams and waterfalls, and a thousand clear, highland lakes mirroring stark glacier-etched peaks and gentle shores of beech and tree fern. That is Tasmania. Parts of it are reminiscent of the pasturelands of Europe, others of its woods. High moorlands suggest Scotland or Iceland. And the mountainous interior has an Alpine look to it.

Here the comparison ends. The exposed west coast is so dominated by the continuous westerly winds that the vegetation is twisted almost horizontal and into an impenetrable mass of interlaced trunks and branches. Eucalypts prevail as the main forest tree, as elsewhere in Australia. The beeches are the Antarctic beech *(Nothofagus)*, a tree whose ancestors branched off from the northern genus probably in the Cretaceous period, over fifty million years ago, and the deciduous beech *(N. gunnii)*, which grows nowhere else in Australia. Some of the freshwater streams contain a primitive shrimp, *Anaspides,* whose nearest relatives, so far as can be determined, are marine fossils from the Permian and Carboniferous periods of Europe and North America, two hundred million years old. Roaming the fern glades and timbered ranges are pademelons, little members of the kangaroo tribe no larger than a hare, and giant gray forester kangaroos, marsupial tiger cats and possums, and most bizarre of all, the Tasmanian marsupial wolf or thylacine which is now probably extinct. The swans that one sees on the surface of the lakes are not white but black. The bird called "magpie," so common about the farms, has nothing in common with the European magpie save its pied coloring; besides, it is one of the best bird songsters in the world.

Tasmania lies directly south from Victoria, separated by the two-hundred-mile-wide stretch of Bass Strait. The island is heart-shaped, one side paralleling the Australian coast, the blunt apex pointing toward the south. Its character suggests in some ways that it is a southward extension of the continent proper, cut off by the rising sea that followed the last glacial retreat. In fact, geologists consider that it has repeatedly been joined to the mainland, with probably three and possibly four periods of junction in the last million years,

each of these corresponding with a glacial maximum. This has ensured a considerable degree of interchange of flora and fauna. Tasmania is poorer in plant and animal species than Victoria; on the other hand, its topography and geology for the most part have remained distinctive.

MOUNTAIN FASTNESSES AND ICE AGES

Tasmania extends from north to south for some two hundred miles and is about 190 miles across at the widest part. It is dominated by a great central plateau three to four thousand feet in height; there are a few peaks reaching more than five thousand feet. The highlands are composed mostly of igneous dolerite, the basic rock of Tasmania but almost nonexistent on continental Australia. There are also very ancient sandstones from the Cambrian period, slates and sandstones that date from the Ordovician, and limestones, conglomerates and quartzites of Silurian age, periods dated 550, 480 and 420 million years ago. The Ordovician and Silurian rocks contain shells and corals, indicating that they were laid down under the sea and that temperatures were warmer then: dense coral beds do not occur so far south today. In the Permian period, 250 million years ago, there must have been glaciation since some rocks on the island show a few telltale striated marks left by moving ice. The next major geological event was the development of fresh-water lakes in the eastern and central parts, as shown by the large areas covered with a thick capping of sandstone, this rock only being laid down under water. The fossils are those of fresh-water species and they are typical animal forms of the Triassic period, showing that these rocks are about 200 million years old. In the Tertiary period, probably starting forty million years ago, Tasmania went through a phase of volcanic activity that must have been widespread and of long duration. Molten rocks intruded along the bedding planes of the sandstone, and spread out to form a sheet over northern parts of the tableland and elsewhere. These varying origins and kinds of rock are of interest to more than professional historians and geologists: they help to explain much of the diverse scenery of today. Hills and valleys vary in shape according to how rapidly they weather and erode. Granites and lavas are very resistant. So are the quartzites, rock hardened by compression. Many of the island's characteristic escarpments are formed of igneous dolerite, while the curious whitish peaks between Queenstown and Macquarie Harbor on the west coast are of quartzite and schists.

The Tasmanian highlands, like those of the east, are largely the results of two periods of uplift, in the Miocene and in the Pliocene. But the final form of much of the uplands is the result of molding by glacial ice. The first glaciation, the so-called Malanna, is believed to have covered between one-third and one-half of the island, including the whole of the center and southwest to a depth of a thousand feet. When it began to retreat, after perhaps 200,000 years, it gouged out deep valleys and ground over the summits of the hills. Great piles of stone were dropped in the valley floors, to create

Tasmania's picturesque glacial lakes were formed when melting glaciers dropped debris across valleys, blocking them off. (Robin Smith)

BASS STRAIT

KING IS.

FLINDERS IS.

Launceston

+ Cradle Mt.

Great Lake

Lake St. Clair

Hobart

Tasmania is famous for its glacial lakes and highlands, forests, pasturelands, and windswept west coasts.

moraines, so giving rise to the many lakes that are such a delightful aspect of the landscape today. The streams ran swiftly, and rivers such as the Derwent, Gorden, Mersey, and Forth were able to form deep gorges.

After an interglacial period of perhaps half a million years, the ice, during the Yolande, or second glaciation, again spread down the mountainsides. Many of the cirques, or amphi-theater-like valleys, now mostly lakes, are believed to be the result of this. Among them are the spectacular cirques of Cradle Mountain and Mount Pelion West in the central high-lands and of Federation Peak in the Arthur Range, fifty miles from Hobart. Two truly magnificent Tasmanian lakes, Lake St. Clair and the Great Lake, are also believed to stem from the Yolande, and it is suggested that two striking harbors of the west coast, Port Davey and Macquarie Harbor, represent areas where the Yolande glaciers carved a path to the sea.

ISLAND ANIMALS AND PLANTS

Tasmania has a considerable rainfall, some sixty inches per year in parts of the west and thirty in the east. This ensures

good forests. The temperature in Tasmania fits into the cold temperate category. The daily minimum temperatures in the highlands in January are 45 to 50 degrees; in July, 30 to 35 degrees. Thus, though the winters are not extreme, the snow season extends for perhaps four months, sufficient to cause many birds either to move temporarily to the lowlands or depart for the mainland, and such temperatures do make Tasmania unsatisfactory for some animal species that require more warmth.

Isolation has had a profound influence on the flora and fauna of the island. The number of species is much fewer than in Victoria. Some of the commonest birds on the Austra-lian side of the strait are absent. There are no lyrebirds (except introduced), yellow robins, willie wagtails, or mistle-toe birds, though the island is plainly suitable for them. A few of the absent species, such as the mistletoe bird *(Dicaeum hirundinaceum),* are probably geologically recent arrivals from Asia, coming after the formation of Bass Strait. Many others, however, are obviously "old Australians."

There are relatively few reptiles in Tasmania, and no tortoises, goannas, gecko lizards, pythons, or snake lizards (pygopods). The total fauna is a mere twenty species, with the tiger snake *(Notechis scutatus)* and copperhead *(Denisonia superba)* the main dangerous snakes. Only two species, both small lizards, are peculiar to the island. The island forests have about 70 per cent of the bird species of southern Victoria, and since reptiles, being cold-blooded, need on the whole a warmer environment than birds, there are no more than 40 per cent of the reptile species. Though there may have been some subsequent colonization of the island from Australia, each of the glacial periods must have had a dire effect, caus-ing the wholesale extinction of lizards and snakes.

Tasmania has many mammals. There are two kinds of pigmy possum *(Cercartetus* and *Eudromicia),* compared to one in southern Victoria, two of marsupial mice *(Antechinus),* the native cat *(Dasyurus quoll),* the tiger cat *(Dasyurops maculatus),* ring-tailed and brush-tailed possums *(Pseudo-cheirus laniger convolutor* and *Trichosurus vulpecula fuligi-nosus),* a pademelon wallaby *(Thylogale billardierii),* a brush wallaby *(Wallabia refogrisea)* and a kangaroo *(Macropus major tasmaniensis),* plus the unique Tasmanian devil *(Sarco-philus harrisii)* and the extinct marsupial wolf *(Thylacinus cynocephalus),* both known only as fossils on the mainland. Numerically, these compensate somewhat for the absentees, the koala and gliding possums other than the sugar glider *(Petaurus breviceps).* This introduces another interesting fact of island life.

Certain species of animals are able to survive on islands after they become extinct in other parts of their range. The fossil record suggests that the thylacine became extinct on the mainland soon after the arrival of the dingo *(Canis dingo),* the wild dog apparently brought to Australia by one of the later waves of aborigines. Since these two animals have many similarities in body form and both preyed on other mammals we presume they were competitors, the dingo winning out. The dingo has never reached Tasmania. There is a parallel in the human sphere. The Tasmanian aborigines, the last of whom died in 1879, were Negritos, racially distinct from and culturally much inferior to the Australian natives. Apparently once occupying much of the continent, they were overrun and absorbed by the Australoids; only in Tasmania did the race remain pure. A more recent example: Europeans brought

Dove and Crater lakes and Cradle Mountain (in center) in the glaciated central highlands of Tasmania. The tops are bare but dense forests crowd the lake edges. (Robin Smith)

the European fox *(Vulpes vulpes)* to Australia for use in the hunt. The introduction of this efficient little hunter, and the drastic changes brought about by settlement, have all but exterminated pademelons from the mainland. They still thrive in Tasmania, however, where the fox does not occur and where large areas of forest still remain.

In a recent study of the plants of Tasmania, Dr. Nancy Burbidge found that some fourteen genera (7 per cent of the island's total) and 20 per cent of the species occurring on the island do not occur on the mainland. This reflects another evolutionary principle: isolation on an island tends to lead to the development of differences and the evolution of new species. These figures would be still higher if some of the plants that occur in the alpine regions of the mainland, and that undoubtedly arose in Tasmania, were included.

Several plants occurring on the mainland as fossils in Tasmania, suggesting that the glacial periods cause some extinction of species. Among these are the araucaria pine, common in the lush forests of New South Wales and Queensland, the Sydney Christmas bush *(Ceratopetalum),* and a kind of bloodwood, *Eucalyptus gummifera.*

HIGHLAND LAKES AND WILDFLOWERS

The highlands of Tasmania have quite distinctive scenery. Lake St. Clair, ten miles long, three to four miles across, and crystal clear, is 720 feet at the deepest part. It is fringed by tall trees, like *Eucalyptus gigantea,* whose white trunks are mirrored in the water, heavy green Antarctic beeches

(Nothofagus), sassafras, and three or four kinds of conifers. Tree ferns grow in abundance along the streams and surround the waterfalls of the area. Forming a steep, purple backdrop to the whole scene is Mount Olympus. Lake St. Clair, now enclosed by a national park, is 2,300 feet above sea level. It was formed when a deep valley was dammed by a glacial moraine. Its outflow gives rise to the Derwent River, Tasmania's biggest stream.

In many ways the most interesting tree in this area is the somber Antarctic beech. This genus occurs also in South America and New Zealand, and its fossilized pollen has been found in various other parts of Tasmania, Grahame Land and McMurdo Sound in Antarctica. To the north it is found in the highlands of New Guinea and New Caledonia, but it is unknown north of the equator. It is one of the plants whose distribution geologists have cited in support of the theory that Australia and South America were once connected by way of Antarctica. In the forests of Tasmania the beech is a rugged, knobby tree whose thick green foliage forms an almost continuous canopy. The bark of the older ones is covered with mosses and lichens, and their antiquity is evident in trunks that are three and four feet thick. The ground beneath them is littered with rotting logs and they support a parasitic fungus *Cytteria gunnii*.

In spring, Lake St. Clair park is notable for colorful flowers, including large red waratahs, pink and white richea heaths, butterfly irises, small orchids, and yellow wattles.

Scores of small lakes, tarns and lagoons adorn the plateaus of these highlands. Many have been tapped for hydro-electric projects. Largest of the lakes is Great Lake, forty miles west of Lake St. Clair, with one hundred miles of shoreline and bays. It is as shallow as St. Clair is deep. Great Lake, like some of the others, has been stocked with brown and rainbow trout, for no large fish occur there naturally. These immigrants wax fat on the myriads of crustaceans and insect larvae in the lake, as well as on the little native minnow *Galaxias*. One of the favorite foods of the fish is caddis flies.

The peaks of the Tasmanian highlands are uniformly impressive. Cradle Mountain rises jaggedly to a series of spires, taking its form from columnar monoliths of dolerite. Federation Peak has high and impressive spires. Ben Nevis, high up on the plateau, is gently rounded. Frenchman's Cap, rising 4,752 feet above the Franklin River Valley, has an overhanging southwest face and crags of shimmering white quartzite. From the quartzite of Frenchman's Cap one gazes across alpine meadows of yellow and cream *Senecio* daisies, little *Anemone crassifolia,* purple-red *Hewardia,* and foot-high heath *Dracophyllum* with its red, bell-shaped flowers. Below, one sees vast tracts of country from Cradle Mountain in one direction to the ocean at Macquarie Harbor in the other. The panorama changes with the seasons and moods of the weather. Winter's snow gives rise to the rain and mists of spring, and then the dancing heat waves of summer. Brilliant sunrises change to the glare of midday and then the pink and orange sunsets of the late afternoon.

THE MARSUPIAL WOLF

There was no more striking inhabitant of Tasmania than the marsupial wolf *(Thylacinus cyanocephalus)*. Now extinct, in all probability it was common in the days of the early settlers,

when it was feared for its powerful physique and hated because of its inroads among the sheep. With such opposition, and its haunts steadily compressed by the clearing of its habitat, it was doomed. Next to the kangaroo, it was perhaps the most bizarre of the marsupials. Though unrelated to the dogs, it had developed a remarkably doglike body and characteristics, with long legs, good for running, an elongated muzzle, large canine teeth and erect ears. It was said to utter a series of guttural coughing barks. Three feet in height and nearly six feet in length, it approached a timber wolf in size. The coat color was tawny gray, and some sixteen dark brown stripes traversed the back, tail base, and flanks. The tail was inflexible and thick at the base, and could not be wagged like that of a dog. The jaws could open to a remarkable width, forming almost a straight line, which must have considerably increased the penetration of the snap.

The marsupial wolf apparently lived in more or less open country. All accounts agree that it hunted singly or in pairs, not in packs like a wolf or dingo. Prey was caught by following a trail until the quarry became exhausted, then brought down with a swift, somewhat clumsy rush. It hunted at dusk or at night, spending the day hiding in a lair. It ate kangaroos, wallabies, and smaller mammals and birds. The destruction of sheep led to the marsupial wolf's being systematically hunted and poisoned, and even to the placing of a bounty on it life.

A recent writer on the thylacine, Dr. Eric Guiler, suggests that the animal fed primarily on blood, sucking it from the jugular vein of its victims, eating nasal tissues, the liver and kidneys, and only occasionally the meat. Other authorities believe that it was not so selective. Certainly, something must have been left behind, for the Tasmanian devil *(Sarcophilus harrisii)* had the hyenalike habit of cleaning up after the thylacine had taken what it wanted.

The last-known thylacine died in captivity in 1933. Mammalogist David Fleay, however, believes that he had one in a trap in 1945, and since that date there have been reports of tracks. This gives hope that a few may still survive, especially in the wild mountainous districts of west and southwest Tasmania.

THE BLACK DEVIL

The thylacine's companion at the kill, so to speak, sharing a wide range with it in southern Australia in the not too distant past, was the Tasmanian devil. It has the dubious honor of being perhaps the ugliest of the marsupials, and as Australia's version of a hyenalike scavenger, it is of great interest. This animal is about the size of a small dog, with a short, heavy-set body, disproportionately large head, and short tail. The black coloring is broken by a white marking across the rump. The attitude is alert, but the snarling pink mouth and wet nose, continuously sniffing, are hardly endearing. The gait is stiff-bodied and cantering. Males weigh from fourteen to twenty pounds and females slightly less.

A scene (at about 3,000 feet) behind Cradle Mountain shows green cushions of Phyllachne *broken by tall spurs of the shrub* Leptospermum. *(F. J. Mitchell)*

The devil thrives in densely wooded areas but often comes about farms looking for fowl. Here its pads may be found, especially in the vicinity of streams. A devil's diet is varied—frogs, snakes, lizards, mammals, insects, lambs—since scavenging comes naturally to them. Apparently their reaction toward each other is little better than that toward a visitor, for Fleay records nights broken by rasping snarls rising to a crescendo of screams, louder and more startling than those of any other bush animal.

The lair is a hollow log or cave among upturned tree-roots and undergrowth, with a bed of bark, buttongrass, and leaves. Four young are produced at the end of May or early June and make their way up to the teats in the pouch. Captives studied by Fleay were nearly three inches long at seven weeks, developed their first fur at from eight to nine weeks, and relaxed their continuous grip on the teats at fifteen weeks of age, when they were well furred and the eyes had opened. From then on they were left in the lair when the mother went hunting, though it was five months before they ceased to rely on her milk. The young were found to be frolicsome and affectionate. They washed frequently, licking both paws and then rubbing them over the face.

SPINY ANTEATERS

Tasmania has its own species of Australia's second monotreme type, the echidna. The Tasmanian echidna (*Tachyglossus setosus*) is distinguished by its larger size and by the fact that its short spines are more or less hidden by fur. There is a description of this animal from as far back as 1792, in the log of the *Providence,* which was commanded by Captain William Bligh of *Bounty* fame. It was written on February 7, when the ship was anchored in Adventure Bay:

> Lieutenant Guthrie, in an excursion today, killed an animal of a very odd form. It was seventeen inches long, and the same size round the shoulders, to which a small flat head is connected so close that it can scarcely be said to have a neck. It has no mouth like any other animal, but a kind of duck bill two inches long, which opens at the extremity, where it will not admit above the size of a small pistol ball. . . . It has no tail, but a rump not unlike that of a penguin, on which are some quills about an inch long, as strong as and like those of a porcupine. These quills, or prickles, are all over its back amidst a thick coat of rusty brown hair; but the belly is of a light greyish color.

The echidna, it will be seen, has little resemblance to the platypus. Nevertheless in the small brain structure, the reproductive system and parts of the skeleton, the two are equally primitive and semireptilian. In both a beak replaces teeth. But the echidna is a terrestrial mammal, it thrives in the forest and in dry, rocky locations, subsisting largely on the ants it excavates from their mounds and burrows by means of its short, thick limbs and powerful digging claws. Apparently, it can live without water. It is extremely hardy and is said to be very difficult to kill. The quills and digging claws are an almost perfect defense, the animal curling up into a spiny ball when surprised or, in soft soil, rapidly digging its way into the soil. Though not a marsupial, the female echidna has a pouch in which it carries the egg until it hatches. The young is also carried in the pouch until the quills become

too large, whereupon it is left behind in a secure hiding place while the mother searches for food.

Echidnas have a wide range in Tasmania. Their presence may be detected by the presence of freshly turned stones and damaged ants' nests. They were a favorite food of the aborigines, but the flesh savors too much of ants to appeal to Europeans.

BIRDS OF FEN, FOREST, AND FARM

Michael Sharland has shown that 230 species of birds have been recorded for Tasmania, about one-third of the number recorded on the Australian continent. Of these, forty petrels, albatrosses, and some penguins may be classed as visitors, frequent or occasional, from the sub-Antarctic seas. About twenty-five, mainly wading and shore birds, are summer visitors from the Arctic. A dozen or so represent rare records of continental birds that have wandered southward or been blown off course by winds. This leaves about 150 species of resident land birds.

Fourteen kinds of birds are considered to be peculiar to Tasmania. The island once had a dwarf emu, but this is now extinct. There is a large rail or water hen known as the Tasmania native hen (*Tribonyx mortierii*); it is twenty inches long and has a greenish-brown body and white flanks. It inhabits river flats, marshes, and lagoons. Recently the Tasmanian native hen has been the subject of scientific study because it is destructive to certain cereal crops. Most of the other birds are counterparts of continental species, but some have undergone a steady change as a result of their isolation. Thus, the green rosella (*Platycercus caledonicus*) resembles the yellow rosella (*P. flaveolus*), and the dusky robin (*Melanodryas vittata*) the hooded robin (*M. cucullata*); the yellow wattlebird (*Anthochaera paradoxa*) has much the same habits as the red wattlebird (*A. carunculata*). Of these the robin has lost its pied male, which is brown, and the wattlebird is larger, more heavily streaked, and has fleshy face wattles of yellow instead of red.

These endemics, as they are called, add zest to bird watching in Tasmania. But many of the other species are racially different from the continental forms, including the brown scrub wren (*Sericornis [frontalis] humilis*) and the strong-billed honeyeater (*Melithreptus [gularis] validirostris*).

Spring finds the birds in full song and vigorously defending their territories. To hear the caroling of the magpies (*Gymnorhina leuconota*) around the fields and farmhouses is a memorable experience. Two or three birds may begin to sing, and inspire the bird who occupies the adjacent territory. Thus, as one drives along a country road, there will be a singing bird on every third or fourth telephone pole. Magpies, about the size of a crow and black and white in color, are resolute nest defenders when they are breeding. A golfer or a boy who wanders too close to one of their large stick nests placed high in a tree will often be sent scurrying by them.

A walk in a field will also draw a quick response from

King River Gorge, where a swift-flowing stream carves a path past steep eucalypt-covered hillsides. (Agent General for Tasmania)

the spur-winged plovers *(Lobibyx novae-hollandiae);* these are predominantly gray and white birds, black on the cap and back of the neck, with yellow facial wattle and bill. Shrill calls of alarm announce the intruder, who soon finds himself circled by indignant birds. From a clump of trees the melancholy call of the fan-tailed cuckoo *(Cacomantis pyrrhophanus)* rings through the air. Swallows *(Hirundo neoxena),* newly arrived from the north, twitter excitedly as they hawk the air for insects.

In the highland lakes of central Tasmania one sometimes sees grebes or dabchicks *(Podiceps novae-hollandiae),* cormorants *(Phalacrocorax melanoleucos),* and teal *(Anas gibberifrons).* The mountain fastness supports the little scarlet and flame robins *(Petroica multicolor* and *P. phoenicea),* gray fantails, golden whistlers, gray thrushes, thornbills, pardalotes, and others. Large currawongs *(Strepera)* enliven the treetops with their melodious, whistling calls.

Yellow-tailed black cockatoos flap lazily across the exposed mountain slopes. And it is rare not to be able to see at least one great wedge-tailed eagle *(Aquila audax)* spiraling high in the sky.

THE BLACK SWANS OF MOULTING LAGOON

In Australia there are no native white swans; they are all black. Small wonder then that they astonished the Dutch navigator Vlaming when he first saw them on the Swan River in southwestern Australia in 1697. Black swans *(Cygnus atratus)* seem to reach a peak of abundance in Tasmania; instead of pairs nesting singly on lagoons, they form huge breeding colonies there. (This also occurs on Lake George near Canberra.) One such large colony is to be found annually on Moulting Lagoon on the east coast where the birds construct their bulky nests of rushes and waterweed in late winter. Four to eight eggs are laid, and incubation takes thirty-five days. The nests are closely guarded, particularly by the male, who aggressively places himself between the sitting female and the intruder. For her part, the female sits closely on the eggs, standing up and making vigorous lunges with her long neck and bill. Cygnets swim well soon after they hatch and it is one of the delights of early spring to see the little parties of gray, downy babies following their parents over the water.

The name Moulting Lagoon comes from the habit of the birds, after breeding, of returning to the lake to molt. Swans, like ducks and certain other birds, become flightless when molting. They then have to take refuge in the center of lakes and swamps. Halfway through the molt the surface of Moulting Lagoon is virtually covered with floating feathers.

The swans can often be seen flying from pond to pond in the late afternoon or early evening, usually in the characteristic V-shaped formation. The long, outstretched neck and white wings standing out from the black body are easy to identify, as are the periodic honking calls.

IN THE TIDAL ZONES

The Australasian seas are rich in marine life, and the exposed, rocky shores of Tasmania are no exception to this. When the tide is full and the westerly swell is churning and boiling against the rocks of the coast, sending fountains of spray

The Tasmanian wombat (Phascolomis ursinus tasmaniensis) *favors hilly country and lives in burrows. (Agent General for Tasmania)*

Facing page: Waterfalls and tree ferns in the Mount Field National Park. (Robin Smith)

The Tasmanian tiger cat (Dasyurops maculatus), *a plucky marsupial carnivore the size of a large marten. (Agent General for Tasmania)*

skyward, there is little to be seen save for masses of seaweed. But when the sea withdraws at low tide, dense encrustations of mollusks, barnacles, worm tubes, and algae cover the rocks. This intertidal life is varied and diverse, with well defined zones.

Usually the life highest on the rocks is a band of orange lichen; then comes a strip of black encrusting lichen; below this is the territory of the small snails. This is the supra-littoral zone, which is never underwater but merely wetted by spray.

The mid-littoral zones or strips below are underwater at high tide. The line of demarcation is sharp, and can be seen extending off into the distance along the rock face. This is the zone where the barnacles, limpets, and mussels live. Both barnacles and limpets look like tiny tents, but they belong to very different groups. The former are crustaceans; the shell is divided into little plates that open out at the top to enable the soft, fernlike feeding tentacles to be extruded. The limpets are mollusks. Barnacles and limpets are equally difficult to remove from the rocks. Their conical shape is obviously ideal for withstanding the force of the waves. The mussels do not favor the more exposed areas, and they are mostly found wedged into crevices and cracks. Also occurring in this mid-littoral zone, and forming a still lower layer, is a corallike algae known as *Lithophyllum*. If one of these is torn apart, a variety of animal types will be found sheltering in it. Isopods and amphipods, polychaete worms, bryozoans, little bivalves, young mussels and chitons, sponges, small crabs and, where there is good shelter, sea urchins and sea stars occur in this middle zone. The lowest zone, the littoral, is underwater during all but the lowest tides. This is the home of the thick, leathery seaweed known as *Durvillea*. It also has a diverse animal life.

It takes a marine biologist to appreciate fully the animal and plant life of the rocks. But the observant amateur will note the differences between animals that live in rock pools, those on exposed rocks, and those that wedge themselves into fissures and cracks.

Despite the hazards of being exposed to the dessicating action of the sun at low tide and, periodically, to violent storms, there are several good reasons for the intertidal zone's being a very rich living area. The churning of the waves causes it to be well oxygenated at all times. Also a fresh supply of food organisms comes in with every tide. When the animals spawn, their eggs and young are easily and rapidly transported to new living areas.

THE MUTTONBIRDS OF BASS STRAIT

The explorer Matthew Flinders, when moving through the stormy waters of Bass Strait in 1802, witnessed a remarkable sight:

> A large flock of gannets was observed at daylight . . . and they were followed by such a number of the sooty petrels as we had ever seen equalled. There was a stream of three hundred yards, or more, in breadth; the birds were not scattered but were flying as compactly as a free movement of their wing seemed to allow; and during a full hour and a half this stream of petrels continued to pass without interruption, at a rate little inferior to the swiftness of the pigeon.

This is our first account of one of the world's most remarkable birds, the short-tailed shearwater or muttonbird *(Puffinus tenuirostris)*. Flinders estimated the numbers of birds at over 150 million, a truly fantastic total and yet one quite believable to anybody who has visited the nesting colonies of these shearwaters.

Bass Strait is the home of some of the greatest sea-bird colonies in the world. The strait is dotted with islands, big and small. The largest, Flinders and King islands, with areas of about four hundred and three hundred square miles, respectively, resemble parts of the mainland, with trees, grassy slopes, wallabies and wombats, and farms. But the smaller islands belong to the seals and sea birds. Some islands are flat and covered with long, yellow dune grass. A few are so precipitous that they have yet to be conquered by man. All have their share of bird life: gulls and terns, muttonbirds and diving petrels, gannets and albatrosses, penguins, cormorants and Cape Barren geese.

The muttonbird or, rather, the young of the muttonbird, is of considerable economic importance to the Bass Strait islanders, who export them in large numbers, pickled, and fresh, to Melbourne and Hobart. Authorities have come increasingly to fear, however, that such exploitation will lead to a falling in the species numbers. A concentrated program of study was, accordingly, a necessity, and a few years ago I had the privilege of accompanying Dr. D. L. Serventy of the Wild Life Division of the Commonwealth Scientific and Industrial Research Organization on one of his expeditions to study the bird.

Our journey through the sounds to the "birdin' isles," as they are known, is by powerful launch with a dinghy following for these waters are most treacherous, a sudden wind abruptly converting a calm surface into a churning mass of giant waves. Dawn is the time of embarkation since it is possible to land on many of the islets only while the early morning calm prevails. From the small port of Lady Barron at the southeastern end of Flinders Island the boat moves swiftly up the beautiful Franklin Inlet. The sound is here dotted with small islands, most of them low hummocks rising to perhaps a few dozen feet above the sea. Some are covered with rather short green grass interspersed with shrubs. Most, however, are yellow with tall dune grass. Ahead, the high peaks of large Cape Barren Island rise a thousand feet above the sea.

The immediate objective is a small grassy island called Little Green Island. In the launch's dinghy, we land beside a hut, pulling the dinghy up on the pebbly beach. We are

Right above: Tasmanian scrub wallaby (Thylogale billardierii), *mother and youngster in log-strewn forest clearing. Because of their isolation and other factors, the smaller kangaroos are not uncommon in parts of Tasmania. (F. J. Mitchell) Right: A black swan* (Cygnus atratus) *and cygnets is a common sight in Tasmania. Australia's only native swan is black; those of the rest of the world are white. (Harold J. Pollock) Far right: The Tasmanian devil* (Sarcophilus harrisii), *the size of a small fox terrier, is perhaps the least attractive but most savage and strong of the living marsupials. Partly a scavenger, it lives mainly on wallabies, birds and frogs, and is destructive to poultry. (Allen Keast)*

Light-mantled sooty albatross (Phoebetria palpebrata), *one of seven species of albatrosses that frequent the stormy waters of Tasmania. (John Warham)*

muttonbirds start to breed at between five and seven years of age, and the males in their seventh or eighth year. Once they leave the colony, young birds do not return for three or four years. Egg laying starts about November 20 to 22 and ends between November 30 and December 2, a schedule that is maintained with remarkable regularity from year to year, regardless of local variations in sea and weather conditions. Only a single egg is laid each year. The first incubation shift, undertaken by the male, lasts twelve to fourteen days, during which time he remains continuously in the burrow, receiving no food. The female then takes over for ten to thirteen days, and so on.

The young bird hatches between January 10 and 23. For two days it is tended, then left alone while both parents forage for food, which consists mainly of a small, surface-swimming crustacean called *Nyctiphanes*. Food is brought back every few days. Growth is rapid and in a month the baby may exceed the adults in weight. Some time in April the very heavy youngster is abandoned by the adults, who leave on migration. For a few weeks, while its wings continue to grow and it assumes adult plumage, the youngster lives on its great accumulation of fat. At night it emerges to exercise its wings, retiring to the burrow during the day. Finally, down to a normal weight, hunger drives it to the sea. The departure takes place at night.

Studies indicate that the muttonbird makes one of the most remarkable of all migratory flights. First these birds move eastward, then northwestward to the waters of Japan and Kamchatka, which they reach in June. By July their "center of abundance," as it is called, is in the central north Pacific. They then appear off British Columbia. Little is known of their subsequent movements until they arrive in Queensland waters in September. Looking seaward from the coastal cliffs of New South Wales any time in October and November, one sees a line of muttonbirds moving south, half a mile or so offshore. Sometimes, apparently because of shortage of food—for pelagic fish that feed on the same plankton are also scarce at the time and the dying birds are ravenously hungry—there may be quite a number of casualties at this time, the birds being washed ashore on the beaches.

Not only do individual birds go to the same island from year to year, but to the same burrow. Finding the burrow must be quite a task. On islands like Big Dog, which is a mile or so across, there are thousands of burrows—and the terrain is remarkably uniform. Nevertheless, the birds do manage to "plop" down—their long wings do not permit them to maneuver in a tight space—within yards of their burrow. Once on land, the bird locates its sitting mate by means of mournful wails. Swift, shuffling steps take the birds along well-trodden paths to the nest. The rest of the night is spent in the burrow. Then, well before the first light of dawn, the birds gather on the runways again, make their way to one of the elevated parts of the island and volplane out to sea.

SNAKES, GEESE, AND ALBATROSSES

An interesting sidelight of the muttonbird islands is that some are almost overrun by tiger snakes (Notechis scutatus), one of Australia's most venomous species. The variety here is particularly large, reaching lengths of six feet. This snake's venom is neurotoxic, causing death by respiratory paralysis.

greeted here by the owners, a family of "birders" who have just arrived from Flinders Island for the muttonbird season. Refreshments over, we are conducted out into the colony in the dune grass. The birder carries a long pointed stick, generally used for carrying the young birds, but also a good precaution against snakes. The ground beneath the grass clumps is virtually honeycombed with burrows. A birder thrusts his arm full length into one of the burrows and pulls out a baby muttonbird. It is so fat that it is almost oval in shape. The coat is soft gray down, soft and resilient.

Presently, we find an adult muttonbird in a burrow. It struggles as it is pulled out of the hole, lashing wildly about with its hooked bill. The size is about that of a pigeon, but the body is slim and the wings long and tapering—powerful instruments for its life over the ocean. It is a dark chocolate brown and the webbed feet are flesh-colored. Released, the bird glides down the slope and disappears out to sea.

Studies over a ten-year period have shown that the female

Prior to the introduction of modern antivenines, the death rate among human beings who had been bitten exceeded 20 per cent. On these islands the tiger snakes seem to feed largely on the very young muttonbird nestlings; after a few weeks the birds become too large to swallow. This means that, as far as we know, the snakes feed voraciously for only a few weeks in the year and apparently subsist the rest of the time on small skinks and their own stored fat! No proper study of them at other seasons has, however, been made.

A number of birders have been bitten by tiger snakes. Usually, however, a man putting his hand on a snake in a burrow is relatively safe since the snake cannot strike in such a confined space. Perhaps the most beautiful of the "birdin' isles" I visited on this trip was Chappell Island. It had become so overrun with snakes that only one family was willing to harvest it. We went ashore armed with a shotgun and killed about half a dozen of the big brutes in the course of a morning.

Bass Strait is the home of a very unusual goose, the Cape Barren goose *(Cereopsis novae-hollandiae)*. Unlike most other geese, this species lives among exposed islands in the sea, feeding on the grassy pastures and roaming far and wide in Bass Strait. It has a silver-gray body, with black tail and wing coverts. A prominent yellow-green cere overlies the greater part of the short blackish bill. The bird stands some three feet high, is from thirty-two to thirty-four inches long, and has a wingspan of about five feet eight inches. Its body weight, ranging from eight to thirteen pounds, makes it a great favorite with sportsmen, who travel from island to island in search of it. The total population of Cape Barren geese is believed to be only about four thousand birds.

My first glimpse of these geese was a thrilling experience. We were returning up the sound in the late afternoon, hard traveling against choppy seas and a strong head wind. Five birds appeared and flew effortlessly overhead, rapid wingbeats carrying them swiftly toward some distant island. Their powerful flight left little doubt of their ability to thrive in this somewhat stormy environment.

The numbers of these geese may well be as great now as at any time since European settlement. While some of the breeding islands have been taken over by sheep, artificial pasture improvement has helped the birds. They remain relatively undisturbed since the graziers only visit their sheep a couple of times a year. With four to seven eggs being laid at a sitting the birds seem quite capable of withstanding a moderate level of hunting.

The Tasmanian echidna (Tachyglossus setosus) *has, in contrast to the mainland species, relatively short spines largely hidden by the thick fur. (Vincent Serventy)*

Tasmanian waters contain the only breeding stations of albatrosses in Australian seas. The breeding species is known as the shy albatross *(Diomedia cauta)* and one colony is on Albatross Island, a nearly inaccessible monolith south of King Island in Bass Strait—and the other on Mewstone Rock off the southern coast. On Albatross Rock the birds nest on the plateau top. Their home is treacherous, however, for a deep chasm bisects the island. The one or two parties of ornithologists who have succeeded in making a landing found many skeletons at the bottom of this chasm; apparently, birds sweeping up on the air currents were caught in a zone of still air and tumbled into the canyon. The island's precipitous sides, central chasm, and boiling white fringe are plainly visible even from an airliner far above. It was easy to imagine the stately albatrosses, erect on their bowl-shaped nests below.

Wave-cut Cliffs, Fern Forests, and Lyrebirds

The Southern Coasts and Their Hinterland

4

Southern Australia is strikingly diverse. Its two thousand miles of seacoast includes huge granitic headlands and monoliths, broad shallow inlets, great stretches of sand beach and dunes, and high limestone cliffs. In places, as on Wilson's Promontory and the Otways, the mountains come down almost to the sea. Over much of coastal Victoria tall eucalypts, with a substratum of tree ferns and dense undergrowth, alternate with lush pasturelands. Beyond the Great Divide, which here swings westward to parallel the coast, are the woodlands and grasslands—the sheep, wheat, and cattle country of today. Finally, marking the northern limits of Victoria is the "Old Man" Murray River, silhouetted against picturesque river gums, its broad, muddy waters enlivened by ducks, pelicans, and white herons.

Where the Divide peters out, the grasslands sweep down toward the sea but beyond, in far western Victoria, are the isolated Grampians, a jagged silhouette of rugged sandstone, named after their Scottish counterparts. Directly north of this, and forming a broad belt to the south of the Murray, are the red sand hills of the mallee, a dense arid scrub of spindly eucalypts with multiple trunk systems.

South Australia contains the lower reaches and mouth of the Murray River, which turns here to meet the sea, flowing through a chain of lakes and wind-swept sand hills. The city of Adelaide lies at the foot of the Mount Lofty ranges, another isolated highland area, its dry eucalypt forests and steep, hilly terrain standing out in relief from the surrounding plains. Northward in the desert the Flinders Ranges are a continuation of the Mount Loftys but now the hills are bare, misty blue in the far distance, finely sculptured and toned with pastel reds, browns, and yellows in close view.

Spencer Gulf, a deep inlet, points toward the heart of the continent. Desert sands and scrubs come down to meet its head. Westward through coastal South Australia is mallee and dry scrub and then, in Western Australia, the Nullarbor Plain, eight hundred miles of virtually treeless limestone plateau. The Nullarbor was once under the sea but now is a seemingly endless plain of dancing heat waves and the scantiest vegetation, for most of the sparse rain that falls soaks quickly into the rock and is lost to the plants. Those clumps of trees that do occur as, for example, near Naretha, are believed by botanists to be leftovers from a time of better conditions, for few seedlings are developing as a replacement. Beneath the Nullarbor are many deep caverns, most with an entrance so small that a human can barely enter. These caverns have their own special race of owl, the cave owl *(Tyto novae-hollandiae troughtoni)*. Just as the Nullarbor Plain is traversed by the longest stretch of straight railway line in the world (291 miles), so it is bordered to the south by the longest unbroken cliffs known, a line extending for 120 miles around the head of the Great Australian Bight.

WIND-SWEPT COASTS AND CHURNING SEAS

Bass Strait, an area of wind-swept islands and turbulent seas, separating Victoria from Tasmania, has an average width of about 120 miles. Projecting out into it like a bastion from the north is Wilson's Promontory, granitic and 2,500 feet in height. It is part of a ridge that once continued through to Tasmania. Other high points on the ridge are Rodondo Island, a monolith of red granite with virtually unscalable walls rising a sheer 1,500 feet above the sea; Hogan Island; the Kent Group; and the large Flinders Island. The strait has had a varied geological history. Its maximum depth today is 240 feet. The famous geologist, Sir Edgeworth David, and others have suggested that it is land that has sunk downwards, the result of faulting to the north and south. But a fall in sea level of about 150 feet would be sufficient to produce a strip of dry land through the shallowest part, the line southward from Wilson's Promontory. There can be no doubt that Tasmania has been in periodic contact with the mainland for, during the Pleistocene glacial periods, when much of the earth's water was bound up as ice sheets, the Pacific seas are known to have fallen 250 to 300 feet. In any event, the submarine ridge running from Wilson's Promontory to Flinders Island is believed to be a horst, an upward bulge of the sea floor, as is that extending from the Otway Peninsula of Victoria to King Island further west.

Wilson's Promontory is itself interesting geologically in that it is connected with the mainland by only a low saddle of sand. Apparently it went through a stage as an island and its junction with the mainland is fairly recent, the result of a later slight fall in sea level and of the accumulation of dune sands.

The large Port Phillip Bay, at the head of which Melbourne stands, and adjacent Westernport Bays represent drowned sections of coast. In western Victoria the shoreline, composed of relatively soft clays, sands, and limestones, is rapidly being

Tree ferns among the gum trees in the forests of the Tarra Valley, Victoria. Such places are a favorite haunt of the lyrebird. (K. P. Phillips)

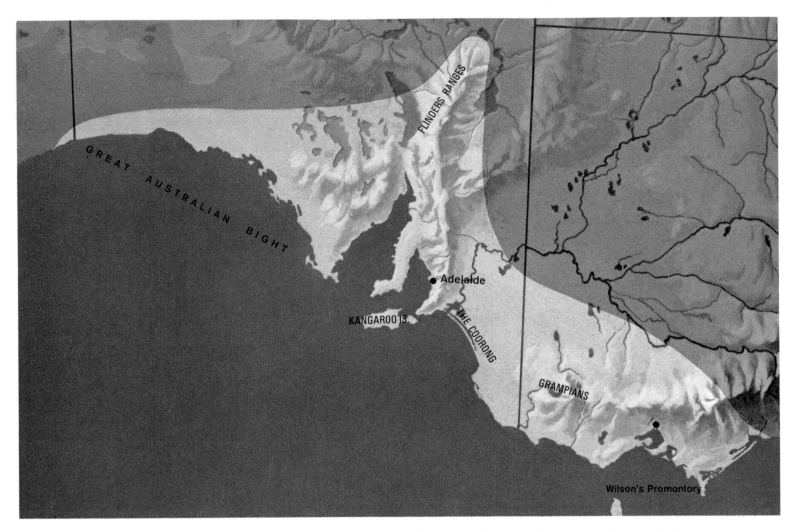

The southern Australian coastlands have a mountainous backbone, gullies of tree ferns and dense vegetation, and island colonies of penguins and seals.

cut back by the sea. Here and there harder masses of rock have been left behind, to form large blocks, rounded hummocks, and even needlelike spires. An irregular line of spires, near Port Campbell, are known as the Twelve Apostles. They are one of the curiosities of the Victorian coast.

PHILLIP ISLAND PENGUINS AND SEALS

Australia has only one species of penguin that breeds on its coasts. This is the little or fairy penguin *(Eudyptula minor),* a small, stubby bird that is blue-gray on the back and white on the breast. It is the smallest of all the penguins, standing from fifteen to eighteen inches high. These penguins abound in the seas of southern Australia, coming ashore onto islands in spring to breed and returning in late summer to molt. The rookery islands extend from Port Stephens in the east to Rottnest Island in the west. None, however, is more famous than that on Phillip Island in Port Phillip Bay. Each evening, between August and December, tourists there see the evening "penguin parade."

The birds wait offshore and their little, puplike yelps may be heard until after dark. Then a group of a dozen or more will surface together and, looking like little old men in white waistcoats, waddle up the beach toward their burrows above the high-tide line. Visitors can observe the penguins by spotlight but are not allowed to disturb them.

Penguins feed on fish, shrimps, and other small marine animals. The eggs are laid between August and November, the clutch being two, and occasionally three. The two parents alternate in keeping the eggs warm, changing places every five to twelve nights. The eggs hatch in thirty-eight days, and the chicks leave for the sea at the age of three months. Penguins must return to their burrows for the annual molt for, like the ducks (but unlike small bush birds, whose molting is a gradual process), they lose most of their body feathers all at once. The few weeks when the penguins are unable to swim is a period of starvation for them. Once fully clad again, however, they are among the most expert of swimmers, progressing by means of short, paddlelike "wings" and steering with the feet. The feathers of the penguin are small and scalelike, shedding water rapidly; a thick underlayer of

An eroded, wave-cut feature near Port Campbell, Victoria. (Robin Smith)
Overleaf: The Twelve Apostles, a curious series of rocky residuals rise like sentinels above the churning seas on the coast of Victoria. The soft limestone cliffs are rapidly being cut back. (Barry Main)

The penguin parade on Phillip Island off the southern coast. These small penguins (Eudyptula minor) *wait in the surf until dark, then come ashore to their burrows among the rocks and tussocks. (Australian News and Information Service)*

fat protects them against the cold. Among their enemies in the water are sharks, in whose stomach a penguin is occasionally found.

Offshore from Phillip Island, on Seal Rocks, is a colony of fur seals *(Gypsophoca dorifera)*. This is an unusually sheltered site for the species, which prefers islands in the open sea. Here the young are born in December and January. The mothers are timid and will take to the water if approached too closely, but the babies remain indifferent to human intruders for the first month or so of life. When old enough to swim, the babies are coaxed into the water by the mother, who guides them with her flippers. Ideally, a rookery island should have small pools in which the young can learn to swim before facing the buffeting of the open sea. The old male fur seal is about six feet in length and the females from four and a half to five feet. As in all of their tribe, their social structure when ashore takes the form of a harem, an old male defending as many as fifty females. Seals live on squid,

cuttlefish, and fish. Heavily persecuted by shooters during the last century, fur seals are now protected in most places. Their numbers are slowly building up again, and it is hoped that the time is not far off when the species will once again be a familiar sight around the coasts of southern Australia.

TALL FORESTS AND HIGH RAINFALL

Southern Australia has a predominantly winter rainfall because it is a part of the Antarctic system, which delivers rain from April to August; in the north of the continent the rain comes from the summer monsoons. But in eastern Victoria, as in coastal New South Wales, the mountains also trap summer rain. The resulting average of sixty inches per annum explains the rich forests of Gippsland, Wilson's Promontory, the Dandenongs, and the Otway Peninsula. Here grow white-trunked mountain ash that rival California redwoods in size. In other places a temperate rain forest results, a few species of softwoods like lilypilly, sassafras, and coachwood, forming dense stands, and tree ferns and bracken being entangled with undergrowth and lush grass that is dripping wet much of the winter. The forest floor here is rich in delicate maidenhair fern and tiny terrestrial orchids.

Where the rainfall is lighter, the tree growth is less spectacular. Along the southern coastline beyond the Otways, in the northern and western parts of the Great Divide, the rainfall ranges from twenty-five to thirty inches per annum. In the Mount Lofty region it ranges from thirty to forty inches, and is twenty to twenty-five inches on the Yorke Peninsula and Kangaroo Island. Here the forests are only about one hundred feet high, and have a much more open canopy. The undergrowth is more sparse, and there is an intrusion of grass in ever increasing amounts. In other words, the conditions are transitional to woodland.

The winter rainfall gives most of southern Australia a Mediterranean type of climate, best described as temperate to cold temperate. Along the coast the mean winter temperature is about fifty degrees; overnight frosting and a fine coating of ice on the ponds are common, but snow is rare. This contrasts with the severer conditions on the higher mountains that make up the backbone of the Great Divide to the north.

THE LYREBIRDS OF SHERBROOKE FOREST

A twenty-five-mile drive from Melbourne brings one to an area of tall gums, tree ferns and lively creeks—a section of the Dandenongs known as Sherbrooke Forest. Here is the best place in Australia to see lyrebirds *(Menura novae-hollandiae),* for long contact with picnickers, along with their naturally tranquil disposition, has made the birds relatively tame. In June and July, when it is cold and damp, the birds are singing at their best. A visitor, if he is patient and has a few hours to spend, has every chance of seeing the majestic male, his beautiful tail elevated and shimmering, singing and dancing at one of his mounds.

The quest takes one among the dense undergrowth, vines, creepers, and moss-grown logs. It is a matter of getting as close as possible without frightening the bird by breaking sticks and rustling the undergrowth. There is no difficulty in locating a male. A hundred feet away the loudness of the call makes one's ears ring. Rich, clear notes cut the air, interspersed with the most varied repertoire of borrowed notes to be heard in the bird world: the resounding crack of the coachwhip bird, the caroling of the gray butcherbird, the chatter of rosellas taking to the air, the wails of black cockatoos, melodious snatches from the golden whistler and gray thrush, followed by the gay laughter of the kookaburra. Some of the calls are loud, others uttered in an undertone so that one has to be close to distinguish them.

Presently, as the watcher stretches and cranes his neck,

71

there is a slight movement in the shrubbery ahead and the singer strides into view. He is about the size of a bantam hen and dark brown in color. The beautiful lyre-shaped tail is elevated over the head, and the fine white underfeathers shimmer in the dim light. As he starts to feed the tail is allowed to fall behind. He runs down a log and the legs are seen to be strong, the toes long and powerful. Vigorously the bird scratches at the fallen leaves, sending them in all directions. He skirts a small tree trunk and his bill is seen to be fairly short, the eye dark and inquisitive. Suddenly the observer is seen. "Whisk-whisk," the lyrebird calls in shrill alarm and in a flash is gone in the undergrowth.

Lyrebirds are found only in the forests of eastern Australia, from about the Bunya Mountains in southern Queensland to the Dandenongs. There are two species, one being confined to the Macpherson Range and adjacent areas in the north. This species, the Albert lyrebird *(Menura alberti),* has the less striking tail. The southern one is said to have the better song, although my experience is that there is not much difference between them. No other bird is so good a mimic. Not only bush sounds but those associated with human activity are reproduced. Stories are legend about the faithfulness with which they learn to copy the sound of a timber mill saw, the neighing of a horse, the rumble of a horse and cart, and a motor horn. One bird caused great confusion among loggers by reproducing the five o'clock "knock off" whistle.

The displays of the males may be carried out either from dance mounds on the floor of the forest or from logs. Each individual has a number of mounds in its territory, freshly scratched patches of earth about a yard across and hidden among the ferns and undergrowth. The male spends much of

Left: Young fur seals (Gypsophoca dorifera) *learning to swim in rock pools on their rookery island off the southern coast. (K. P. Phillips) Below: Fur seal pup being taught to swim. (Don Stephens)*

his time during the winter breeding season in song and dance. In late afternoons, particularly, the air rings with the songs of males whose territories may be a quarter of a mile apart. Each appears to be striving to outdo the other.

Lyrebirds eat worms, small snails, and amphipods or sand fleas, uncovering them with their powerful claws. The nest is a rounded structure, somewhat larger than a soccer football, made of sticks and lined with moss and the soft underfeathers from the breast of the female. It is placed on a sloping hillside, in a cave, or on top of a tree fern, a prime requisite being that the bird is able to glide downhill when it has to leave suddenly. The single egg, slate gray and with umber, purplish, and brown blotches, is laid in June or July. The youngster hatches in about six weeks and leaves the nest in September. Nest building, incubation, and the rearing of the young are solely the work of the female—a social system that is not without its good points!

FROM TINY PARDALOTES TO GIANT COCKATOOS

The forests of Victoria are rich in bird life, many species having an intricate relationship to the eucalypts that dominate the landscape. The tiny three-inch-long pardalotes, rarely seen as they forage high among the leaves, are assiduous destroyers of the scale insects that infest eucalypts. A forest in winter or spring will be enlivened by their melodious piping so that the ornithologist knows there are really a good number of them at work. At the other extreme of size is the giant black cockatoo, *Calyptorhynchus funereus.* This large parrot is an inhabitant of the high ranges, where it breeds in hollows in the tallest trees. One cannot mistake its loud, plaintive call, a common sound in the early morning or late afternoon when the birds are moving between roosting and feeding areas.

The black cockatoo has a unique role in the economy of the gum tree, that of destroying the burrowing grubs and caterpillars that infest the trunks. On other continents this is the task of the woodpeckers, but Australia lacks woodpeckers; so the cockatoos have taken over this role. Lacking the pointed, drilling beak of the woodpeckers, their parrot bill, adapting to the task, has grown huge. The boring insects are obtained by a tearing motion. A curious and characteristic sight after a flock has left a tree is the great strips of bark hanging from the infected area.

HONEYEATERS AND FLOWER POLLINATORS

An even more important role in the economy of the eucalypts is played by the honeyeaters, or Meliphagidae—that of pollinating the flowers. With sixty-nine species, the honeyeaters are the largest family of birds on the continent except for the warblers. They live in forest and desert alike, subsisting on a diet of nectar and insects. Basic characteristics of the group are a somewhat long bill, whose base is grooved to provide a channel for the nectar, and a protrusible tongue that is brush-tipped. Some have bare areas behind the bill and about the eye, an advantage in that the fouling of the feathers by the sticky food is reduced. The alimentary canal is also distinctive, the opening of the esophagus and intestine into the stomach being close together in a little chamber partly separated from the stomach. By this means, nectar, which is easily digestible, can pass straight into the absorptive intestine, while insects and berries are retained in the stomach for further treatment.

Just as the birds are adapted to nectar feeding, so many Australian plants are structurally modified for using the birds to convey pollen from flower to flower. Mr. O. H. Sargent, a Western Australian botanist, believes that birds are the chief pollinators of *Eucalyptus,* though these flowers are also visited by large numbers of flies and bees. In the gum blossom the nectar collects in the shallow basin at the center of the flower, which is surrounded by large numbers of erect and curved pollen-bearing stamens. The bird must brush against these to get at the nectar—often, the heads of honeyeaters are yellowish or white with accumulated pollen. The blossom does not need petals and does not have them. Comparable, and often better, structural adaptations for bird pollination characterize the flowers of other Australian shrub genera such as *Banksia, Beaufortia, Callistemon* and *Epacris.* As is characteristic of "bird flowers" the world over, the blossoms of most of these plants are red or yellow.

THE POSSUM AND THE BANDICOOT

No two marsupials are more typical of the forest, and yet have adapted themselves better to civilization, than the brush-tailed possum or phalanger *(Trichosurus vulpecula)* and the two bandicoots *(Perameles nasuta* and *Isoodon obesula).* The former is arboreal and the latter a ground-dweller. Both are nocturnal. Both range widely, the possum in fact extending far beyond the limits of the forest out into the arid interior. The bandicoots are represented by close relatives in other parts of the continent. It is obvious that this adaptability stood them in good stead when European man began to change conditions drastically. The possum learned to live in roofs and to nibble the tender rose and citrus leaves in suburban gardens. Householders, for their part, took to putting food out for the possums at night, learning that a well-fed possum is not so tempted to eat garden plants. Bandicoots are about the size of a big rat and have long snouts and powerful digging forelimbs. The food is mostly burrowing grubs, which they dig out by means of snout and claws. When gardens border the bush the bandicoots come up to hunt on lawns, leaving telltale snout holes behind.

The brush-tailed possum, which is about the size of a large cat, has gray fur. It has a somewhat doglike, mischievous-looking face, with prominent ears and eyes. Its daytime retreat under normal conditions is a hollow limb or trunk. From this den it moves out to feed by night on tender foliage. Adults have their own territories, and three males studied by Dr. George Dunnet had home areas that measured three

Right above: A male lyrebird (Menura novae-hollandiae) *rests on a sunlit branch above the fern-covered forest floor. (Harold J. Pollock) Right: A bellbird* (Manorina melanophrys) *at its nest. In the dense coastal forests colonies of these birds make the air ring with the sound of little bells. (J. D. Waterhouse) Far right: A yellow robin* (Eopsaltria australis) *seeks its insect food on the forest floor beside a clump of toadstools. (L. H. Smith)*

hundred by one hundred, three hundred by fifty, and four hundred by seventy-five yards respectively. They drove rival males from these areas, though they tolerated younger males and females. The adult females had somewhat smaller ranges.

The name possum stems from Captain Cook, who saw one in North Queensland in 1770 and thought it looked like the American opossum. Though the latter is also a marsupial, it belongs to a very different group. The Australian animal has a prehensile tail but is vegetarian and is a much more attractive and appealing animal. Their fur is soft, and they were at one time killed in thousands for their pelts. The koala never recovered from a similar slaughter, whereas the possum is still one of Australia's most common mammals.

The breeding season is in March-April and there is a second, lesser one in August-September. Birth occurs within twelve to twenty-four days, the baby making its way to the mother's pouch as in all marsupials. It is then blind and naked. Two to three weeks after arrival at the teat males may be distinguished from females; the prehensile nature of the tail is discernible at forty-eight days; and the eyes open after one hundred to one hundred and ten days. The duration of the stay in the pouch is four to five months, so that the babies conceived in the major breeding season emerge onto the mother's back in August or September. By November, at the age of about seven months, the baby is largely independent of the mother.

Possums come readily for bread and jam when it is placed on a fence post or edge of the verandah. They emerge as soon as darkness falls. Sitting erect on his hind limbs, the possum lifts the titbit with its hands, munching like a squirrel. In many homes in Melbourne and Sydney it is part of a regular evening ceremony for children to feed the possums before being put to bed.

In comparison, bandicoots seem to lack personality and so are less well known and liked than possums. They can often be seen on the forest floor by a searcher with a flashlight. The animal has a slow, bounding gait. The fur is coarse and hairy and is of no interest to the fur trade. A curious characteristic of the bandicoot is that its second and third toes are bound together, an adaptation, it is thought, for preening the coat.

Bandicoots live in burrows, under logs or in crevices. They may have young at any time of the year, the litter varying in size from one to five. From man's point of view they have one shortcoming: they are apparently an important intermediate host of the dog tick, a scourge that kills off many household pets each summer.

THE MARSUPIALS

The mammal fauna of Australia numbers about 230 species. Of these, three, the platypus and two species of echidna, are egg-laying monotremes. There are about one hundred and ten marsupial mammals, in which the young are not fully developed in the womb, and there are about one hundred and twenty species of "advanced" or placental mammals in which the young are held in the uterus of the mother until fully developed. The latter are either rats and mice, or bats, plus the dingo, whose ancestors were brought in by the aborigines. It is in the marsupials that most interest lies, for in the fifty million or so years of isolation on the Australian continent these mammals have developed the widest range of body

forms. Many have assumed a body structure and way of life similar to placental mammals on other continents. Thus there are marsupial "cats," a marsupial "mole," a marsupial "anteater," and a marsupial "wolf." The smallest of them are called marsupial "mice," but actually these are insect- and flesh-eaters, not vegetarians like the true mice. The wombat, a large terrestrial burrower, has developed a body much like that of a marmot; the brush-tailed possum looks somewhat like a raccoon; and so on.

The forest and woodland areas of Australia are the richest in the number of species of marsupials. Here live the great gray or forester kangaroos (Macropus major), the males of which may stand six feet high. Other members of the kangaroo tribe are the wallabies and small rat kangaroos, the latter no bigger than a hare. Unfortunately the rat kangaroos are now almost extinct. The macropodids, as all of these are called, are vegetarians, consuming grasses and shrubbery.

The phalangers, arboreal marsupials, include the brush-tailed possum and the ring-tailed possum (Pseudocheirus laniginosus), a smaller, browner, and daintier species, is still quite common. It tends to keep to the dense bush, preferring thickets. Tiniest of all is the pigmy or dormouse possum (Cercartetus nanus), which is no bigger than a mouse. It too has a prehensile tail. Several members of the group have gliding membranes that stretch between the fore and hind limbs, permitting them to volplane from tree to tree. They do not fly in the true sense, but simply glide downward; hence they progress through the forest by climbing a tree and leaping from the top of it to a lower point on an adjoining tree. The largest member of the group, the greater glider (Schoinobates volans), has been recorded in glides of up to three hundred and sixty feet. Those of the smaller, squirrel-sized sugar glider (Petaurus breviceps) are shorter, but still spectacular. The smallest of the gliders is the mouse-sized feathertail glider or flying "mouse" (Acrobates pygmaeus).

Victoria has an endemic phalanger, Leadbeater's possum (Gymnobelideus leadbeateri), which was long thought extinct but rediscovered in Gippsland a few years ago. It is quite similar to the sugar glider but is browner in color and lacks the gliding membranes.

PREHISTORY OF THE MARSUPIALS

Marsupials survive only in Australia, New Guinea, and South America. The single North American marsupial, the Virginia opossum, is not a native but a recent immigrant from the south. Australia has three-quarters of the known marsupial species. But marsupials are found as fossils both in Europe and North America, showing that at one time they had a much wider range. Presumably they arrived in Australia prior to that continent's separation from Asia, toward the end of the Cretaceous period, some sixty million years ago. Whether or not a land connection existed at this time is not known. Professor G. G. Simpson, the famous zoologist, has postulated that, if there was not, the ancestral marsupials must have

A dense fern gully near Melbourne. The cone-shaped trees are sassafras (Doryphora). *(Australian News and Information Bureau)*

been able to cross water gaps, whereas the early placental types, already coexisting with them, could not.

We know nothing of the early evolution of marsupials in Australia because the fossil record does not extend back beyond the Oligocene period, thirty or so million years ago. The single fossil from that period is a possum type. By the time of the Miocene period kangaroos had evolved. In the Pleistocene, extending back for a million years or so, there was a rich fauna that included giant forms now extinct. Included in these are *Diprotodon*, a four-footed herbivore with the bulk of a rhinoceros, and a curious predator, the panther-sized *Thylacoleo* with strange shearing teeth and prehensile claws.

WILDFLOWERS AND THE CYCLE OF THE SEASONS

Unlike the northern continents, Australia does not have extreme seasonal changes. Spring is the season of renewed life here as elsewhere. Summer is hot and the winter somewhat cold. But the seasonal influences may be fairly subtle. The trees are evergreens. The main flowering periods in the coastal areas are spring and summer, but some species bloom in autumn and others in winter. Insects reach their peak of abundance in spring and summer, but their availability all year is revealed by the high proportion of nonmigratory birds. Most birds breed in spring, but there are a few summer nesters, and hawks, owls, and the lyrebird have their eggs and young in winter.

Near where I lived in Sydney the spring wildflowers were always breathtaking, but Christmas, which falls in midsummer in Australia, had its striking types, notably the Christmas bush *(Ceratopetalum)* and Christmas bells. Autumn brought many wattles into bloom, plus various heaths and pea flowers, while the winter was characterized by other wattles as well as boronias.

A similar pattern characterizes colder southern Victoria. Spring begins in September with the early nancies *(Anguillaria)*, which spread over the landscape like thin snow. The banks are festooned with the tiny purple creeper *(Hardenbergia)*, and the shrub *Dillwynia* opens up with its yellow and brown pea flowers—the "ham and eggs" of schoolchildren. October brings white milkmaid *(Burchardia)*, yellow bulbine lilies, buttercups, field daisies, and wild violets into flower. With November comes the trigger plant *(Stylidium)* and the sickle greenhood orchid *(Pterostylis)*. In December, when the grasshoppers begin clicking in the long grass, blue pincushions *(Brunonia)*, bluebells *(Wahlenbergia)*, fringe lilies *(Thysanotis)*, and curled everlastings *(Helichrysum)* come into their own. One of the most conspicuous January flowers in southern Australia is the pink hyacinth orchid *(Dipodium)*, a leafless plant that draws on tree roots for nourishment. Here, as farther north, February, March, and April see the flowering of a few wattles (which offer only a foretaste of what is to follow in spring), the bell-shaped *Correa,* the purple fanflower *Scaevola,* and others. In midwinter the landscape offers the

A male lyrebird displaying on his mound among the ferns of a valley floor. The tail of shimmering white filaments is spread over the body. (Roy P. Cooper)

white-flowering heath *Epacris,* yellow stars *(Hypoxis)*, sundews, greenhoods, and minute helmet orchids.

SEASONAL CHANGES IN THE WORLD OF BIRDS

In the bird world the changing of the seasons is quite striking. Most of the winter song has been only intermittent, with many species communicating by short snatches of song. But with the coming of August the dawn is enlivened by the first spring songs. Yellow robins, gray thrushes, yellow-tailed and striated thornbills *(Acanthiza chrysorrhoa and A. striata)* start to build in this month. At the beginning of September the first of the returning migrants arrive, bringing with them songs not heard for many months. There is the joyful cadence of the bush canary or white-throated warbler *(Gerygone olivacea)*, the loud, ringing notes of the rufous whistler or eachong *(Pachycephala rufiventris)*, and the mournful scale of the pallid cuckoo *(Cuculus pallidus)*. By October most of the residents, and the first of the migrants, have started to nest: wood swallows, cuckoo-shrikes, peewees, wagtails, quail, and others. With November come the later migrants. The large dollarbird *(Eurystomus orientalis)*, so called because of the white blotch on its wing, takes up his hunting perch on top of a dead tree, and the cicada bird *(Edoliisoma tenuirostre)* makes the hilltops ring with his buzzing call. These birds breed locally but two other summer visitors do not: the migratory swifts from China and Japan *(Chaetura caudacuta and Apus pacificus)*. Usually these arrive on the tail of a northerly wind or at the beginning of a rainstorm. One sees them fluttering and spiraling high in the sky, sweeping up the flying insects in their wide, gaping mouths. But they do not stay long in any one spot. One may encounter them half a dozen times in a summer.

Nesting is usually over by early December, for then the weather is starting to become hot and is unsuitable to delicate nestlings. Later migrants like the rufous fantail *(Rhipidura rufifrons)*, however, continue to nest into January, and the fruiting of the mistletoe may persuade the tiny mistletoe bird *(Dicaeum hirundinaceum)* to go on into February. The dozen or so migratory forest species start back north at any time from late January to April. But by the time they go they have already fallen silent, so that it is difficult to say just when they leave.

EARTHWORMS TEN FEET LONG

One of the zoological curiosities of the higher rainfall areas of southern Victoria is the giant earthworm *(Megascolides gippslandicus)*, a species far larger than any other in the world. These worms live in the rich loam of the Bass River Valley of Gippsland where they may be located by their weird gurgling and bubbling sounds. They are about the thickness of a man's thumb but they can be stretched to as much as ten feet. The large ones weigh ten ounces and more. When handled they defend themselves by squirting fluid from pores on the body surface.

Giant worms were long thought to be confined to Gippsland but in 1952 David Fleay found one in southern Queensland that was three feet long and extended to four and a half feet. And in 1957, Elizabeth Pope of the Australian Museum

found one of equal size in the red basaltic soil near Kyogle in northern New South Wales.

THE GARDENS OF THE GRAMPIANS

Rising suddenly from the plains of western Victoria, the rugged Grampians are famous for two features, the bizarre shapes of the rocks—for sandstone weathers rapidly—and the variety of the plants. Tourists come from far and wide to see the wildflowers in spring, when the landscape is alive with color and the diversity in species is great. There are, for example, eighty-four different kinds of terrestrial orchids alone. Many of the plants, moreover, do not occur elsewhere on the continent.

When I visited the Grampians in September 1956, my high expectations were fulfilled. From a distance the range is a thrilling sight; on approaching closer one is struck by the rugged beauty of the sandstone cliffs, the piled masses of fallen rock, and the innumerable honeycombed caves. One could see all the curious rock features described in the literature: the "giant mushroom" (a flattened rock perched on a narrow vertical base), the "Christmas turkey," the "railway engine," the representations of human heads, needles, and domes, the great boulders perched precariously on the edges of precipices, and others wedged in chasms or lying broken on the valley floor. To this jumbled mass of stone the wildflowers and the gums clung in complete disorder. The beauty of the flowers was a delight: the white bush heath-myrtle, red fuchsias, golden acacias, white- and pink-flowering tea trees, the blue tinsel lily with its star-shaped flowers, pink boronias, yellow pea flowers and goodenias, purple scaevolas, and various *Epacris* and *Grevillea*. Many of the genera were familiar to the visitor from eastern Australia but the species, and the colors and shapes of the flowers, were often different. The gums of the Grampians, like eucalypts everywhere, showed a remarkable ability to thrive in areas of broken stone, but the finest trees grew in the valleys. An interesting species was the Grampians' endemic eucalypt, *Eucalyptus alpina*. Grass trees *(Xanthorrhoea)*, a curious plant with a three-foot, rounded base of grasslike leaves and a six- to seven-foot flower stalk adorned with tiny white blooms, were numerous. I had seen them near Sydney and in other parts of the continent but here they were particularly fine.

THE LOWER MURRAY AND MOUNT GAMBIER

In southeastern South Australia, where the cliffs have given way to long, sandy beaches and dunes, the Murray River enters the sea. To do this it swings southward and runs through a relatively arid part of the continent that in ancient geologic times was a deep inlet, the so-called Murravian Gulf. Part of its journey is through mallee but in the lower reaches, around Murray Bridge, its flood plains support a substantial dairy industry. The river here is broad and muddy, a haven

The upper reaches of the Yarra River (which flows into the sea at Melbourne), showing shallows and gum trees. (Dacre and Pauline Stubbs: J. Allen Cash)

The little grebe (Podiceps novae-hollandiae) *sits on its nest in a marsh. When frightened these birds cover their eggs with weeds before flying away. (Eric Lindgren)*

for waterfowl. Pelicans and black swans dot the surface, little skeins of ducks pass swiftly upstream, and herons stalk in the shallows.

The mouth of the river is largely blocked by a sandbar that dams the water back into the shallow lakes Alexandrina and Albert, and the Coorong. The edges of these lakes are shaped into low headlands and shallow bays. The terrain is sandy and arid, and covered with low bushes. Farther north, near Naracoorte, are true salt lakes.

The Coorong is curious. It is a long narrow lagoon, stretching for ninety miles from east to west, only a mile or two back from the sea and separated from it by sand dunes. It is famous among ornithologists as the nesting place of large colonies of pelicans *(Pelecanus conspicillatus),* who choose the sandy islands for their rookeries. This striking bird is white, with the wing and tail black, and a pale pink bill. The pouch that hangs beneath the bill is buff pink. The body length is from five feet to almost six feet, and the wingspread ranges from eight to eight and a half feet. The birds weigh from ten to fifteen pounds. The bill is fourteen to eighteen inches long and is capable of holding up to three gallons of water. The take-off of the pelican from the water is lumbering and leaves behind a train of broken water; the landing creates a surge like a miniature powerboat.

Pelican nests are slight hollows scraped in the ground. The two to three eggs that are laid are white with a thick coating of lime. The newly hatched young are naked, gawky, and

ugly. From their nesting colonies the pelicans disperse widely over southern Australia in the summer, autumn, and winter, being found as far afield as central coastal Queensland.

Black swans also nest in large numbers on the Coorong, and in past times the aborigines used to come to this waterway for an annual feast of eggs.

East of the Murray, at the town of Mount Gambier, are a series of curious volcanic lakes—deep bodies of water collected in old cones. That of Mount Gambier itself is the most impressive. Its crater wall rises six hundred feet and within the crater are several small bodies of water. This area is the westernmost extremity of recent volcanic activity in Australia. There is an old aboriginal legend referring to an "area of fire" here, and it seems possible that the volcanoes were still active at the time of the first aborigines.

KANGAROO ISLAND AND MOUNT LOFTY

Many of the plants and animals of the eastern forests peter out by near the Grampians or the Millicent coastal area of southeastern South Australia. In fact, there is a progressive reduction in the number of species westward from the Dandenongs, beyond which the lyrebird and other species do not occur. Then, to the west of the arid Murray–Coorong strip in South Australia, are two extensive tracts of rather dry forest. One of these is in the Mount Lofty ranges, and the other is offshore on Kangaroo Island.

Kangaroo Island is about eight miles long and thirty to forty miles across. It lies twenty to thirty miles offshore and was connected to the mainland at times of lower sea level. It has been known since the earliest days and was frequently visited by sealers, for its coasts and offshore islets contained great colonies of these animals. The first settlers found a dwarf species of emu on the island, but this was quickly exterminated. Archaeologists have found evidences that the aborigines once occupied the island; it has been suggested that they died of nutritional deficiency. At any event they were apparently an earlier type of man, similar to the Tasmanian, who lacked dogs, for no dingo remains occur on the island.

Kangaroo Island contains excellent tracts of forest and the reaches of a few small streams, like American River, are a delight. Much of the terrain, however, is sandy and covered with coastal scrubs and heathlands. The island has its own endemic race of the forester kangaroo. There is a population of the glossy black cockatoo *(Calyptorhynchus lathami)* on the island, a hundred or so miles to the west of its main distribution. Many of the small birds have formed races on the island. Thus populations of thornbills are visibly different from those on the adjoining mainland and some of the common birds on the adjacent coast, such as the singing honeyeater *(Meliphaga virescens)*, do not reach the island. The seal colonies on Kangaroo Island are slowly building up in numbers again and are not difficult to observe.

The Mount Lofty ranges, like the Flinders behind them, apparently originated during the great Miocene uplift. The

Loftys (high point 2,384 feet) and Yorke Peninsula represent this upthrust, whereas Spencer Gulf and St. Vincent's Gulf represent a sinkage during the same period. The dry forests of these ranges harbor many eastern forest birds. Here are such honeyeaters as the spinebill *(Acanthorhynchus tenuirostris)* and the blackcap *(Melithreptus lunatus)*, kookaburras, thornbills, thrushes, and blue wrens. As on Kangaroo Island, many of them have differentiated into races. Among the mammals the eastern native cat occurs, or did occur.

A minor, but interesting, area nearby are the marshy grasses and heathlands of Mount Compass. Here are isolated populations, possibly now extinct, of emu wrens *(Stipiturus malachurus)*, so called because their filamentary tail feathers resemble the plumes of an emu, and the rare and elusive ground parrot *(Pezoporus wallicus)*. This bright green bird, about the size of a rosella, is a true ground dweller, living on seeds and herbage in scattered areas of marshy grassland along the southern and eastern seaboard of the continent. Through this habitat it moves with the skill of a rodent but takes to the air when approached too closely, flies swiftly for a hundred or so yards and then drops precipitously to ground again. The nest, with its four to five white eggs, is hidden low in the undergrowth.

The emu wren and ground parrot are two species in South Australia that are steadily being eliminated by the increasing dryness of the country. In the not too distant past, damper

Young individual of the southwestern race (hypoleucus) *of the gray or brushtail possum* (Trichosurus vulpecula), *the common phalanger of the Australian forests. (Vincent Serventy)*

Grampian Mountains, western Victoria, where the sandstone has weathered into bizarre shapes and forms. (Robin Smith)

conditions must have prevailed around the mouth of the Murray and permitted free interchange of forest and wet grassland animal species between east and west.

THE RED AND PURPLE OF THE FLINDERS

Extending northward from the Mount Loftys, for some two hundred miles out into the desert, are the Flinders ranges. Like the former they are, geologically, a giant horst, and had their origin in the marked land movements of the Miocene. Within the ranges sharp ridges and steep gorges alternate. Some of the latter contain thick vegetation. Water flows in the creeks only intermittently. To the north the peaks become higher and bleaker, their bare purple and red rock strongly reminiscent of the McDonnells to the north. Mount Remarkable reaches 3,178 feet, and St. Mary Peak, 3,900 feet.

The Flinders ranges are a major tourist attraction. Visitors enjoy the parklike country of the south, with its covering of cyprus pines, eucalypts, and grass. At Warren Gorge are stark rocky outcrops, around which the gums cling precariously, but the bottom has a well-defined creek fringed by tall white-trunked gums. Wilpena Pound, in the north, is one of the natural wonders of the continent—a vast plateau-top amphitheater or basin nearly twelve miles long and five miles wide, surrounded by steep escarpments of quartzite. It can be entered only by a narrow gorge on the east side through which, on the rare occasions when it is running, Wilpena Creek flows out onto the sand plains.

The Flinders ranges are the haven of one of the most delightful little members of the kangaroo family, the yellow-footed rock wallaby *(Petrogale xanthopus)*. They are brown with yellowish markings and yellow feet, and have a banded tail. They live high on the rocky slopes, taking shelter in caves by day and coming out at dusk to feed on the vegetation of the hills and valleys. The animals have ridged, "skidproof" soles, which permit them to move about with the nimbleness of a mountain goat. One has to be lucky to see the rock wallabies today for like other marsupials they were once heavily slaughtered for their pelts. If an observer does catch a glimpse of them, it is likely to be in the form of a few little heads, high on the slopes, silhouetted against the evening sky.

Pelicans (Pelecanus conspicillatus) *and silver gulls* (Larus novae-hollandiae) *on the banks of the American River, Kangaroo Island. (K. P. Phillips)*

Grasslands, Kangaroos, and Ibises

The Murray–Darling Basin

5

Extending from the Great Divide into the interior of New South Wales and Queensland, and from south to north for almost the length of the continent, is a tract of savanna woodland and grassland country known as the western plains. Although these plains have become the center of the Australian wheat and wool industry, they are specially interesting as the home of the red kangaroo, the stately emu, the great flocks of white and pink cockatoos, and as the location of marshlands where, in favorable years, myriads of water birds breed. The southern two-thirds of this plains country forms the drainage basin of the Murray and Darling rivers and their tributaries, great streams by Australian standards but insignificant compared to those of other continents. They rise from the western slopes of the Great Divide and follow sluggish, contorted pathways west and south, falling as little as from four to nine inches in a mile.

Much of the basin has an erratic rainfall. "Normal" years are interspersed with drought years, when many of the streams dry away to a series of pools. Alternatively, floods may sweep out over the plains, changing the course of streams and leaving behind marshes and the oxbow lakes called billabongs. Westward from the Great Divide, the amount of rainfall decreases steadily from an annual average of forty inches at Sydney to twenty inches at Dubbo (150 miles inland), twelve at Bourke (300 miles inland), and eight at Broken Hill, on the fringe of the desert (450 miles inland). These changes, along with soil differences, give the western plains of New South Wales and Queensland a fair measure of diversity in vegetation. A north-south belt of woodland extends inland for a variable distance from the divide, changing to savanna grassland with scattered trees. In some places tracts of cyprus pine occur, and in others mulga *(Acacia aneura)* dominates the landscape. Great areas of the flatter country are covered by the stunted saltbush and bluebush. Finally, in areas of red sand, and especially along the lower Murray River, there is mallee. But the most striking feature of the Murray–Darling basin is the stately river gum *(Eucalyptus camaldulensis)* that lines the waterways, big and small.

These giant trees are commonly eighty to one hundred feet high, have bright green foliage and attractive white trunks with patches of brown bark. They extend in an unbroken line across the landscape, marking the courses not only of the continuously flowing streams but of those that hold water only intermittently. They and another eucalypt, the coolibah *(E. coolibah)*—of *Waltzing Matilda* fame—line the billabongs, providing shade and shelter for the wild ducks, herons, and parrots.

MAN'S INFLUENCE

In his one hundred and seventy years in Australia, European man has wrought many changes in the western plains country. There has been considerable clearing, and sections that were woodland broken by patches of grass are now open paddocks and fields with scattered clumps of trees. An extensive network of roads, a few of them paved, radiate across the country. Sheep are dispersed through the paddocks or straggle across the areas of light woodland, grazing and stirring the dust as they go. It is the land of the drovers, and they, with their sheep dogs, are a common sight. Overstocking of the land has been serious in places, and erosion and silting have occurred along the waterways. But the worst agent of destruction has been the European rabbit *(Oryctolagus cuniculus)*.

The domesticated rabbit was introduced to Australia as early as 1788, but it was not until the wild rabbit was introduced in Victoria, in 1859, that rabbits established themselves. Adjusting rapidly to the country, and having a phenomenal reproductive rate, the rabbits spread like wildfire. By 1880 they had crossed the Murray River into New South Wales, and in 1886 reached Queensland, having traversed New South Wales at an average rate of seventy miles a year! In due course they reached the Gulf of Carpentaria but, the more northern areas apparently proving unsuitable, they died out in much of Queensland. The impact of the rabbit was catastrophic. Country that had supported lush grass was now eaten down until it resembled a bowling green. At times of drought the rabbits died by the millions, but before doing so they ring-barked and killed shrubs and bushes, and ate grass down to its roots. The number of sheep that could be grazed in a given area was drastically reduced, and hundreds of men were employed in keeping down the number of rabbits. During World War Two, with the withdrawal of manpower for the services, these controls were lifted and the rabbit numbers built up enormously. To see valuable grazing properties a moving, almost solid mass of bobbing white tails, as I did near Coonamble in 1947, was sobering indeed.

In 1950, following extensive study, scientists introduced the virus disease myxomatosis, which had originated in South American rabbits, into the rabbit population. Initially, the results were disappointing. Apparently the weather in the first year was not conducive to the spread of the disease. Then came one of those years of flood. Mosquitoes, the main

Budgerigars are common in the grasslands of the Murray–Darling basin. This huge concentration occurred at Queen Victoria Springs, a desert waterhole in Western Australia. (Vincent Serventy: Paul Popper Ltd.)

transmitting agent, built up enormously, and far and wide across the land there were dead and dying rabbits. The rabbits were cut to perhaps a tenth of their former numbers. Country that had been virtually wasteland became green again and in some places grass grew to heights such as farmers had not seen in their lifetimes. Today, fifteen years later, the rabbits remain low in numbers, although they have developed some degree of immunity to the disease. The campaign against the rabbit in Australia has thus far been a triumph for the Commonwealth Scientific and Industrial Research Organization and for the biologist directing the program, Francis Ratcliffe.

The net effect on the native wildlife of the despoliation of the grasslands of eastern Australia has been great. The loss of cover meant an early extinction of many species. A recent study by Basil Marlow of the Australian Museum has indicated that half of the sixty-odd species of marsupials occurring in New South Wales have not been reported since 1910, and most of the extinct species were from the grasslands. Among them were the attractive rabbit bandicoot (Macrotis lagotis), a dainty marsupial with soft gray fur and long ears, which lived in shallow burrows. Today this species is known only in central Australia, where it survives in small numbers. Small birds such as the striated grass wren (Amytornis striatus), which once occurred on the lower Namoi, are now found only hundreds of miles farther west.

Compensating to some degree for these losses has been an increase in the grassland species that need open areas, examples being the red or plains kangaroo, such parrots as the galah (Kakatoe roseicapilla) and white cockatoo (K. galerita), the ground-feeding magpie (Gymnorhina tibicen) and peewee (Grallina cyanoleuca).

THE MURRAY RIVER SYSTEM

Far more than any other feature, the western rivers have imprinted themselves on the Australian landscape. They are responsible for much of what one might describe as the identity of Australia: cool avenues of trees through dry plains, alternating drought and flood, picturesque gums overhanging still reaches, colorful parrots drinking at dusk, the flickering campfire of a swagman or drover under a cloudless night sky. The grandfather of these streams is the Murray River, the only one that can be counted on to keep flowing (it has stopped only twice in one hundred years). It is also the widest, and, since the others pour into it, the ultimate conveyor of the western waters to the sea.

The Murray River rises in the Australian Alps, where it is fed by melting snows, and then pursues an east-west course for a thousand miles, during which it receives streams from Victoria to the south and New South Wales and southern Queensland in the north, and then turns south to enter the

Inland from the Great Divide lie hundreds of square miles of plains country, much of it covered with grass, where a network of meandering streams may spread widely in times of flood but drain away to a series of waterholes during drought. It is the land of the red kangaroo, the emu and colorful cockatoos.

Right above: Budgerigars (Melopsittacus undulatus) live and migrate in flocks. These favorite pets range widely over the inland areas of Australia. (Stan and Kay Breeden) Right: Grassland meets a parklike grove of gnarled gum trees in a dry stream bed on the western slopes of the Flinders Ranges in South Australia. (K. P. Phillips)

European rabbits (Oryctolagus cuniculus) *concentrated at a drying waterhole in time of drought. In over a hundred years millions of these creatures have degraded the grasslands and caused huge economic losses. (Australian National Travel Association)*

sea just east of Adelaide. At one time the Murray was a major avenue of transportation, with paddlewheelers plying its entire length from Albury to South Australia. The Darling was likewise navigated for a thousand miles northward to Bourke, and beyond. But the erratic flow of these streams, their variable water levels, and their meandering courses, led to their being supplanted by road transport. Today only a couple of the old paddlewheelers remain, functioning as tourist attractions and plying the southern reaches of the Murray, between Mildura and Swan Hill. The mean annual discharge of the Murray River is ten million acre feet, which simply means the amount of water that it would take to cover this area of land to a depth of one foot. This flow is only about half that of the Danube, one-seventh that of the Nile, and one-fourteenth that of the Ganges. The flow varies greatly from year to year, reflecting the marked annual differences in rainfall over the catchment areas. A stream may be flowing one year and only a stream of pools the next.

Many of the tributaries of the Darling, of course, arise in the drier inland country and reach the main stream only during the infrequent floods. The Paroo, no more than a dry, sandy riverbed outlined by a mixture of gums and tangled shrubbery, is a classic example. Normally its waters are lost in lakes and marshes thirty to forty miles from the Darling, but in the great floods of 1870 the river was sixty miles wide and was navigated by a river steamer for 180 miles. The Darling River has a clearly defined course, with banks thirty to forty feet high, but during floods these are not only over-topped but the water spreads out on the plains to a width of fifty miles. The degree of this overflow is explained partly by the low gradient of the drainage pattern of the Darling: at the Queensland border it is five hundred feet above sea

level, but at its junction with the Murray, 1,350 miles to the south, it has fallen only four hundred feet. Parts of the lower Murray and Darling today cut through old river sands and silts one hundred feet and more in depth, indicating periods of much greater flow in the last few hundred thousand years. This accords with the wealth of evidence from various sources that much of Australia was once well watered, the land of "swift-flowing rivers and full-bosomed lakes" that Professor W. R. Browne described it as once having been. The fossil remains of *Diprotodon,* the extinct giant, herbivorous marsupial, found on the crumbling banks of the Darling and on the dry salt bed of Lake Calabonna in South Australia, are mute testimony to this.

BIRDS OF THE WESTERN PLAINS

The western plains are a wonderland of birds. As one drives along, flocks of pink and gray galahs rise from the ground and flap across the plain, pink when their breasts are toward the watcher, silver when they turn against the blue sky. Sulphur-crested white cockatoos are common too, screeching from the tall river gums. Large flocks of little red-rumped parrots *(Psephotus haematonotus)* with bright, grass-green bodies, rise from the side of the road and are overtaken, perhaps, by a careering mass of little green budgerigars *(Melopsittacus undulatus)* or leisurely gray and white cockateels *(Leptolophus hollandicus).* Yellow rosellas *(Platycercus flaveolus)* and blue-bonnet parrots *(Psephotus haematogaster)* fly between the trees or, if it is early spring, can be seen investigating hollow branches and trunks as nesting sites. Black-and-white magpies walk over the grass picking up insects and lizards, or are heard caroling—they are among the world's best songsters—from the tops of telegraph poles or from exposed limbs. Whistling eagles *(Haliastur sphenurus),* disturbed in their roosting place, flap away with loud protesting cries. From time to time one or two wedge-tailed eagles, Australia's counterpart of the famous golden eagle, will be flushed, too, but they are more often seen spiraling on air currents high in the sky.

Prominent among the smaller tree-frequenting birds are various honeyeaters, the species changing with the habitat. The best place for birds is, of course, the gums along the river. Here dozens of different species may be seen at once: gray thrushes and rufous whistlers, weebills and pardalotes, wagtails and jacky winters, rainbowbirds and ravens.

THE POPULAR BUDGERIGAR

Though the western grassland is a rich area for birds, the seasons are apparently unpredictable enough to make much seasonal movement a necessity. The numbers and kinds of birds in any part of the area vary greatly from year to year. Most of the movements are nomadic rather than migratory, their direction, extent and timing being different from year to year. Typical of many of the birds is the budgerigar, the little green parrot that is now so common as a household pet throughout the world.

Budgerigars, or budgies, occur throughout the inland parts of Australia. They feed on the seeds of grass and other plants found on the ground. Flocks sometimes number less than a

An "old man" red kangaroo (Macropus rufus) *hops across the grass plain in the Riverina district of New South Wales. (Graham Pizzey)*

dozen birds, and sometimes they are hundreds strong, the larger aggregations occurring when the birds gather for migration or are concentrated by drought into restricted areas. They move north in the autumn and return southward in the spring, the former bringing them to country watered by the summer monsoon and the latter to where the winter rains assure good spring conditions. But, unlike the true migrants of the northern hemisphere, they do not return to the same place each time, being abundant in a district one year and completely absent from it the next. This seems to be the result of concentrating where conditions are best.

Budgerigars are fond of nesting in dead trees standing in swamps; on occasion, up to a dozen pairs may breed in the same tree. Four to eight eggs are laid in a hollow limb or

trunk and take seventeen to eighteen days to hatch. The young, which are fed partially digested seed and other plant material, remain in the nest some six weeks. The aborigines coveted the fat nestlings as food, and the bird's name is derived from two aboriginal words, "boogeree," meaning good, and "gar," meaning food.

One of the most interesting aspects of bird biology in the inland plains is that the habit of breeding at a fixed time peculiar to the species is much less developed than elsewhere; here the birds of almost all species usually nest after rain. Greatly interested by this phenomenon, I carried out a survey from 1957 through 1960 of the nesting of the birds in western New South Wales. It was found that if the weather was reasonably normal, nesting would take place in the spring. When a

Two emus (Dromaius novae-hollandiae) *on the plains of the Riverina district, New South Wales. Next to the African ostrich they are the world's largest birds. (Graham Pizzey)*

drought had set in, however, breeding was either eliminated or reduced, those birds that did build nests often laying fewer eggs than usual. The birds had a remarkable capacity for responding to rain, the breaking of a drought being marked by an outburst of courting song and the collecting of nesting material. This occurred even in midsummer, or if the birds have already started to molt.

The capacity to suspend breeding when conditions are unfavorable, and to make up rapidly for the delay when

favorable conditions return, is certainly one of the more interesting adaptations of the birds inhabiting the drier parts of the Australian continent. This habit, along with the mobility that enables many of the species to leave drought-stricken areas and concentrate where conditions are most favorable, enables the birds to thrive in this erratic climate.

MARSHES, IBISES, AND WILD DUCKS

When the rivers run high, the water spreads out over the countryside, forming marshes and lakes. On these the water birds converge from far and near and form huge nesting colonies, constituting one of the wonders of the inland country. There are many of these areas along such meandering

western streams as the Murray (e. g., Lake Hattah in the Victorian Mallee), the Murrumbidgee (especially the Riverina segment), and, in the south, the Lachlan. One of the most famous, and now a wildlife reserve, is the Macquarie Marshes in central western New South Wales, not far from the town of Warren. On the Gwydir, the marsh known as the Watercourse is almost permanent. Others occur in Queensland, including the terminal lakes of the intermittent rivers (for example, Lake Bulloo) and the arid lower reaches of the Diamentina and Cooper's Creek near their junction with Lake Eyre.

An unusual characteristic of these nesting colonies, which rival those of the Florida Everglades and the great Danube marshes in ornithological interest, is that their location varies from year to year, depending on which rivers are running.

The colonies are inhabited by three species of ibis, two kinds of spoonbills, three species of cormorants, four different egrets, two or three other herons, two species of bittern, the black swan, water hens and coots, reed warblers and grassbirds, and half a dozen different kinds of ducks.

A visit to one of these inland marshes at breeding time is an unforgettable experience. Preparation for such a trip should include correspondence to learn just where the birds are concentrating, arrangements for a jeep or pack horses, a flat-bottomed boat, mosquito nets, and preferably a guide since it is easy for a novice to get lost in such a marsh. The approach is likely to be over many miles of flooded country with the water ranging from a few inches to several feet in depth. Ample incentive is provided, however, by the songs of the smaller bush birds breeding in the surrounding gums

A mob of plains kangaroos in western New South Wales. (Sydney Morning Herald)

and the distant white specks that field glasses reveal are thousands of ibises spiraling and circling in the sky.

Such was my experience on a visit to the Macquarie Marshes one October. This marsh, well wooded along its margins, with vast areas of reedbed and lignum bushes from four to eight feet high, interspersed with drainage channels, is one of the largest in New South Wales. We had not gone far before we were among the colonies of egrets and spoonbills in trees—hundreds of snow-white birds perched on or about flat stick nests, craning their necks to peer at the intruders or protestingly taking flight as the party drew too close. A few trees were crowded with little pied cormorants and little black cormorants *(Phalacrocorax melanoleucos* and *P. sulcirostris)*. Maned geese *(Chenonetta jubata)* and black ducks *(Anas superciliosa)* honked and squawked as they flew past. Red-rumped parrots and budgerigars chattered above. At the end of the line of trees was the ibis colony, a vast expanse of untidy lignum bushes dotted with snow-white forms, mostly straw-necks *(Threskiornis spinicollis),* but with a liberal sprinkling of white ibis *(T. molucca)*. Nests, untidy structures of sticks an inch or two across, were wedged wherever there was support—in the center of bushes, at the top, or almost touching the water. Bedlam broke out as we

drew near, the air filled with hundreds of protesting adults and the larger young scrambled out of the nests and attempted to conceal themselves in dense foliage. On closer inspection we saw that the nests contained eggs and young in all stages of development, indicating that the arrival of the birds for breeding had not occurred all at the same time, some birds coming much later than others.

The areas of open water partly covered with aquatic plants and water lilies were aglow with color and shimmering with reflections. A pair of majestic black swans paddled nervously ahead of us, scattering dozens of coots while the black-tailed native hens, cormorants, and grebes dived out of harm's way. A black duck and a gray teal *(Anas gibberifrons),* each in charge of a string of ducklings, hastily disappeared into the shelter of the adjacent reedbed. The water itself was swarming with life, including the aquatic bugs known as water boatmen *(Rhynchota),* water beetles of various kinds, dragonfly nymphs, and gyrating myriads of minute fresh-water crustaceans. The accumulation of all forms of life, not to mention the luxuriance of the water plants themselves that followed the flooding, had converted the marsh into a biologist's paradise.

It was interesting to camp overnight on high ground on

one of the islands, mosquitoes notwithstanding. As the shadows lengthened on the still waters, the ducks and coots seemed to lose their fear and paddled close inshore. The cormorants, egrets, and ibis returned to their respective colonies to noisily settle down for the night. A brown bittern *(Botaurus poiciloptilus),* the legendary "bunyip" of the aborigines, boomed from the heart of the marsh. And as the setting sun picked out the tops of the reeds in gold and the marsh life began to quieten, we were left with the melodious evening song of the reed warbler *(Acrocephalus australis).*

KANGAROOS

The Australian national coat-of-arms consists of a shield supported by a kangaroo and an emu. The open plains are the home of the giant flightless emu, second in size only to the African ostrich among the birds of the world, and of the slim, erect red kangaroo. Both species are found all across the continent, but their most familiar setting is the interior of New South Wales and Queensland. Emus have been discussed in Chapter 1. On the plains emus subsist on a mixed diet of berries, herbage, and insects, and characteristically occur in parties ranging from three to about a dozen.

The kangaroos are met in small groups called "mobs." They are generally dominated by a large male, ginger-red and perhaps five-and-a-half feet in height, the females being bluish-gray and smaller. There will be a few subadult males and young of various sizes in the group, for kangaroos take many years to reach full size; also, there is no regular breeding season in the red kangaroo, the young leaving the pouch at any time of the year. In the morning and afternoon the kangaroos will be seen in the open, standing up to gaze at an intruder, then turning and bounding away across the plain, only to stop and gaze back a little farther on. Their whole manner is one of curiosity and guilelessness, qualities admirable from the viewpoint of the tourist with a telephoto lens on his camera, but all too often fatal to the animal. In recent years kangaroos, ever regarded as food competitors of sheep, have been slaughtered in millions.

When feeding, the kangaroos have a habit of moving slowly along on all fours, placing the weight alternately on the hindlegs and forelegs. In full flight, when large males may attain a speed of thirty miles per hour for short distances and are said to make individual leaps of twenty-five feet,

Right: The trapdoor spider, found widely in southern Australia, retreats into its burrow, closing a small, ingeniously constructed lid behind it. (Stan and Kay Breeden)

Overleaf: Picturesque river gums (Eucalyptus camaldulensis) *fringe the rivers, streams and billabongs of the Murray–Darling basin. Periodic inundation does not necessarily hurt them, provided it is not too protracted. (Douglass Baglin)*
Right above: A mulga parrot (Psephotus varius) *approaches its nesting hollow. This seed-eating, ground-feeding parrakeet ranges widely over the dryer parts of southern Australia.*
Right: Rainbow birds (Merops ornatus) *favor the vicinity of streams, hawking the air above them for dragonflies and other insects, and nesting in hollows excavated in their banks. (Both by Michael Morcombe)*

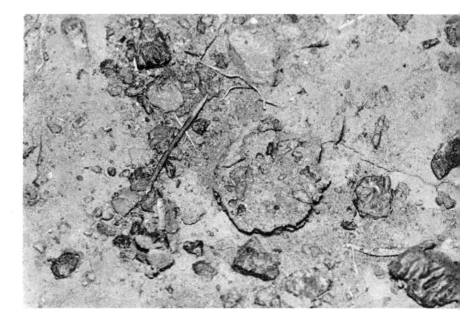

the animal's powerful tail extends behind as a sort of balancer. The tail also functions as a prop, the third leg of a tripod, when the males are fighting; the animal then stands erect with the weight resting mainly on the tail, and grapples with its somewhat puny forelimbs. In the *coup-de-grâce*, the kangaroo holds the opponent with the forelimbs and slashes downward with the big nails of the hindlimb, which can be devastating. When a man trains kangaroos as circus performers the problem is not to teach them to box, which is a natural action, but to persuade them to forego their equally natural desire to disembowel the trainer!

During the heat of the day kangaroos lie in the shade of trees or bushes. They are very clean animals, frequently licking themselves in cat fashion and running their paws through their fur. The young spend part of the time playing and sparring.

Since kangaroos are marsupials, their development takes place partly in the mother's uterus and partly in the pouch. The uterine period is from thirty to forty days, the baby when born being very incompletely developed and only three-quarters of an inch long. At this time the blind, hairless mite has overdeveloped forelimbs, which enable it to make its way upward through the mother's fur to the pouch. There it fastens itself so firmly to a teat that pulling it free tears the skin, and the mother's milk is virtually "pumped" into it. The pouch life lasts some six months, during which time the baby acquires fur and develops the kangaroo's characteristic body proportions. When it first emerges from the pouch it is all skin and bones! Thereafter, for perhaps six weeks, it spends part of its time mouthing tender grass shoots beside the mother, diving head first into the pouch when danger threatens. When mother kangaroos are pursued while carrying a baby in the pouch, they are said to abandon it but return later to retrieve it.

Just why Australia, alone of the continents, has large hopping animals is a mystery. The hopping gait is largely characteristic of animals inhabiting open spaces: thus the American jack rabbit and African jerboa are mainly desert dwellers. But this gait appears to be chiefly advantageous only when small obstacles abound and, in contrast to a running gait, it is apparently rather tiring.

Kangaroos, the Macropodidae, are divided into some thirty species, all occurring either in Australia or New Guinea. The group is diverse, ranging from rabbit-sized rat kangaroos with stocky bodies, through various wallabies, to the large gray kangaroos, red kangaroos, and euros. Extreme adaptations include the arboreal tree kangaroos of New Guinea and the North Queensland rain forest, which have enlarged forelimbs, and the cliff-frequenting rock wallabies, with "nonskid" soles on the hindfeet. The entire group is descended from arboreal phalanger stock, though transitional types have not yet been traced in the fossil record. The earliest known fossils, from the early Miocene, some twenty million years ago, are quite similar to the modern kangaroos.

THE REMARKABLE MALLEE FOWL

In spring the vast belts of mallee that extend over parts of Victoria and New South Wales are a delight, for then the eucalypts and acacias are in bloom and they are alive with birds. The nectar feeders are there in abundance, especially species like the yellow-plumed, yellow-fronted, and white-eared honeyeaters (Meliphaga ornata, M. plumula and M. leucotis). One may even be fortunate enough to see the elusive and very nomadic little black honeyeater (Myzomela nigra). A short walk through the shrubbery will surely yield the resplendent little black-backed and purple-backed wrens (Malurus melanotus and M. assimilis), the latter with brilliant orange-red shoulders. The tantalizing ventriloquial calls of the crested bellbird (Oreoica gutturalis) lead one ever deeper into the scrub. Dusky miners (Myzantha melanotis), the guardians of the bird world, chide and harass the interloper. One may come upon an emu unexpectedly. And in time four characteristic mallee birds will be seen, the scrub robin (Drymodes brunneopygia), the chestnut-backed quailthrush (Cinclosoma castanotum), the striated field wren (Amytornis striatus), and the Gilbert whistler (Pachycephala gilberti).

But there is one inhabitant of the mallee that is a truly unique bird of Australia. This is the lowan or mallee fowl (Leipoa ocellata), one of the continent's three "incubator-birds." These do not hatch their eggs by normal means, but place them in specially prepared mounds, or incubators, of rotting vegetation and sand, depending on the heat of decomposition and of the sun to hatch out the young. This family, the megapodes, ranges from the Philippines to Sumatra and the Andaman Islands, thence east to New Guinea and Australia. Included in it is an ingenious species in New Britain that places its eggs in warm sands on the sides of volcanoes. Of the three Australian species, the jungle fowl is an inhabitant of the coastal scrubs of the north and northeast, and the brush turkey of those of the eastern coastal region. Some of the mounds of these birds may grow, with annual use, to structures thirty feet across and six to seven feet high. Alone of the group, the lowan inhabits semi-arid country, a habit that would appear to complicate enormously its domestic affairs since moisture, necessary for the fermentation process, is at a premium there.

Mallee fowl, the size of small turkeys, brown in color and with golden flecks on the wing, are still common in places. The slow disappearance of their habitat, the cover it provides, and the acacia seeds and other berries that make up their diet is a major threat to the survival of the species.

The lowan was first studied in detail in the 1950's by Dr. H. J. Frith, in the Griffith area of New South Wales. It was found that the birds commence to build the big nesting mound in April, scraping together fallen leaves, sticks, and loose sand from up to one hundred yards around. A little later the bird modifies the top to form a saucerlike depression, and it is then evident that the organic material is concentrated in the center. In due course the winter rains fall, the vegetation becomes saturated, and fermentation is initiated. The first egg is laid at the end of September, when the temperature reaches about ninety-two degrees. Thereafter, eggs are laid at from four- to eight-day intervals, the male, who is in charge of the mound, opening it up each time so that the egg can be placed in the center, and closing it again with sand to retain the heat. The laying period continues for the remainder of the

The long-legged, white-headed stilt (Himantopus leucocephalus) *wades in marshy shallows as it hunts aquatic insects.* (Michael Morcombe)

spring season, through the summer, and into early autumn.

But the role of the male is by no means a simple or easy one during this time. He is constantly at work adjusting the temperature. Dr. Frith found that in spring most of the heat comes from the rotting vegetation, by summer the heat from this source is reduced, but the sun's heat is so intense as to create a genuine danger of overheating. To adjust for this the bird piles sand in a thick insulating layer over the eggs. By autumn, however, the problem is to obtain sufficient warmth since the heat from fermentation is no longer available and the sun's rays are growing weak. The male responds by opening the mound during the middle of the day, spreading the sand out over the ground to warm it, and later packing a layer of the warmed sand over the eggs to keep them developing well into the night. By March, the struggle to keep the eggs developing becomes too great, the mound is abandoned, and the last few of the eggs laid during the season fail to hatch.

FRESH-WATER FISHES

As might be expected on so dry a continent, Australia has relatively few species of fresh-water fishes, a mere one hundred eighty, out of a possible two thousand species in the seas around the continent. While it contains two relatively ancient types, the lungfish *(Neoceratodus)* and the barramunda *(Scleropages),* of Queensland, the others are probably all derived ancestrally from the sea.

The Murray–Darling river system has a few dozen species, including several that are excellent as food. Most famous of these is the Murray cod *(Maccullochella),* which grows to about six feet in length, one hundred eighty pounds in weight, and has an excellent flavor. The fish is olive-green with fine spots and is yellowish below. It is a predatory species, taking crayfish, mice, insects, and other fish. In spawning it drops its eggs, which sink to the river bottom and hatch there. Another well-known native food fish is the yellowbelly or yellow-bellied perch *(Plectroplites).* This species grows to two and one half pounds in weight and sixty feet in length. It, too, is a predator, waiting in shady places and dashing out at passing prey. Spawning takes place during flood time, the eggs being shed and left to the mercy of the currents. The most distinctive of the Murray–Darling fishes, however, is of little importance as food; it is the slippery or blackfish *(Gadopsis).* Superficially this species looks like a European codfish but it is in fact so distinctive that some ichthyologists have created a special order for it. The blackfish is usually less than a foot long. Next to the lungfish and barramunda it is Australia's most ancient fresh-water species.

The unpredictable nature of the rivers has undoubtedly placed a premium on the ability to withstand extreme conditions. Certain gudgeons and *Galaxias* have been dug up beneath dried mud in the bottom of streambeds, and a number of species probably have the capacity to estivate—that is, go into suspended animation—underground when the waters

A group of straw-necked ibises (Threskiornis spinicollis) *and white ibises* (T. molucca) *rest in a quiet backwater of the Kiewa swamps. (Australian News and Information Bureau)*

A white-faced heron common along the rivers and marshes of southern Australia. (Robin Smith)

dry up. These inland species must be able to withstand the warming up of the water: one species, the grunter *(Hephaestus),* has been recorded living in waters registering one hundred two degrees. There are a number of records of fish coming up in artesian water, but there is disagreement as to whether they were actually living underground or merely lying dormant in surface mud until freed by the water. Dispersion following flooding is well developed in some species and, in the Murchison area of Western Australia, the ichthyologist Bruce Shipway recorded little grunters *(Madigania)* swimming along wheel-ruts a couple of miles from the nearest stream. When the water dried up the fish were left stranded and dying.

LAKE EYRE AND ITS DRAINAGE BASIN

The interior plains of northern Queensland are drained by a series of intermittently flowing streams a few thousand miles

long. Best known of these are the Diamentina and Cooper's Creek. Their headwaters are on the western slopes of the Great Divide; they flow southwestward across that state, heading for Lake Eyre, in the most arid part of the continent. Falls in their catchment area are scanty and occur only in summer. Occasionally, however, an incredible amount of rain will fall, such as eleven inches in a single day. The rivers then spread upward of fifty miles over the country: in full flood Cooper's Creek is said to reach a width of ninety miles in South Australia. Only occasionally do they reach Lake Eyre itself, although there is a huge deltaic area at the entrance to the lake where Cooper's Creek is recorded as having deposited four feet of silt in forty years. The dissipation of the waters is due in part to the division of the rivers into a large number of channels, producing the so-called "channel country."

Lake Eyre has a drainage basin of some 480,000 square miles, one of the largest in the world for an inland lake. The lake itself, five thousand square miles in area, is, however, only a vestige of a much larger Pleistocene lake, named Dieri by geologists, which embraced other major dry lakes such as Gregory, Blanche, Callabonna and Frome and must have covered forty thousand square miles and have been perhaps one hundred eighty feet deep.

In the middle of 1950 Lake Eyre filled with water for the first time in living memory, following extraordinary rains in Queensland, and in succeeding years it has contained water on at least one other occasion. Today Lake Eyre is in a closed basin, but in past ages it drained southward to the sea at the head of St. Vincent's Gulf in South Australia.

Some of the tributaries to Lake Eyre periodically form extensive marshes. One of the most nearly permanent of these is Goyder's Lagoon. The grasslands of central Queensland and even the parched terrain near Birdsville respond miraculously to rain and the flooding of the country. The grass flourishes and wildflowers appear. There is an influx of birds; even bustards *(Eupodotis australis)* occasionally occur. Birds breed everywhere. Sandy depressions that are now full of water soon support writhing masses of brine shrimps *(Apus)* and other fresh-water crustaceans, as well as water beetles. Frogs come out of estivation and contribute

Mallee fowl (Leipoa ocellata) *on their incubator mound in the brushwood known as mallee. The male is testing the temperature of the center of the mound while the female waits to lay. (Roy Cooper)*

tadpoles to the temporary ponds. Then, as the weeks go by, the ponds dry up and the rivers and swamps shrink to small holes. The birds disperse and the frogs go underground. The little shrimps, their eggs shed for the winds to blow far and near, lie dead, their carapaces reflecting the withering rays of the sun.

Caked surface of Lake Eyre, Australia's largest dry lake. It has contained water only twice in living memory. The ridge on the horizon is a camp. (Jeff Carter)

Palm-Fringed Beaches and Green Jungles

Eastern Queensland and Its Tropical Coasts

6 Queensland contributes tropical luxuriance to the Australian scene: vast mountain blocks heavily draped in jungle, somber rain forests with vines and epiphytes, arboreal orchids, spectacular waterfalls, clear streams fringed with slender-shafted palms, crimson firewheel trees, tulipflowers *(Stenocarpus sinuatus)* and golden silk oaks *(Grevillea robusta)* and wattles. The white beaches of northern Queensland are fringed with pandanus, coconut palms, and casuarinas. Passages and channels of deep blue skirt the coast and surround high, green islands. And offshore the Great Barrier Reef, a series of coral ramparts alive with colorful fish and other marine life, stretches over twelve hundred miles.

Elsewhere are tracts of tall eucalypt forest, lily-covered lagoons, inlets fringed with mangroves, rocky seacoasts, the curious volcanic spires of the Glasshouse Mountains, and the rugged sandstone gorges and cliffs of the Carnarvon Ranges. Much of Cape York and the north are covered with tropical savanna woodland similar to that of the Northern Territory. West of the Great Divide, the downs country and grasslands give way to vast plains. Finally, a thousand miles away, in the southwest corner, the country is as arid as central Australia. As noted previously, the interior here is drained by infrequently flowing rivers, which may, on rare occasions, reach Lake Eyre.

MOUNTAINS AND ISLANDS

The Great Divide is poorly defined in Queensland. The Herberton Plateau represents the Great Divide in the north, the Carnarvon Ranges in the center, and the McPherson and

Pacific breakers roll ashore at Coolum Coves in southern Queensland. Pandanus characterizes coasts throughout the tropical Pacific. (Adelie Hurley)

Coastal, tropical Queensland contains rain forests, lush vegetation and waterfalls. But most of it is covered by tropical savannah woodland, parklike and somewhat dry.

Bunya ranges in the far south, but for some seven hundred miles it runs through tableland country where in places it is only a thousand feet above sea level.

In New South Wales the Great Divide is generally parallel to the coast, but in Queensland it makes a wide curve inland: it is seventy miles inland near Brisbande, three hundred fifty miles from the sea at the Tropic of Capricorn, and only twenty miles from it near Cairns. Charles Hedley has pointed out that there is a seaward extension of the continental shelf at a point that corresponds in latitude to the peak of the curve of the Great Divide. Accordingly the Great Barrier Reef, which rests on the outer fringe of the shelf, is well out to sea at this latitude. The reef, in the view of most authorities, could have developed only during a steady sinking of the ocean bottom. The divide here is composed of uplifted sediments of the great inland sea that existed in Cretaceous times, some hundred twenty million years ago. The eastern block of Queensland, it has been suggested by some geologists, has undergone a progressive tilt, or dip, seawards, with the coastal mountain ranges forming the axis.

Along the coast there is a discontinuous series of ranges, unconnected with the Great Divide except in the far south and north. Some of these are higher than the divide itself. The Bellenden Ker ranges, near Cairns, forty miles long and about ten miles wide, rise almost sheer to between four and five thousand feet; the tallest peak is Mount Bartle Frere at 5,287 feet. The irregular groups of peaks and ridges near Townsville that make up the Mount Elliott Range—a wedge-shaped block twenty-five miles long and four to ten miles wide—reach nearly four thousand feet.

Many of the highest mountains in Queensland owe their majesty to volcanic rocks, which resist erosion. The McPherson Range is a series of volcanic plateaus, deeply slashed by gorges; the more lofty peaks are of rhyolite and trachyte. Basalt also caps the Bunya Mountains, though their present elevation may be partly due to upthrust. The high country of the Darling Downs shows basalt capping. The rugged inland Carnarvon Ranges, whose sandstone has weathered into many bizarre shapes, have a thin basalt capping here and there. The Atherton Tableland is partly formed of basalt. The striking series of domed and conical peaks in southern Queensland, which Captain James Cook was inspired to name the Glasshouse Mountains, are the remains of the necks of old volcanoes. Other such plugs make up the Peak Range near Clermont, and occur near Mackay and Rockhampton. Australia today is a very stable land mass. There are no active volcanoes, and earthquakes are rare. The widespread distribution of lava clearly shows that this was not always so. Volcanoes, active from several million down to perhaps a hundred thousand years ago, have left behind a twofold legacy: high, erosion-resistant peaks, and vast areas of rich soil.

The perennial eastward-flowing rivers of coastal Queensland can be divided into two groups, short rivers that flow directly from mountain to sea, and longer, meandering rivers that resemble the inland streams. The larger rivers, notably the Burdekin and the Fitzroy, belong to the latter category.

Gnarled old Antarctic beeches (Nothofagus moorei) *in the Lamington National Park, southeastern Queensland. (Derek Duparcq)*

The former, four hundred twenty-five miles long, rises less than forty miles inland. Its gradient is slight. For the ninety-five miles before it reaches the falls it drops four feet to the mile, and between there and the sea, two feet to the mile. Farther south, the Fitzroy River is said to have a fall of only 1.4 feet to the mile from the headwaters of its largest tributary, the Nogoa, to the sea. The Burdekin and the Fitzroy have the largest drainage systems in eastern Australia, basins of 53,500 and 55,600 square miles respectively. They are obviously much older than the short and steep rivers, and geologists have advanced two alternative theories to account for their characteristics. Some believe that prior to the uplifting of the Great Divide they flowed westward, and were subsequently forced to reverse their courses. Others maintain that they have always flowed to the east and their meandering patterns result from the uplift of the coastal ranges across the rivers' paths to the sea. There is, of course, ample proof of periods of geological uplift in eastern Queensland. The Brisbane River, for example, is entrenched four hundred feet deep in its upper reaches, and one hundred feet deep in its downstream segment.

The lowness of the mountains in central Queensland has had important biological effects. The climate is dry and of the inland type, hence much of the Fitzroy and Burdekin river systems are covered by grassland and savanna woodland, not forest. Inland birds of various kinds follow the broad river valleys down to the coast. The little peaceful dove (Geopelia striata), various quails, the white-breasted wood swallow (Artamus leucorhynchus), the fork-tailed kite (Milvus migrans), and others, are common about Townsville and elsewhere. At St. Lawrence, a number of miles to the south, the railway passes through an immense marshland where Australian cranes or brolgas (Grus rubicunda) are present in the hundreds.

The beautiful coasts of Queensland, their estuaries, and high wooded islands separated by passages and corridors, have their origins in the same earth movements that fashioned the mountain and river systems. The high islands close inshore are hills that were cut off by the sea, and some of the passages separating them from the coast, and from each other, are drowned river valleys. The agents involved have been down-faulting of the ocean floor and the rising water level that followed the melting of the glaciers in the northern hemisphere. All told, Queensland has some six hundred islands within the sixty-mile-wide belt along its coasts. The majority of these are so-called high islands, but there is a considerable number of low coral cays scattered along the Great Barrier Reef.

THE RUGGED McPHERSON RANGE

Back from the sea, along the borders of New South Wales and Queensland, is a magnificent mountain sector of lush jungles, tall eucalypt forests, and misty valleys. It is the Lamington National Park, a reserve of 36,000 acres, created in 1915

A flock of scaly-breasted lorikeets (Trichoglossus chlorolepidotus) *rest after their morning feast of nectar. (Harold J. Pollock)*

mainly as the result of the campaigning of a young pioneer, Romeo Lahey, who was appalled at the rapid reduction of the best forests by timber interests. Today, from guesthouses in the center of the park, tracks radiate out to high points with such fascinating names as Mount Bithongabel and Mount Hobwee (upwards of 3,800 feet), where grow the gnarled and ancient Antarctic beeches (Nothofagus moorei), through dense forests and thick scrubs, and along swift-running creeks and still pools. These are the forest haunts of rare jungle birds like the Albert lyrebird (Menura alberti), rufous scrub bird (Atrichornis rufescens), riflebird (Ptiloris paradiseus), and olive whistler (Pachycephala olivacea). Some inhabitants—forest wallabies (and their smaller relatives the pademelons), koalas and large fruit bats or flying foxes—are not uncommon; several striking lizards and snakes are here that do not occur in the more open forests to the south. The McPhersons contain the last of the really large surviving tracts of southern or temperate rain forest since those of the upper Clarence and Dorrigo were reduced. The importance of the park in the survival of the animals peculiar to this habitat is, accordingly, considerable.

The giant Antarctic beeches of the McPhersons, heavily buttressed at the base, with arched roots rising to fifteen feet, their trunks covered with hanging mosses and ferns, are said to be more than a thousand years old. This is the northernmost stand in Australia; other stands are on isolated mountaintops at Dorrigo and Barrington in New South Wales. The trees have a wider distribution in Victoria and Tasmania. Associated with them in the McPhersons is the olive whistler, a bird with olive-brown back and buff-brown breast. It is in many ways a mystery bird, for its flutelike and somewhat ventriloquial "peeee-pooo" call carries long distances through the high mountain forests, though the bird is seldom seen. In July 1948, I spent several days searching for the olive whistler. The quest was made particularly difficult by the moving patches of mist that obscured the upper parts of first one tree, then another. It was not until almost dusk and the mists cleared that I saw a bird "fossicking" for insects high in the outer foliage, its breast tinged with gold by the rays of the setting sun. Olive whistlers are inhabitants of sea level in the more southern parts of their range, but in the McPhersons, which are inhabited by a distinctive race, they keep to heights of three thousand feet and more.

The trees of the McPhersons include the giant tristania (Tristania conferta), rough-barked hoop pines (Araucaria cunninghamii), the huge stinging trees (Laportea gigas), as well as cedar, bloodwood, beefwood, and carbeen. The main flowering trees are the flame tree (Brachychiton acerifolius) and Moreton Bay chestnut, both of which begin blooming in November, and the firewheel (Stenocarpus sinuatus), or tulip-flower, whose wheel-like arrangements of deep-crimson tubular flowers are a feature of the area in January and February. Cunjevoi lilies (Alocasia) and piccabeen palms (Archontophoenix), with their scarlet fruit, ferns of many kinds, lawyer palms, and, in open places, tall grass trees (Xanthorrhoea arborea), are some of the more striking forms of the lower levels of the forests.

Flowering orchids adorn many of the trees in late spring. They include the spider orchid (Dendrobium tetragonum), with its long spidery flowers, the lovely orange-blossom orchid (Sarcochilus falcatus), which resembles an orange blossom in both its scent and color, the yellow-green olive orchid

A small, cave-dwelling bat (Hipposideros bicolor), *a rare tropical species from the far north. Australia has twenty seven species of bats that eat insects and nine that eat fruit and blossoms. (Stan and Kay Breeden)*

(S. olivei), the white and mauve sprays of the ravine orchid (S. fitzgeraldii), and the green orchid known as the snake-flower (Cymbidium suave). On the floor of the forest the Christmas orchid (Calanthe veratrifolia), its white sprays containing as many as fifty to sixty flowers, makes its appearance in midsummer.

The McPherson trails are famous for lookouts on high cliffs from which the entire northeastern corner of New South Wales can be seen spread out like a relief map. There is the spectacular, spirelike Mount Warning, the meandering Tweed River, the Terranora Lakes sparkling in the sun, the coast extending away to the south as far as the eye can see. Dropping away from the cliffs at one's feet are gorges, precipices,

and waterfalls. They echo and seem to amplify the notes of the birds from the forest canopy below, the loud whipcrack of the coachwhip bird *(Psophodes olivaceus)*, the "walk-to-walk" call of the brilliant-colored pitta *(Pitta versicolor)*, the "calung-calung" of the pied currawong *(Strepera graculina)*, the bubbling notes of the wompoo pigeon *(Megaloprepia magnifica)*, and the excited screeches of a flock of rainbow lorikeets *(Trichoglossus moluccanus)*.

The birds are among the main attractions of the McPhersons, for they include many rain forest forms that are rare farther south. The male riflebird, resplendent in iridescent greens and purples, sends pieces of bark tumbling to the forest floor as he prods the cracks and fissures of trees for insects with his long, down-curved bill. The dainty little rufous fantail *(Rhipidura rufifrons)*, his tail a widespread fan of orange-red, flutters and dances along the tracks. There are several different kinds of fruit pigeons, and the tiny green fig parrot *(Opopsitta diophthalma)* feasts high in the tall figs. The Albert lyrebird sends out showers of fallen leaves as he scratches among the debris; when disturbed, he half runs, half flutters down into the protection of the undergrowth below. The black-and-gold male of the regent bowerbird *(Sericulus chrysocephalus)*, the species that rarely builds a bower, flies across a jungle clearing. Finally, there is the rufous scrub bird, of particular interest to scientists in that, lacking furcula or wishbone, it belongs to the same primitive group as the lyrebird. A small bird, inhabiting a few restricted areas of dense undergrowth, it is known for two things, the loudness of its voice, and its habit of keeping to a few areas of special habitat. For the most part it keeps well down in the dense undergrowth but, on occasions, will provide the patient observer with a fine view.

FLYING FOXES

Perhaps the most striking, and certainly the most noisy, mammals of the jungle scrubs of southern Queensland are the large fruit bats or flying foxes *(Pteropus poliocephalus* and *P. scapulatus)*. I first met with these as a boy when, in late summer, large numbers would come migrating southward to Sydney to raid the ripening fruit in gardens and orchards. Every night they would appear just after dusk and spread out through the suburbs. Often they flew so low that one could almost hit them with sticks. Curiosity seemed to be one of their most marked characteristics, for an approaching bat would veer toward any object thrown into the air. A spinning hat held a special fascination, the bat often buffeting it with its body before continuing on its way. Dead bats would sometimes be found entangled in electric light wires, and on one occasion I had an orphan youngster as a pet for several months.

Flying foxes spend the daylight hours in large roosts or "camps" consisting of thousands of individuals; one flock was estimated by biologist Francis Ratcliffe, who made a study of them, at half a million strong. These camps are very noisy; the individuals, which hang upside down from the branches, quarrel incessantly. The area soon comes to have an overpowering musky odor. When frightened the fruit bats defecate and urinate so that it sounds momentarily as if rain is falling. Captain James Cook had a feeling of revulsion when he visited a camp near present-day Cooktown, north

Queensland, in 1770, writing of the flying foxes as follows: "It was a most peculiar animal about the bigness of, and much like, a one-gallon keg. It was as black as the Devil, and had wings; indeed, I took it for the Devil, or I might easily have caught it, for it crawled very slowly through the grass."

Five species of *Pteropus* occur in Australia. They have a long, foxlike face (hence the name flying fox), prominent brown eyes and long sharp teeth. Most species have red-brown or dark-gray fur. The wings are of pliable black skin, and are supported by long thin bones like the ribs of an umbrella. The body proper is about the size of a half-grown cat, and the largest Australian species has a wingspan of about four feet. Their toes, by which they hang, are long and clawed. One young is born at a time and, until it can fly well, it is carried by the mother, clinging to her body as she flies.

A MILLION YEARS ON THE DARLING DOWNS

On the western slopes of the Great Divide, sixty to eighty miles west of Brisbane, are the Darling Downs, gently rolling terrain with broad valleys. Today they make up some of the richest farmland in Australia. Their black and red-brown soils are derived from the dissected and eroded remnants of Tertiary basaltic rocks to the east, deposited as alluvia in the valleys. The rainfall is an adequate thirty inches a year, most of it falling in late summer. The total area of cultivation is now nearly a million acres.

The early settlers thronged to the rich downlands country, striving to get a segment before all was distributed. Soon their plows began to turn up the fossil bones of giant animals. These were sent to the famous paleontologist, Sir Richard Owen, in London. Owen was delighted, for he had just received batches of bones from the Wellington Caves in New South Wales, the first mammal fossils to be found in Australia, and scientists were most curious to know what the ancestors of the marsupials were like.

The Darling Downs fossils are found mainly in the old alluvia in gullies and creeks; they are usually well preserved, but seldom complete, the streams having long since scattered the bones. The range of forms represented is, however, considerable, and they give a good picture of what life was like in the Pleistocene period, a million years ago. Kangaroo remains are numerous. Some of these animals had body proportions like those of the largest living kangaroos but exceeded them in size. Others were stockier, wallaby types. One that has no surviving relatives was *Procoptodon*, which had a curiously short, blunt face, a high skull, and strongly ridged molars.

The largest marsupial ever to have lived was *Diprotodon*, a heavy-bodied quadruped with the bulk of a rhinoceros, a ponderous herbivore, six feet high and from ten to twelve feet long. Its remains crop up over wide areas of the continent, for it was apparently prone to being trapped by muddy lakes and creeks. A common fossil on the downs, it is found along with other members of the Diprotodontidae such as the browsing *Nototherium* and *Euowenia*, each the size of a large bullock, and the smaller and more lightly built *Palorchestes*, which Dr. J. T. Woods, Director of the Queensland Museum, describes as having the skull structure of a grazer.

Flying foxes (Pteropus) *in Palm Swamp, Queensland. Largest of the fruit-bats, they roost by day in remote parts of forests. (Stan and Kay Breeden)*

There was also a wombat, *Phascolonus gigas,* with a five-foot-long body. Not yet found on the downs but probably contemporaneous with this fauna is *Euryzygoma,* a large herbivore with a skull broader than long. These skull proportions were the result of the exaggerated sideways extensions of the upper jaw, presumably to support cheek pouches. This animal, described by the paleontologist Heber Longman, is known from the skull only.

Thylacoleo, a jaguar-sized marsupial carnivore, preyed on the large herbivores. The species has long been known for its short, heavy skull and the huge pair of shearing premolars in its cheek region. Only in recent years, in a cave in South Australia, has an intact skeleton been discovered. Studies made by Professor R. A. Stirton of the University of California have

shown this animal to have had retractile claws, the first marsupial known to have this character. It is not known whether the *Thylacoleo* was predominantly hunter or scavenger, but it must have depended largely on the diprotodons, for it became extinct when they did.

The marsupial wolf, *Thylacinus,* and the marsupial devil, *Sarcophilus,* now surviving only in Tasmania, are found as fossils on the Darling Downs, as are the giant goanna *Megalania,* which was fifteen or sixteen feet long, a few kinds of large flightless birds, and a heavy fresh-water crocodile.

Just what forces caused the extinction of these gigantic Pleistocene animals are not known. Certainly the gradual desiccation of the southern part of the continent must have been important for we know that during much of the Pleistocene the interior enjoyed a more or less temperate climate and good rainfall, and was studded with rivers and fresh-water lakes. Radio-carbon dating indicates that *Diprotodon* survived at least up to seven thousand years ago, and probably long after that. There is evidence of the coexistence of the dingo and some of the extinct mammals, their remains having been found side by side in the Wellington caves. Thus, it would seem possible that early man, who brought the dingo to the continent as a pet, may have been the ultimate factor responsible for the extermination of the fabulous Pleistocene mammal fauna.

AN ANCIENT LINEAGE—THE LUNGFISH

Lungfish, or the Dipnoi, are an ancient group of fishlike animals that, judging from the fossil record, flourished in great numbers in the Devonian geological period, 400 million years ago. Today they survive only in the three southern continents, Australia having one genus *(Neoceratodus),* South America one, and Africa one. Lungfish are confined to fresh water and apparently they have always been so, for their fossils are only found in fresh-water deposits. Their name comes from the fact that they have lungs and hence can breathe air.

The fins are curious in that, instead of being supported, as in other fishes, by a series of rays, they have a stout central axis that branches into two, with the terminal supports arising from these. The limb, in other words, is of the same basic type as that of all the land animals and man. The lungfish is not now thought to be the direct ancestor of land animals, which was once suspected to be the case, a related group of fishes, the Crossopterygii, having functioned in that respect.

The Australian lungfish is today confined to two of the coastal rivers of southeastern Queensland, the Mary and the Burnett, though it has now been introduced to other waterways. Fossils are known from as far away as the dry salt lakes of central Australia. The lungfish is rather sluggish and though it has gills from which it normally breathes, it can rise to the surface to gulp in air when the water becomes

Left: Two tiny azure kingfishers (Alcyone azurea) *perch above a jungle pool, waiting for a tasty water beetle or fish to drift past. (Stan and Kay Breeden) Right: Palm-fringed pool in the rain forests of the Atherton Tablelands. (Adelie Hurley)*

The spotted cuscus (Phalanger maculatus nudicaudatus), *inhabitant of the rain forests of Cape York Peninsula. These rather sluggish marsupials spend the day curled up high in the trees. (Herbert Chargois)*

foul. The Australian species has only one lung. It grows to a length of six feet and is known, from captive specimens, to live as long as thirty-three years. The fins are paddle-shaped and the tail is rounded, not indented as in most fish. It apparently feeds mainly on vegetation. The eggs and young are not unlike those of frogs.

VALLEY OF RUINED CASTLES
TO THE VALLEY OF LAGOONS

Extending north and south in Queensland between the coastal strip and the inland plains is a tract of elevated country that embraces the headwaters of most of the rivers. It is pleasant and well-watered terrain, some of it undulating downs country with an abundance of grass and trees, but it also includes vast tracts of dense myall and brigalow scrub, rugged ranges and lagoon-filled valleys.

This is the country that the famous explorer Ludwig Leichhardt traversed after leaving the Darling Downs on October 1, 1844, a journey that extended from Queensland to Port Essington in the Northern Territory and took fifteen months. The expedition is of special significance because Leichhardt was a botanist and John Gilbert, the deputy leader, was an ornithologist. Hence, its journals contain not only good descriptions of the terrain but detailed lists of the animal species observed.

Two areas that particularly impressed the explorers, and are still particularly interesting today, are the rugged Carnarvon Ranges and the lagoon country of the upper Burdekin. The Carnarvons, about three hundred fifty miles northwest of Brisbane, are a wild jumble of ranges, composed of sandstone with a basaltic capping. They exceed three thousand feet in height, the highest peak being Mount Percy. Superficially they resemble the Hawkesbury sandstones about Sydney with their vertical cliffs, broken scarps and caverns, and honeycombed rocks, even to having such trees as the large pink-barked *Angophora lanceolata* (often called Sydney red gum), *Livistona* palms, *Macrozamia,* and the white flannelflower *(Actinotis).* Such vegetation, and the permanent water of the ranges, permits many coastal animal species to occur much farther inland than would otherwise be the case. Thus, included in the avifauna of the Carnarvons are the brush turkey *(Alectura lathami),* yellow-tailed black cockatoo *(Calyptorhynchus funereus),* king parrot *(Aprosmictus scapularis),* kookaburra *(Dacelo novae-guineae),* gray fantail *(Rhipidura fuliginosa),* yellow robin *(Eopsaltria australis),* figbird *(Sphecotheres vieilloti),* buff-breasted scrub wren *(Sericornis laevigaster),* white-throated tree creeper *(Climacteris leucophaea),* and Lewin honeyeater *(Meliphaga lewini).*

One valley in the Carnarvons reminded Leichhardt and Gilbert of ruined castles, and Leichhardt wrote of it: "Our admiration of the valley increased at every step. High sandstone rocks, fissured and broken like the pillars and walls and high gates of the ruined castles of Germany, rise from the broad sandy summits of many hills on both sides of the valley." He named it Ruined Castle Valley.

Five months after leaving the castlelike sandstone, the party reached the Burdekin River, which flowed through a beautiful valley. Leichhardt wrote: "We discovered an extensive valley with large lagoons and lakes, and a most luxurious vegetation, bounded by distant blue ranges, and forming the most picturesque landscape we had yet met with." The valley had a sizeable native population, which subsisted in part on the bulbs of the blue water lilies that covered the ponds. Exceptionally abundant were large and striking waterbirds; brolgas *(Grus rubicunda),* jabirus *(Xenorhynchus asiaticus),* pelicans *(Pelecanus conspicillatus),* and magpie geese *(Anseranas semipalmata),* as well as stilts, plovers, egrets, herons, and the long-toed lotus birds *(Irediparra gallinacea).*

Australia has more than half a dozen species of water lilies, most of them in the genus *Nymphaea.* All grow in shallow water. The fleshy roots are rich in starch; the colors of the flowers may be white, blue, yellow, or pink, depending on the species. The sacred lotus *(Nelumbo),* which ranges from Egypt to the Orient, also occurs here. Its blooms, deep pink with greenish-gold centers, may be nearly a foot across; small wonder, then, that the lotus is a sacred emblem of the Buddhist faith, and was a basic form in the art of the Assyrians and Egyptians, and later the Greeks and Romans.

WATERFALLS AND CRATER LAKES

The most fascinating part of Queensland is the large tropical "pocket," some two hundred miles long and thirty wide, that extends from the Bloomfield River to the Herbert River in the northeastern corner of the state. Here, on the Atherton Tableland and the Bellenden Ker Plateau, is the greatest belt of tropical rain forest to be found on the continent, the habitat of striking plant and animal forms with strong New Guinea affinities, tropical orchids, butterflies, cassowaries, tree kangaroos, and cuscuses. With its steep, verdant slopes, cliffs, and spectacular cataracts and waterfalls, this country affords some of the most interesting mountain scenery in Australia. Tourists at the edge of a scarp can look out over the coastal lowland a thousand feet below—a vista of white, sandy beaches fringed by coconut palms and pandanus, deep blue sea, and distant reef islands.

Large sections of these highlands have now been set aside as national parks. On Bellenden Ker is a reserve of seventy-nine thousand acres that includes the two highest peaks in the state, Mount Bartle Frere and Mount Bellenden Ker.

Of the region's waterfalls, the Wallaman Falls on the Herbert River have the greatest drop, one thousand feet; while on the Tully, the Elizabeth Grant Falls and the Tully Falls tumble from heights of nine hundred feet into precipitous gorges below.

Two crater lakes, Barrine and Eacham, occur at two thousand four hundred feet, near the top of the tableland. One comes upon them suddenly from the jungle—clear, deep bodies of water that reflect the sky. The lakes are surrounded by ridges of coarse volcanic ash, now covered by dense vegetation, showing that these old craters, in their heyday, were of the explosive type.

Altitudinal differences from mountaintop to sea produce a range of climatic conditions that give northern Queensland a considerable biological diversity. On the plateau the average annual temperature is about sixty-five degrees, compared with seventy-five in the lowlands. The plateau's summer average is about seventy-five degrees, that on the coast being eighty to eighty-five and accompanied by a heightened humidity.

The average annual rainfall over much of the highlands is fifty to sixty inches. On the eastern side and coast it ranges from eighty inches, to the Australian maximum of 160 inches in a small area near Innesfail. This range makes dairying and vegetable growing possible in the highlands, and the cultivation of sugar cane, bananas, and pineapples along the coast.

LUXURIANCE AND DIVERSITY—THE RAIN FORESTS

The visitor strolling along a road or track through a tropical rain forest will note that it differs from other forests in many ways. The trees are tall, commonly between 150 and 180 feet high, and they grow so closely together that their foliage is continuous, providing a closed canopy that shuts out sunlight. The interior is, accordingly, in dense shade, and the ground vegetation is scanty. Instead, a carpet of rotting leaves, an agelong accumulation, lies an inch thick. Here and there are fallen branches and trunks, their wood moldy and crumbling. Huge vines, some the thickness of a human thigh, hang like cables between the trees. Creepers are intertwined around the branches, and others cling in sinuous curves around the trunks. Epiphytic ferns, orchids, algae, and lichens abound. Mosses give the fallen logs a woolly texture. The humidity is high and the still air has a somewhat earthy smell.

The millions of large trees in the Atherton–Bellenden Ker forests include kauris *(Agathis), Cardwellia, Flindersia,* hoop pine, red cedar, maple, walnut, and many others. The number of species that grow to sufficient size to be used for timber has been estimated at four hundred. These rain forest trees are basically different from the other trees on the continent; in the rain forest, softwoods predominate, and they are of Malaysian origin. The true Australian genera, such as *Eucalyptus, Acacia, Casuarina* and *Melaleuca,* are absent. Among the more curious trees of the rain forest are the strangler figs, or banyans. Scattered by flying foxes and birds, the seeds lodge and germinate on a tree branch, producing roots that grip the host tree. A woody, potatolike lignotuber with a leafy shoot develops, and then drops a root to the ground. Other roots follow and fuse with one another until finally the host is enmeshed in a stout cage of fig roots. When the tree has been strangled, the banyan inherits its position. It may subsequently grow to a height of eighty feet.

The major climbers in the Atherton Tableland forests include the matchbox bean *(Entada),* and the snakewood *(Lonchocarpus),* and the creepers include peppers *(Piper), Freycinetia, Pothos,* and *Raphidophora.* There are various palms, including *Calyptrocalyx,* and several species of lawyers *(Calamus),* the most obstructive of all vegetation, equipped with prickly cane stems and long, hooked tendrils. The most plentiful of the tree ferns is the tall, thick *Cyathea.* Staghorn and elkhorn ferns are prominent in the trees. They grow outward from a huge bowl-like holdfast, which gathers debris; the plants may be said to have a soil of their own making. Arboreal orchids include various species of *Dendrobium, Sarcochilus,* and *Cymbidium.*

Progress through mature and undisturbed Queensland rain forest is not altogether unpleasant, though the clingy, clay soil, muddy areas, and rotting logs prove tiring. Along creeks and in areas where trees have blown over, light permits undergrowth to develop, and progress is nothing short of tortuous. In such places the lawyer palms grow thickly and their thorny tendrils, six or more to each plant, tear at one's clothing, hands, and face.

The diversity of the trees of the rain forest is unbelievably great. Rough counts for the Cairns-Tully section by Dr. L. F. Webb have given a figure of one hundred sixty species in one and a half hectares, a diversity that ranks with that of Sarawak (one hundred thirty species), and Mount Makeling, Luzon (one hundred twenty-seven species). In a comparable tract in southern Queensland, a rough count indicated less than one hundred species.

Alfred Russel Wallace, during his pioneer researches in Malaya, was the first to draw attention to the richness of the flora of rain forests. In 1878 he wrote:

Above: In the flying phalanger (Petaurus norfolcensis), *as in "flying squirrels," membranes of skin between fore- and hind-limbs permit gliding flight. (Stan and Kay Breeden)*

Brush turkeys (Alectura lathami), *one of the megapodes or mound-builders, construct huge incubators in the jungle, depending on the heat of decomposing of soil and leaves to hatch the eggs. (Ederic Slater)*

Right: Brown tree-snake (Boiga irreguloi-des), one of the colubrids or back-fanged snakes which are only slightly venomous. It is fairly common in the forests of coastal Queensland. (J. Clark)

If the traveller notices a particular species and wishes to find more like it, he may often turn his eyes in vain in every direction. Trees of varied forms, dimensions and colors are around him, but he rarely sees any of them repeated. Time after time he goes toward a tree which looks like the one he seeks, but a closer examination proves it to be distinct. He may at length, perhaps meet with a second specimen half a mile off, or may fail altogether, till on another occasion he stumbles on one by accident.

The diversity of species in rain forest trees extends to other plant groups. For example, two biologists in 1917 counted forty-eight species of epiphytes on the trunk of a fallen tree at Mount Tambourine, southern Queensland. Of these, sixteen were vascular plants.

Although rain forest trees belong to a vast number of different groups, they tend to have several common features. The trunks are, as a rule, straight and slender, and there are no branches until near the tops of the trees. Plank buttresses, flangelike outgrowths, often extend out from the bases, providing additional support. The bark is generally thin and rarely has deep fissures. The leaves are large, leathery, dark green, oblong-lanceolate to elliptical, often finely serrated or toothed along the edges, with an acumen or "drip-tip" present. Large and strikingly colored blooms are uncommon; instead, most of the trees have small white or greenish flowers. These tend not to be produced in the crown but project from the leafless, woody stems and larger branches, a habit known as "cauliflory." On some trees the flowers are suspended from long stringlike penduncles. They have no distinct flowering seasons, though there are times of maximum blossom and of leaf production.

Various theories have been advanced to account for the various peculiarities of the rain forests. Great biological diversity is, of course, typical of much of the tropics. It applies to insects and birds, as well as plants, and the richness of life on coral reefs is legend. This diversity is generally ascribed to the availability of a large number of ecological niches or ways of life. Again, it is believed that the relatively rich physical environment permits a great variety of minor specializations, which would reduce competition. But what of trees? There are certainly not innumerable differences in soil and moisture conditions within a small area. Is it, then, pure chance that permits many different seeds to lodge and grow in a given place? Actually, biologists have no satisfactory explanation for the diversity of tree species in rain forests. The "mosaic theory of regeneration" advanced by the French botanist Professor A. Aubreville might be noted, however. This stresses that the composite of trees in rain forest is not constant and that when a gap is created by a tree's falling, a different tree or composite of trees may fill it. This theory sees the species in a place at any one time as largely a matter of chance.

A common sight in a rain forest is the tree with buttresses. It has been suggested that buttresses help withstand wind and gravity forces, and that they assist in the transport of nutrients from the roots. Trees leaning over water commonly have the buttressing on the side towards the water. At other times, however, there is no link between degree of buttressing and position.

Drip-tips to the leaves, another peculiarity in the rain forest, are regarded by botanists as an adaptation that speeds draining, for a water film apparently decreases the amount of water flowing into the leaves from the stem. One theory of the advantage to rain forest trees of bearing flowers on the trunks and woody stems, is that the flowers there are more accessible to shade-loving butterflies. In another hypothesis, physiologists state that since the food substances do not need to be transported right up to the twigs in such species there must be a saving in energy in having the flowerheads lower down.

ANT-HOUSE PLANTS

Among the botanical curiosities of north Queensland and of the Pacific tropics are the several genera of ant-house plants. Two, *Hydnophytum* and *Myrmecodia,* occur in Australia. Both are epiphytic, growing on the trunks of large jungle trees. The base of the plant is tuberous, fleshy, and greatly distended, measuring perhaps six inches across. It is armed on the outside with spines. The plant is honeycombed with tunnels and galleries; small ants use these as their home, apparently doing neither good nor harm to the plant.

RAIN FOREST BIRDS

Looking for birds in the rain forest is tantalizing, for the dark foliage above and the dense undergrowth round about ring with the voices of birds, yet much of the time a dim silhouette is the watcher's only reward. There is an improvement, however, where the bush track enters open areas and secondary growth persuades the treetop species to come within viewing distance. Then the sight of a variety of rare birds is ample reward. Atherton Tableland has a very rich avifauna. The total number of species recorded from the area is about two hundred fifteen, and in one week in September 1953, a group from the Royal Australasian Ornithologists Union recorded ninety-five species from the Lake Barrine area alone.

The early morning is, of course, the best time to see birds, for then they are feeding actively. One of the tamest is the tiny yellow-breasted sunbird *(Cyrtostomus frenatus)* flitting among the hibiscus flowers a few feet away. This dainty bird bears a superficial resemblance to the humming-bird.

The flame trees and umbrella trees reveal a number of different species of honeyeaters, which are all but oblivious of the observer as they tumble among the blossoms. Some of these are restricted to the far north of the continent, even to the Atherton block itself, but others have a wide range. Thus, there is the little black-and-white-banded honeyeater *(Myzomela pectoralis),* the dusky honeyeater *(M. obscura),* the spinebill *(Acanthorhynchus tenuirostris),* the lesser Lewin honeyeater *(Meliphaga notata),* the Macleay honeyeater *(M. macleayona),* and the white-throated honeyeater *(Melithreptus albogularis).* Scrub wrens *(Sericornis lathami)* and log

Laguna Bay at the mouth of the Noosa River, with the peak of Mount Timbeerwah in the background, one hundred miles north of Brisbane. In the foreground is a she-oak or Casuarrina. *(Derek Duparcq)*

runners *(Orthonyx spaldingi)* rake over the debris of the forest floor. Gray and rufous fantails flutter about the low shrubbery, taking insects on the wing. Yellow robins and gray-headed robins *(Eopsaltria australis* and *Heteromyias cinereifrons)* drop down from their tree-trunk perches to pick up insects on the ground. The pied flycatcher *(Arses kaupi)* hops around the gnarled trunks and vines. Whistlers and shrike thrushes search the branches and leaves; these include little-known northern species like the Bower shrike thrush *(Colluricincla boweri),* which is replaced by the rufous shrike thrush *(C. megarhyncha)* below two thousand feet, and the gray whistler *(Pachycephala griseiceps).*

As the sun climbs over the hills and illuminates the valleys, a clifftop will reveal the little gray swiftlets *(Collocalia francica)* fluttering over a gorge, and topknot pigeons *(Lopholaimus antarcticus)* feeding in the treetops below. A crested hawk *(Aviceda subcristata)* is perched on an exposed branch. Occasionally a party of large white cockatoos *(Kakatoe galerita)* will come screeching over a ridge and make their leisurely way down the valley.

JUNGLE FOWL, CASSOWARIES, AND BOWERBIRDS

Three large birds of exceptional interest frequent the rain forests: the jungle fowl *(Megapodius freycinet),* brush turkey *(Alectura lathami),* and cassowary *(Casuarius casuarius).* All three will be seen on occasion crossing the jungle tracks or roads. The first two are mound-nest builders, depending, like the mallee fowl, on the heat generated by rotting vegetation to hatch the eggs. The sizes of the mounds after some years of use may be enormous—forty to fifty feet across and seven to eight feet high. Cassowaries, giant flightless birds, stand about five feet high and are black in color, with the head and neck bare and preponderantly blue. A large red wattle hangs from the foreneck. The wings are rudimentary, the legs very powerful, with the inner toe having a greatly enlarged nail, used in defense. Cassowaries are shy and difficult to see in the scrub, and their keen hearing makes it difficult to approach them. When alarmed they run through the undergrowth with amazing speed. They feed mainly on large berries and palm seeds. The nest is a flattened structure of grass and dried fern fronds. Four pale green eggs are usually laid, and are found from July to October. The young birds are striped. Cassowaries are one of the many New Guinea elements in the Australian bird fauna that extend south to the limits of the Atherton-Bellenden Ker scrubs.

Two of the most striking rain forest birds keep to the higher range country, and one must travel far up the timber tracks into the remote forests to see them. These are the golden and tooth-billed bowerbirds *(Prionodura newtoniana* and *Scenopoeetes dentirostris).* The display structure of the golden bowerbird, built against small saplings, is huge. The walls are three-and-a-half feet or more high, twenty-four inches apart, and there is a runway elevated ten inches or more. Lichens, strewn on the runway, continue to grow in the moist air. The male, brilliant gold and brown in color and about the size of a small thrush, glows like a fireball as it displays. The tooth-bill has a serrated beak, a development apparently associated with its habit of sawing off large leaves for use in its "circus-ring" play area on the jungle floor. The latter is a cleared space some three feet across. One's attention is drawn to it because the leaves are scattered about, with their silvery undersides exposed. The tooth-bill is a rather plain brown bird, male and female being alike. The bird's notes are a mixture of musical sounds interspersed with the mimicked calls of other species in the neighborhood.

TREE KANGAROOS AND CUSCUSES

The rain forests of northeastern Queensland are the home of some very interesting mammals: several kinds of kangaroos and wallabies, three species of ring-tailed possums, the striped possum *(Dactylopsila picata),* two kinds of cuscus *(Phalanger nudicaudatus* and *P. orientalis),* the tiger cat *(Dasyurops maculatus),* the long-nosed bandicoot *(Perameles nasuta),* and giant fruit bats. Most interesting of the kangaroos are the musk kangaroo *(Hypsiprymnodon moschatus),* the most primitive member of its family, and tree kangaroos *(Dendrolagus lumholtzi* and *D. bennettianus),* which have forsaken a terrestrial existence for life in the trees.

The musky rat kangaroo is a stumpy marsupial about a foot high. Unlike the other members of its group, it is not herbivorous but a mixed feeder whose diet includes worms and insects obtained from the debris of the forest floor. Its teeth, and certain other anatomical characteristics, are intermediate between the true kangaroos and the arboreal phalangers from which these were derived. The animal is not found outside the northeastern rain forests, where it is not uncommon. I have flushed them from the undergrowth many times, and individuals are often found dead on the roads.

Tree kangaroos probably originated in New Guinea, where there are several species. Two of these have invaded Australia, apparently in relatively recent times. Despite their bulk, they are not easily seen under the dense rain forest canopy, and it was there that they moved quickly on the few occasions I have seen them in the wild. Tree kangaroos have a lengthened forelimb, long, thick, sharp claws for climbing, and "skidproof" foot pads that help them in their leaps among the branches. The tail, however, is not prehensile like that of the phalangers, functioning merely as a balancer. They have by no means lost their capacity for moving over the ground: individuals surprised in exposed positions may drop from heights of as much as fifty feet above the ground and bound into the undergrowth. Tree kangaroos are mainly foliage feeders. Of the two species Lumholtz's tree kangaroo is the more attractive animal, a fine grizzled-gray above and yellowish-white below, the face, chin, and toes black.

Cuscuses are bright-colored, woolly, arboreal marsupials that have somewhat baboonlike faces, protruding eyes, and small ears. The body is up to three-and-a-half feet long and as big as that of a large cat, being heavy and powerfully built. The body movements are sluggish. Cuscuses are nocturnal feeders but I have occasionally seen them by day, curled up high in a tree. The diet is a mixed one, consisting of fruits and berries, insects, and birds' eggs. Adult males have a heavy, penetrating odor and zoo enclosures holding individuals soon become disagreeable. Most of the species

Mangroves at low tide on Nudgee Beach, Moreton Bay, to the north of the mouth of the Brisbane River. (Derek Duparcq)

Mangrove seedlings on Moreton Bay, near the southern end of Moreton Island. (Derek Duparcq)

occur in New Guinea, but one has extended its range westwards through the island archipelagoes to the Celebes.

The striped possum has thick, woolly fur, white on the back with three blackish-brown longitudinal stripes. One of the fingers of the animal is long and thin and has a long nail, a device for extracting insects from cracks in bark paralleling that of the Madagascar aye-aye. The species is a nest-builder like some of the other possums and insects; foliage and berries are the food. The striped possum is also of New Guinea origin. It, too, has a sharp, unpleasant odor.

TROPICAL BUTTERFLIES AND GIANT PYTHONS

One of the great delights of walks along rain forest trails is the butterflies. The majority of the three hundred fifty different kinds recorded from Australia inhabit the northern rain forests. Most brilliant is the metallic-blue and black Ulysses or imperial swallowtail *(Papilio ulysses)*, perhaps four inches across. Most often one sees it dancing down the avenue of trees fringing the trail, or fluttering past the high foliage. The large birdwing *(Troides pronomus)* is green and black and is a powerful flier. When hovering in front of a red hibiscus, or the white, pendant flowers of the papaya or pawpaw, it is a delight. The tailed emperor is creamy-white with black edges to the wings. Among a variety of brown, reddish, blue, yellow, and white butterflies, large and small, there is the glass-wing, whose forewings are almost transparent. Another curious species is the leaf-wing, whose wings, when folded above the back, resemble a leaf—a splendid example of camouflage.

The largest snake in Australasia, the New Guinea amethestyne python, is a rain forest inhabitant of the far north, but it is rarely seen. Large specimens grow to twenty feet. These big snakes, which kill by strangulation, probably subsist largely on wallabies and possums. Another interesting rain forest reptile is the green dragon lizard *(Goniocephalus)*, an arboreal species. Smaller species of snakes and small lizards may be seen sunning themselves in those areas where sunlight flickers down to the floor of the forest.

122

A PENINSULA AND ITS ISLANDS

The Cape York Peninsula is one of the most remote and inaccessible sectors of the continent. Its backbone is the Great Divide, which extends north almost to the tip, and from which short eastward-flowing and somewhat longer westward-flowing rivers run. It is covered by tropical savanna woodland, dominated by eucalyptus, with a grassy substratum that is tall and dense after the summer monsoons. There are also tea tree areas along the watercourses.

A number of isolated pockets of rain forest occur on the east coast of the peninsula, for example, along the Jardine and Pascoe–Lockhart rivers and in the Cooktown–Cedar Bay segment. Mangroves, with their fauna of crocodiles, flying foxes, black butcherbirds *(Cracticus quoyi),* and mangrove kingfishers *(Halcyon chloris),* occur in some of the wide inlets. On Cape York the faunas of woodland and rain forest are quite distinct, that of the mangroves moderately so.

The peninsula is of interest biologically in that it is the channel through which most of the recent exchanges of fauna between New Guinea and Australia have taken place. Studies by the writer have shown that at present New Guinea is contributing mainly rain forest species to Australia, while Australia supplies savanna woodland species to the island. The exchange has obviously gone on intermittently over a vast period of time, successful establishment being dependent on habitat needs and specializations. A rough idea of the length of time a species from New Guinea has lived in Australia might be gained by comparing the immigrant species' color, body form, and habits with those of the original parental stock.

Many of the more striking animals peculiar to the Atherton rain forest block are of New Guinea origin. Likewise, on the tops of some of the peninsula's higher mountains are found the only Australian representatives of such New Guinea plants as *Bubbia, Balanops, Rhododendron,* and *Agapetes.* Today these are isolated not only by Torres Strait but by the dry savanna woodlands of the peninsula, which are an unsuitable habitat for the plants. It follows that they reached their present home at a time of higher rainfall, when rain forest was continuous down the length of peninsula.

Many of the migratory birds that winter in New Guinea and on the islands to the north use Cape York as their jumping-off place, for not only is the strait narrower here but there are intermediate islands. Among the birds that have been observed migrating in flocks across the strait, or have alighted on ships in this region, are long-tailed kingfishers *(Tanysiptera sylvia),* black-faced cuckoo shrikes *(Coracina novae-hollandiae),* and tree martins *(Hylochelidon nigricans).* Torres Strait, which separates Australia from New Guinea, is a shallow stretch of water dotted with innumerable reefs and islands of every size and kind. Continuing the line of Cape York Peninsula is a series of rocky islands, and many of them, such as Prince of Wales, Horn, and Moa, are quite large. They are mainly of porphyry, that is, of the same geological formation as the northern parts of the peninsula. These stony islands are, nevertheless, well-wooded in places. There are muddy foreshores and areas of mangroves; and all the islands have fringing reefs. The main settlement in the region and the center of the local pearl oyster industry is on Thursday Island, twenty-four miles northwest of Cape York. Thursday is one of the smaller islands, only about one square mile in area, and rises to a height of 375 feet. These "high islands" are the remains of the land that once connected Australia and New Guinea.

Innumerable coral islands and reefs stud Torres Strait, especially between the area of high islands and the Great Barrier Reef. All are oval sand cays, low but well vegetated. They represent a great hazard to navigation.

A series of volcanic islands, the Murray Islands and Darnley Island, lie in a triangular area of some seven hundred square miles at the northeastern extremity of the strait. They have no relation to the mainland, but are remnants of the summits of extinct volcanoes that once had built up from the sea bottom. On the island of Mer in the Murray group, the rim of the crater, 750 feet high, is still intact and shows little signs of weathering, good evidence that the volcano is not long extinct. A dense tropical vegetation grows on the fertile basic lavas and tuffs and, as on many volcanic islands, it is very beautiful. Mer is the only one of the Murray Islands permanently inhabited by the Torres Strait Islanders.

Apart from bats and cuscuses on the more fertile islands, these Torres Strait islands have little in the way of mammal life. The birds of the high islands are a replica of those of Cape York, except that fewer species occur, sunbirds, scrub fowl, flycatchers, drongos, and small green fruit pigeons, being the main species. Reef herons, cormorants, and migratory waders live on the reefs, and the coral cays support large colonies of sea birds, such as the bridled tern *(Sterna anaetheta),* black-naped tern *(S. sumatrana),* and Caspian tern *(Hydroprogne caspia).*

But the most striking species in the strait area are the Torres Strait pigeons *(Myristicivora spilorrhoa).* These are strong-winged birds, white with black wingtips, that fly with the speed and assurance of a falcon. They sleep and nest in large numbers in the mangroves of the islands. At dawn they leave for the jungles of the mainland to feed on berries and wild fruits. One of the most pleasant memories one can have of the Torres Strait islands is of flocks of these birds coming home at dusk, forcing their passage against the strong sea wind until, gaining the lee side of the island, they swoop down onto their perches among the mangroves.

World of Coral

The Great Barrier Reef

7 The Great Barrier Reef, extending some 1,260 miles from the vicinity of the Tropic of Capricorn north along the Queensland coast to southern New Guinea, is one of the zoological and scenic wonders of the world.

The reef is not a single unbroken chain or breakwater but a composite of reefs of varying shapes and sizes, some entirely beneath the surface, others reaching the surface and separated by channels. Only the six hundred miles of it north of Cairns is a continuous rampart. On its seaward margin the reef, there known as the Outer Barrier, rises precipitously from great depths. East of Cairns the ocean bottom drops away to 780 fathoms (about 4,600 feet). The reef proper, rising from the edge of the continental shelf, is about 180 feet high. Between the Outer Barrier and the coast are a jumbled and irregular series of inner reefs; hence its name, the Coral Sea. Among these reefs is Willis Island, two hundred miles from the coast, the site of a weather station.

The Outer Barrier is farthest from the coast in the south and center and closest in the north. Thus, the Swains Reefs, a thirty-mile-wide area of coral patches separated by intricate channels and marking the southern limits of the reef, are about one hundred miles out to sea. The reef is fifty miles from the coast opposite Townsville, twenty miles at Cairns, and only seven miles at Cape Melville, two hundred miles farther north.

The great distance of the southern parts of the barrier reef from the mainland explains Captain Cook's failure to discover it until he sighted the Low Isles, forty miles north of where Cairns is today. The following morning the ship ran aground on Endeavour Reef. The next voyager to sight the breakers of the barrier was Captain William Bligh in 1789, twenty-six days after he was set adrift in an open boat by

One Tree Island in the Capricorn Group is a typical small, grassy cay resting on a reef nearly a mile across. Thousands of terns nest on the island. (Keith Gillette)

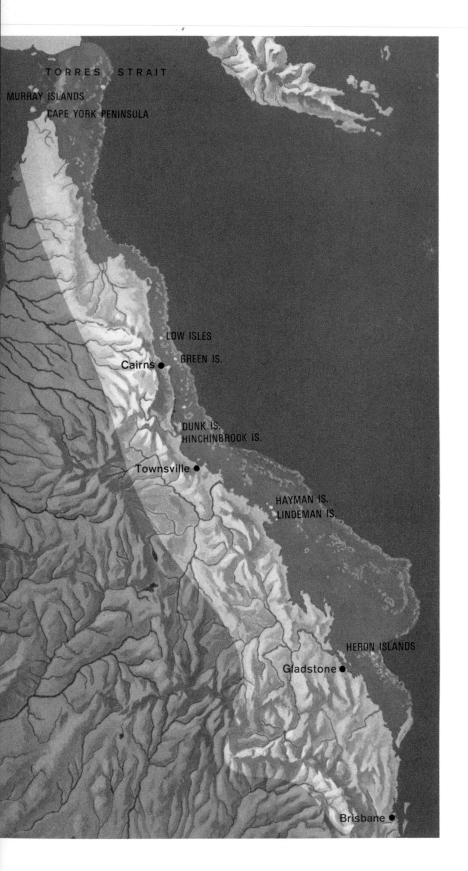

The Great Barrier Reef, the longest coral reef in the world, extends for 1200 miles along the coast of Queensland, forming a rampart against the Pacific tenanted by marine animals of bewildering variety and color. The little cays that occur here and there on the reef's surface contain breeding colonies of thousands of gulls, terns, noddies and mutton birds. Cumbersome turtles struggle ashore after dark to lay their eggs above the high tide line.

the *Bounty* mutineers. The party went ashore on what they named Restoration Island, obtaining fresh water, wild fruit, and shellfish, and staying some days before leaving for Timor. Bligh returned to the Great Barrier Reef in 1792 to map Torres Strait and some of the northern reefs, a work that still continues.

THE REEF AND CORAL CAYS

The Great Barrier Reef is estimated to cover an area of eighty thousand square miles, an amazing structure considering that many of the coral polyps that make it up have bodies the size of a pin point. Solitary and colonial corals occur in all the oceans of the world, from the poles to the equator, but the reef-builders cannot grow where the temperature of the sea water is lower than about sixty-nine degrees. This confines them to the equatorial belt bounded by the tropics of Cancer and Capricorn. They also cannot thrive in depths greater than thirty fathoms. The reefs are mainly limited to the eastern sides of the larger land masses, for on the west there is commonly a growth-stunting cold current.

The fossil record shows that reef-building corals have had a long history on the earth; extensive reefs were laid down as far back as the Silurian period, perhaps 400 million years ago. Silurian and Devonian coral rock is known from many parts of the world, including Australia. Although these ancient reef-builders belonged to different orders, families, and genera from modern corals, they can be considered ancestral to the latter.

The circumstances of the beginnings of the Great Barrier Reef remain obscure. As in the case of the formation of atolls, two alternative theories have been advanced. Charles Darwin postulated that the reef arose on the edge of a gradually sinking continental shelf, the rate of upward growth equaling that of subsidence. The "glacial control theory," advanced by R. A. Daly, contrasts sharply with this. This theory holds that when the sea level was lower during the last Ice Age, wave action cut into the coast of Queensland, redistributing the material on the adjacent sea bottom to form a shelf; as the seas gradually rose again, the reefs developed on this platform. The famous American biologist Louis Agassiz, who visited the reef in 1896, supported these views. As time passes, however, geological evidence for block faulting and sinking along the Queensland coast has mounted, and Darwin's ideas now find general acceptance.

Two kinds of island occur along the Queensland coast, the high islands and the coral cays (or keys). The cays are true coral islands, built up from the sea and surrounded by extensive reefs many times their own area. Cays are formed by wave and current action at high points of reef. They never rise more than a few feet above the high tide line, and are made up of coarse fragments of coral, fine coral sand and, in places, so-called beach rock.

Beating against the face of a reef, the sustained force of wind and sea breaks off lumps of coral and washes them, along with finer fragments, sand and silt, across the reef into

Double Island, one of the inshore high islands originally cut off by a sinking coast and a rising sea level. (Janet Finch)

A small screw-pine or Pandanus, *the most striking tree of the Great Barrier Reef and many other Pacific shorelines. (Sven Gilsater: Tio)*

the eddies of still water beyond. On the lee side, these materials gradually accumulate along the shore. Then seeds are washed in and grass appears, followed by fleshy plant known as pig's face or *Mesembryanthemum* and, as nesting sea birds fertilize the soil with their guano, by shrubs and trees. Here and there along the shoreline is beach rock, composed of coral fragments and sand cemented together by calcium carbonate. The solvent is the summer rains, the dissolved lime being redeposited under the intense heat of the sun at low tide. Beach rock may form part of the ultimate shoreline of the cay. Elsewhere there will be wide beaches of pure white coral sand. In the most exposed sections, a sloping mass of broken coral, its fragments interlocked, may form a shingle rampart.

Coral cays occur throughout the length of the Great Barrier Reef. In the south are the Capricorn and Bunker groups, thirty to fifty miles out from Gladstone. One of the former is Heron Island, a tourist resort and the site of a biological research station. Green Island, near Cairns, to which there is a daily launch service, has the most visitors. Most of the other cays are known only to big game fishermen, marine biologists, and ornithologists. Cays are fascinating, even to the uninitiated, because no two are alike in size, vegetation, or the species of seabirds that nest on them. Moreover, in such a group as the Capricorns all stages of cay development can be seen, from reefs with only a sandy bank protruding above the high water mark to those that are heavily wooded and extend many acres. The largest of the Capricorn group,

Northwest Island, has an area of 260 acres. Lastly, there is nothing to equal the marine life of the reefs near the cays. These reefs, as has been noted, greatly exceed the cays themselves in size, those next Heron Island, for example, measuring almost four miles long by one-and-a-half wide.

NODDIES, TERNS AND SEA EAGLES

The journey to one of the Great Barrier Reef cays is a delightful experience in every way. It lies across mile after mile of fleckless blue sea, calm—if one is moderately lucky—with a light breeze to check the ardor of the sun. Flocks of dainty brown noddies circle the boat or flutter about the surface of the water as they feed. Occasionally a flying fish leaps into the air ahead of the vessel and glides for fifty yards. And often one or more amusing dolphins take up a station at the bow of the boat.

Dolphins may accompany a boat for hours. They will maintain a fixed position and distance from the craft without effort; then, with a sudden twist of the body, sweep to one side in a frolicking chase. Presently, one after another, they leap clear of the surface, exposing their horizontal tails. Then, in a flash they return to their former position near the boat.

On the journey to Heron Island, dark patches on the horizon herald the first cays of the Capricorns. As one approaches closer, the gently churning water of the fringing reef discloses a low sandy mass, its shoreline sprinkled with *Pandanus,* or screw palm, and the horsetail casuarina, beyond which rises the dense *Pisonia* forest of the main part of the island. Some of the islands, such as Masthead, have extensive grassy areas, and in spring a dense mass of fluttering, scolding terns hangs over these. The white of the birds and the ring of glittering white coral sand stand out strikingly against the green of the island and the blue of sea and sky.

Landing on a cay can be accomplished only at high tide, the large launch being anchored out in the lagoon and a smaller boat used to cross the reef to the beach. Ashore, one wanders through the outer zone of tournefortia shrubs with wide leaves, and pandanus, a curious plant with twisted white trunks crowned by a radial fan of leaves. Horsetail casuarinas, *Casuarina equisetifolia,* characterized by long drooping needles, overhang the beach in places, casting beautiful patterns on the sand, both by sunlight and moonlight. A little way back from the beach, pisonia takes over. This forms a dense forest, the trees having large leaves and throwing long patches of shadow—a welcome relief from the heat of the sun.

The pisonia trees are the realm of the dainty white-capped noddies *(Anous minutus),* slim, ternlike birds with dark brown bodies, white caps, and long tapering wings. They stream in from beyond the reef, converge down avenues between the trees, and flutter to their nests in the branches. The nests are simple structures, flattened platforms of dried pisonia leaves cemented together by droppings. There may be seven or eight nests to a tree, in a variety of positions. On a trip to the island in January we found that some nests held a solitary egg but that others had chicks of various ages, indicating a protracted

North Molle Island in the Whitsunday Group, a cluster of high islands that were once coastal hills and are not true coral islands. (Robin Smith)

nesting season. The noddy colony can only be described as a bedlam of yelping birds, with the excitement rising to a crescendo each time a group of birds wheels in from the sea.

It is a relief to get beyond the noddy colony and resume one's journey across the island. Suddenly, the visitor sinks ankle-deep into a burrow of the wedge-tailed shearwater or muttonbird *(Puffinus pacificus)*. A few feet farther on he stumbles again, this time going down to the knees, shoes filling with sand. He realizes he has entered the colony area of the muttonbirds: the whole stretch of the friable, sandy soil is honeycombed with burrows. But none of the owners of the burrows are to be seen, save when the visitor has the misfortune to fall in on a sitting bird—which generally retaliates with a painful stab in the leg.

A little bar-shouldered dove *(Geopelia humeralis)* rises with a clamor of wings from a spindly tree, and a white-eye *(Zosterops lateralis)* utters its spring song in the foliage above. On the tallest tree on the island, a pair of white-breasted sea eagles *(Heliœetus leucogaster)* have long had their nest. It

is not difficult to find the spot, for the nest is a great mass of sticks perhaps five feet across and six feet high, the birds adding to it from year to year. The eagles are by now spiraling overhead, beautiful, big white birds with long wings. They protest the intrusion with loud chattering nasal calls. These birds are fortunate: they have been able to build at a height of some forty feet. A pair on isolated One Tree Island on the outer edge of the Capricorn group, visited a few days later, had their nest a mere six feet above the ground in a stunted *Pisonia,* the only tree on the island.

Because it is so well wooded, Heron Island does not have any tern or gull colonies. For these one must visit such islands as Masthead or One Tree, on which there are large areas of grass or exposed shrub. Apart from noddies there are six species of terns breeding in the Capricorns—the roseate *(Sterna dougalli)*, crested *(S. bergii)*, lesser crested *(S. bengalensis)*, black-naped *(S. sumatrana)*, bridled *(S. anaetheta)*, and little *(S. albifrons)* tern. Masthead and One Tree islands have colonies containing thousands of birds, especially crested

Above: Terns and gulls on a beach near Double Island. (Derek Duparcq)   Right: Osprey (Pandion haliaetus) and young, found on many Barrier Reef islets. (Vincent Serventy: Paul Popper Ltd.)

Overleaf
Left above: Rookery of sooty terns (Sterna fuscata) on Michaelmas Cay, near Cairns. The spotted birds are young. (Graham Pizzey) Left below: Part of a nesting colony of white-capped noddies (Anous minutus) in the branches of a pisonia on Heron Island. (F. G. H. Allen) Right: Dense pisonia forest on Heron Island (pandanus in background). The ground is honeycombed with burrows of the mutton-bird (Puffinus pacificus). (Douglass Baglin)

Coral at low tide on Lindeman Island. (Queensland Government Tourist Bureau)

terns, whose eggs are scattered over the ground a few feet apart. Some of the islands have nesting colonies of silver gulls *(Larus novae-hollandiae)*. No boobies nest on the Capricorns, but the brown booby *(Sula leucogaster)* has colonies in the Bunkers to the east. Three gannet species, as well as frigate birds, have colonies on the Swain's Reefs on the outer edge of the barrier. The sooty tern *(Sterna fuscata),* the dominant breeding tern on the more northern cays, colonizes on Michaelmas and Upolo cays.

LIFE ON A CORAL REEF

The reefs that surround the coral cays are a world unto themselves. They can be studied from a glass-bottom boat or with the aid of diving apparatus, but most investigation is carried out at low tide, when the reef is exposed. The rise of the tides is great, reaching up to fifteen feet. Hence, the volume of moving water and the speed with which it withdraws is considerable. At various points, big coral boulders, tossed

up on the reef by a violent storm and rounded off by wave action, break the surface of the water. As the tide recedes, we can see that the reef covers many acres. But it never becomes entirely exposed: here and there broad expanses of water from six inches to six feet deep are held back by the high outer rim of the reef.

The beauty and diversity of the life of the coral reef is famous. Beneath the surface the coral takes every shape and color—great rounded masses of dark brown brain coral; solitary mushroom corals; treelike, branching *Acropora,* and so on. Where the reef breaks the surface, the coral is dead and bleached: one must peer into the pools to appreciate the true reef life. There one sees waving masses of pale yellow soft coral, clumps of pale brown sea anemones, sponges of many colors, and little flat platforms of mauve porites coral. A large brain coral, its center killed by exposure, forms a brown ring with a white core. A fascinating sight is the colorful serpulid worm; we see a fan-shaped ring of feeding tentacles timorously protruding from coral masses. A blue *Linkia* starfish shares a depression with a black *bêche-de-mer* and with a needle-spine sea urchin whose brittle, foot-long spines threaten any intruder. A brittle star makes its way on long, spidery legs to the shelter of a tuft of seaweed, disturbing a brilliant crimson nudibranch mollusk floating through the water with matchless grace. And through and about and over all, the little reef fishes dart, some blue, some white, some yellow, and some all the colors of the rainbow.

Reef life reaches its peak of luxuriance under open sea conditions; hence the farther out from the coast, the better it is likely to be. The richest reef I have seen is the one surrounding One Tree Island, twelve miles east of Heron Island. This islet is much exposed on the seaward side, but to the landward it is protected by a series of crescent-shaped reefs separated by lagoons. An outstanding spectacle there is the "forests" of branching blue *Acropora*, which grow upward from depths of about fifteen feet to within six feet of the surface.

MUTTONBIRDS AND TURTLES: NIGHT ON A CAY

In the transition from day to night a profound change occurs in the bird activity on coral cays. The noddies and terns, their last meal gained in the yellow half-light of the setting sun, retire to land and, after a period of clamor in the gathering dusk, settle down for the night. For an hour or so all is silent save for the rustling of the waves on the sandy beach and the occasional "plonk" as a sedate reef heron seizes an unwary crab.

Then, after nightfall, the wedge-tailed shearwaters, or muttonbirds, come to land. These birds are close relatives of the Bass Strait muttonbirds. Initially, one might not notice them; they come sweeping in from the sea on silent wings, and spend some time circling and gliding over the colony as though trying to locate their own burrows. Then one after another they drop through the trees to the ground, their plump bodies making a series of "plops," and start toward their burrows with awkward running shuffles. Muttonbirds do not have the most agreeable disposition; when one collides with a neighbor there is much raucous squawking. Returning birds call out greetings to their mates in the burrows. Within minutes, the moans and wails of a few birds swell into the cries of dozens and then of hundreds, bursting finally into an appalling crescendo of squealing and squawking.

At the end of two or three hours all the birds are ashore. But the noise still does not abate. The only recourse for a human visitor is to behave like an ornithologist and regard it as music.

The wedge-tailed shearwater has a wide range in the Pacific like all other petrels, it is wonderfully adapted for life over the sea; its long, tapering wings carry it through the worst storms. It comes ashore for only a few months in the year, seeking out remote islands on which to form colonies. The burrows are three to four inches in diameter, extend underground for two to four feet and terminate in an enlarged

Right above: Acropora *coral and tropical fishes on the Great Barrier Reef. (Australian National Travel Association) Right: Giant clam* (Tridacna) *on the Great Barrier Reef. Such clams, which lie embedded in the coral and coral rock, may be three feet across. (Vincent Serventy: Paul Popper Ltd.)*

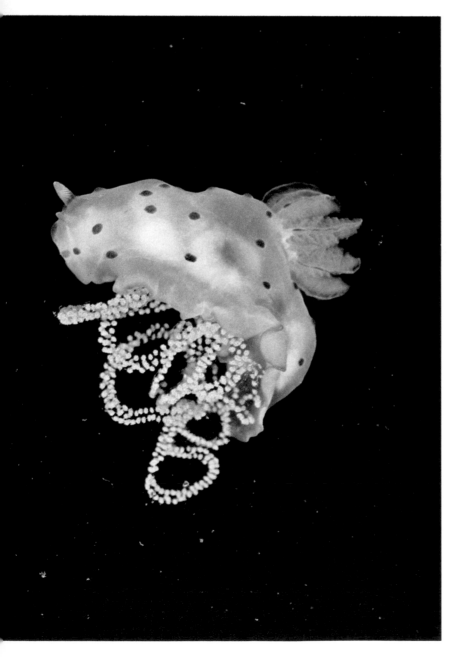

nesting chamber. A single egg is laid at the end of November, and male and female both take turns at incubating, each shift lasting some eight to twelve days. The incubation period lasts about six weeks, and the young bird remains in the burrow until April. As with other petrels, the nestling, by then a plump mass weighing about two pounds, is abandoned before it can fly, and lives on its fat for the last two weeks of its development.

The number of birds in some of the Great Barrier Reef colonies is amazing. Counts can best be made just before dawn, when the birds converge on pathways en route to the sea. One count, made by ornithologist Eric Pockley on Northwest Island twenty years ago, indicated that the birds were passing along some of the pathways at the rate of ten per second, a total of some thirty thousand using one pathway in an hour. While some pathways obviously had more traffic than others, and the rate of passage varied from time to time, there were at least a few hundred pathways, suggesting a possible population of two million birds for that island.

The other fascinating nocturnal inhabitant of Heron Island and other southern cays is the green turtle *(Chelonia mydas),* which also comes ashore on the islands after dark to lay its eggs. The green turtle inhabits a wide range of tropical waters. One of four marine turtle species in Australia's waters, it lives on seaweed among the reefs. It was the basis of the famous turtle soup of former times, and a canning factory of Northwest Island once helped to supply this delicacy.

The carapace of the green turtle may attain a length of forty-eight inches, a width of forty-two inches, and weighs four hundred pounds. The males are only about two-thirds the size of the females.

The turtles come in to the beaches at a time of high night tides between the end of October and the end of February. Though they are skillful in the water, their flippers are poorly adapted to life on land. The journey up the beach is a laborious one. Slowly the female makes it way to above the high tide mark, "rowing" with its forelimbs and leaving a characteristic trail behind it. When a suitable site is found, the long task of excavating a hole for the eggs commences, an exhausting process for the heavy reptile. Once the turtle is engaged, the observer can come and sit alongside it. Using its hind flippers, it casts out the sand in little sprays. In an hour the hole is three feet deep, and the laying begins. The eggs, which are white and about the size of table-tennis balls, are dropped for perhaps fifteen minutes, until from fifty to two hundred have been laid. Then, slowly and with much puffing and wheezing, the female fills in the burrow, and roughs over the surface so that the site of the nest cannot be found. She then drags herself back down the beach.

Left above: Nudibranch mollusk (Chromodoris quadricolor) with the flower-like exposed gills at rear that give the group their name. They lack shells. (Anthony Healy)   Left: Nudibranch mollusk (Glossodoris sp.), one of the most colorful reef inhabitants of the reef, laying its eggs on Heron Island. (Keith Gillette)   Right: A group of golden demoiselle fishes pass over a coral reef. (Allan Power)

Overleaf: Coral reef fishes on the Great Barrier Reef. (Frank Hurley: Rapho-Guillumette)

Left above: Reef fish and table corals near Heron Island illustrate the remarkable diversity of life around a coral reef. (Gordon de'Lisle) Far left: Close-up of the Venus tusk fish, a brilliantly-colored denizen of the coral reef. (Ron Bacchi) Left: Moray eel (Lycodontis pictus) lurks in its hiding place in the coral. Subdued in color but with sharp teeth, morays can inflict a nasty bite. (Allan Power)

Right: Green turtle (Chelonia mydas) swims over the coral. These turtles, which may attain a carapace length of four feet and a weight of four hundred pounds, come ashore on the Capricorn Island beaches to lay their eggs. (Allan Power)

Studies have shown that a female may come ashore as many as seven times in a season. The young take ten and a half weeks to hatch. With unerring instinct the babies make their way down to the sea, running the gauntlet of gulls and herons by day, and crabs and reef sharks at night. Little is known of the life history thereafter until, as an adult, it comes ashore to lay.

THE HIGH ISLANDS OF COASTAL QUEENSLAND

Northward from the Capricorns all the inshore islands are high; they were formerly hills of the mainland. They are not truly part of the Great Barrier Reef system, though tourists regard them as such. The animals and plants on them are mostly those of the mainland, though ospreys *(Pandion haliaetus)*, reef herons, and migratory waders abound on the foreshore. There are, however, no colonies of nesting seabirds or turtles, and the marine life, though sometimes abundant, does not compare with that of the cays. The main high islands are Hayman, Hook, Whitsunday, Lindeman, Brampton, the Molles, Long, Magnetic, and Lizard. Most of these rise to heights of six hundred feet but Hook Peak reaches 1,478 feet and Lindeman has three peaks over one thousand feet high. Whitsunday Island, near Bowen, is the largest of the tourist islands, and is separated from the mainland by a long channel, the famous Whitsunday Passage, used by shipping. Just north of it is the even loftier Hinchinbrook Island. Most of the islands are well-wooded, some having fine groves of pines, while a few, like Dunk Island, are jungle-clad, others are dominated by steep, grassy hills, and a number have magnificent cliffs. These islands are most picturesque and are famous for the beauty of their surrounding seas.

Lily Lagoons
and Billabongs

The Tropical North

The tropical northern fringe of Australia is a land of contrasts: lush woodlands, lily-covered lagoons, mangrove-fringed bays and inlets, barren ranges of red rock, quiet creeks, and vast grasslands. The climatic changes are the most marked on the continent. There is a hot, wet summer, three or four months long, during which forty to sixty inches of rain may fall. Rivers flood and spread out for miles over the surrounding alluvial plains, and the grass reaches heights of six to seven feet. For the rest of the year little rain falls. By the end of the dry season the streams are reduced to a series of pools and the grass has died away almost completely. These extremes affect animals as well as plants. The little coastal wallabies, which found the undergrowth almost too dense, are hard put now to find cover. The river fish, compressed into small pools, go through a period of starvation. The water birds of northern Australia are, by necessity, nomads. During the rains they spread out far over the flooded country, but now they concentrate on the little water that remains. Some, like the black duck and gray teal, as leg banding has recently shown, may leave the north entirely and migrate into the southern parts of the continent.

The aborigines of Arnhem Land have their own names for the distinct phases of the seasons. The start of the rainy season (October to mid-December) is "storm time," its climax (mid-December to mid-February) "rain time," the subsequent period of decreasing rainfall and overflowing rivers and swamps, "close-up time." This period, as the natives told anthropologist W. E. Harney, is disagreeable because their food-gathering activities are restricted. The swamps are too

deep for the gathering of bulbs, the grass is wet and unpleasant to move through, the winds keep the native bees in their hives, and flooding kills many of the mangrove crabs. At the end of March the wind changes to the southeast and blows strongly for perhaps a week. The tall grasses are bent and pushed over; they call this "knock 'em down time." April introduces rain-free, pleasant days and gentle southeast breezes, drying out the swamps. Roots and bulbs now become accessible, and tortoises and fish can be caught. As the grass dries it turns brown and is often fired by the natives to facilitate their hunting of wallabies and other game ("burnt-grass time"). April to September is "cold weather time." Finally, the aborigines state, the imminent rains are heralded by the return of warm, humid days and northwest winds, and this they call "warm-up time."

MONSOON FORESTS AND LUSH WOODLANDS

The key fact about rain in northern Australia is that virtually all of it falls between October and March. Since these are the hottest months and the evaporation rate is high, the benefit to plant life is small. The high evaporation and marked seasonability of the rain impose limits on the kinds of vegetation that can grow. Rain forest, for example, cannot stand such extremes. Nevertheless, there is a somewhat parallel formation in monsoon or "pseudo rain forest," as it is sometimes called. This is composed of softwoods, not eucalypts, and there is a more or less continuous canopy fifty to eighty feet from the ground. The floor is littered with dry leaves. Lianas are abundant, and some ferns such as *Dicranopteris, Blechnum,* and the climbing *Stenochlaena,* occur. There are, however, no arboreal mosses, ferns, or lichens, and only a few orchids.

Monsoon forests are restricted to places where the percentage of water in the soils is relatively high, as along permanent fresh-water streams and the edges of marshes, and sometimes in swampy terrain adjacent to mangroves. This means that they usually take the form of long, narrow strips. Notwithstanding their limited and patchy distribution, the monsoon forests of northern Australia from the Roper River to the Kimberleys are of considerable significance to animal life, accommodating many species that require shade and dense foliage. Various eastern rain forest birds occur here, including rufous fantails *(Rhipidura rufifrons),* green-wing pigeons *(Chalcophaps indica),* and the jungle fowl *(Megapodius freycinet).*

The most spectacular and characteristic vegetation formation of coastal northern Australia is the tall *Eucalyptus* woodland. This is mostly dominated by the Darwin stringybark *(E. tetrodonta)* and the woolly butt *(E. miniata).* The bark covering the trunk and limbs of the former is shaggy and fibrous; in the latter this bark is restricted to a "stocking" at the base of the tree, the limbs being smooth and white. Both trees have straight trunks, from the upper half of which

Rugged Cape Range, northwest Australia, showing eroded tableland typical of great areas of Arnhem Land, the Kimberleys and the Hamersleys. Water drains from it rapidly, and since the rains fall only in the hot summer it is relatively arid. (Michael Morcombe)

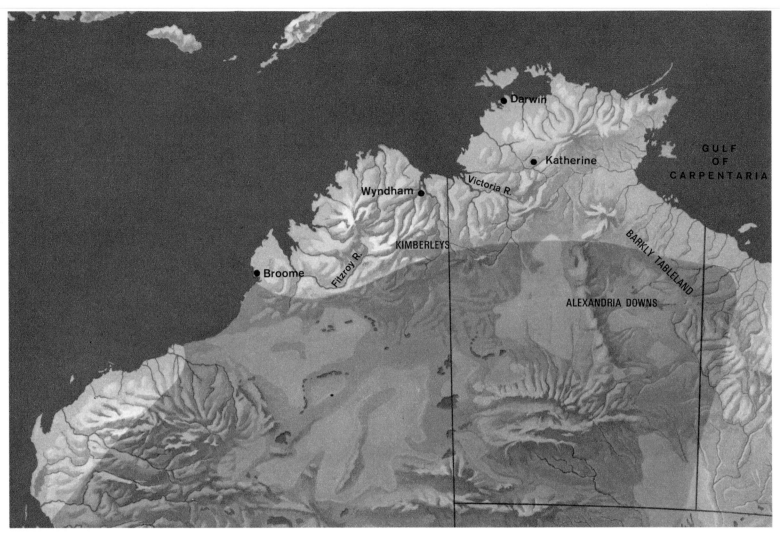

Tropical northern Australia is a mixture of savannah woodlands, lily-covered lagoons, flood plains and barren stony ranges. Giant termite mounds are one of its most familiar sights.

branches extend outwards to form an open canopy. The understory of the woodlands includes some shrubs, but is mostly made up of tall grasses. These, as noted, may be six feet tall at the end of the rainy season.

Apart from the eucalypts, the most striking plants are the palms *(Livistona benthamii* and *L. humilis)* and the somewhat palmlike cycads *(Cycas media)*. The palms reach heights of sixty feet, the cycads about twelve feet. Both tend to occur in clumps, but individuals are scattered throughout the woodlands. *Livistona* has an interesting distribution in Australia. It occurs mainly in the east and north, but isolated species occur in the Macdonnell Ranges of the central desert and in a rocky gorge on the Fortescue River on the arid west coast. These two relict stands indicate that good conditions formerly extended much farther to the south than they do now. Cycads have a coarse trunk surmounted by a ringlike crown of glossy, dark-green, frondlike leaves, beneath which are clumps of stalked seeds. They are ancient plants, first known from the Jurassic period, 150 million years ago. Today there are only two regions of the world where three genera of cycads occur naturally—Australia and Mexico. The Australian forms are the northern *Cycas,* of which there are several species, the southern *Macrozamia* (about a dozen species), and the east Queensland *Bowenia* (two species). One of the southeastern species of *Macrozamia* sometimes attains a height of sixty

feet, and individuals are known (e. g., on Tambourine Mountain in southern Queensland) that are estimated to be ten to fifteen thousand years old.

Tea trees *(Melaleuca leucodendron)* have a wide distribution in northern Australia and form distinctive stands in low-lying areas. They reach heights of twenty to sixty feet and have conspicuous white trunks. The bark, the so-called "paperbark," is composed of a large number of layers of paperlike thickness that can be pulled off in sheets. The leaves of the melaleucas are tiny, but at certain seasons the trees are covered with white blossoms and attract large numbers of nectar-feeding birds. One of my greatest delights is to sit against the trunk of a streamside melaleuca and watch these feathered gems jostling amongst the flowers overhead. Most of the honeyeaters here are species that do not occur in southern Australia. Notable are the dainty little banded honeyeater *(Myzomela pectoralis),* the large gray-bodied friarbird *(Philemon argenticeps),* and the plainer red-throated honeyeater *(Conopophila rufogularis),* white-throated honeyeater

"Ant hill" country near McKinley, northwest Queensland. Termitaria are prominent features of the northern Australian landscape, some rising fifteen feet high. (Janet Finch)

(*Melithreptus albogularis*) and white-breasted honeyeater (*Ramsayornis fasciatus*).

GIANT TERMITE MOUNDS

So large and abundant are the "white ant" mounds, or termitaria, in the woodlands of northern Australia that they constitute a striking feature of the landscape. The columnar

Magnetic anthills, constructed by the magnetic termite, or meridian ant, south of Darwin. These mounds, up to ten feet tall and eight feet broad but a mere three inches across, have a north-south axis and it is believed that the shape minimizes heat intake in summer and maximizes it in winter. (Robin Smith)

structures raised by one of these tropical mound-builders, *Nasutitermes triodiae*, reach heights of over twenty feet. The most bizarre mounds, however, are constructed by the magnetic termite or meridian ant. These take the form of flat slabs, up to ten feet tall and eight feet broad but a mere three inches or so across. Their long axis invariably points north and south. Several theories have been advanced to explain this strange shape and orientation, the most generally accepted one being that of Dr. G. F. Hill: that they serve to minimize heat uptake in summer and, since the broad axis is east-west, obtain the maximum benefit from the sun's rays in winter. Hill's behavior studies showed that many kinds of tropical termites are unable to tolerate excessive heat and retire to the bottom of the galleries by day, returning to the high levels only when the temperature falls at night. Furthermore, in winter there is a marked daily movement to the warm eastern side of the mounds in the morning, and to the western side in the afternoon. Many species of termite construct ground nests, which may vary greatly in form. Those of a species I photographed near Tanami in the south varied from low cones to spires that terminated in rounded turrets. Arboreal termitaria, which at first glance look like excrescences on the trees, also occur in northern Australia, as elsewhere. Most of the gallery space in all termite mounds is devoted to food storage, as opening them up will show.

One hundred and fifty species of termites occur in Australia; the total for the world is about two thousand one hundred. In Australia, however, there are many "primitive" species whose body structure and social organization show them to be ancient forms. One of the genera, *Mastotermes,* as we know from the fossil record, became extinct on the other continents in the middle Tertiary period, thirty million years ago. Termites are notoriously destructive insects. Over large areas of Australia special precautions have to be taken to protect the foundations of wooden houses and the buildings themselves. Until wooden railway sleepers and telegraph poles were replaced by metal structures, the loss in them was heavy. Some of the arboreal termites gradually eat out the core of the trunk and branches of the trees that harbor them. Fruit trees, sugar cane, and vegetable crops may be attacked. In places, grazing lands are damaged too. No extensive study of this has been carried out in Australia, but a recent termite-extermination campaign in Natal, South Africa, restored rich grassland in areas that had long been regarded as relatively barren.

LILY PONDS AND WILD GEESE

The lagoons and billabongs are among the more beautiful sights of northern Australia, for many of them are covered by the large-flowered blue water lily *(Nymphaea gigantea,* variety *violacea).* This flowers in winter, that is, at the middle

Right above: Although mainly a ground-dweller, the three-foot-long goanna lizard (Varanus gouldi) can climb well. (Eric Lindgren) Right: A frilled-neck lizard (Chlamydosaurus kingi) signals its alarm by raising its skin-flap—to make itself appear much larger—opening its mouth and hissing. (Stan and Kay Breeden)

of the dry season. The fruits, which are sought after by the natives, germinate in the mud during the following wet season. Blue lilies also occur on the quiet reaches of the larger rivers. In the shallower ponds, however, they may be replaced by yellow-flowering water plants, so dense they form a carpet.

The lily lagoons are a haven for many distinctive birds: the little green pigmy geese *(Nettapus pulchellus)*, the long-legged tree ducks *(Dendrocygna arcuata)*, the migratory gray teal, and the large magpie geese *(Anseranas semipalmata)*. Here, too, the lotus bird or jacana *(Irediparra gallinacea)* runs over the lilies, supported on its astonishingly long toes. Tortoises abound, as do the little Johnstone's crocodile *(Crocodilus johnstoni)* and many kinds of small fish, including the curious archerfish. Introduced Asian buffalo have found the lagoon areas and their adjacent grasslands and woodlands a home away from home.

The most striking bird living in the northern lagoons and flood plains is the magpie goose, a long-legged species about the size of the domesticated goose (the male weighs six pounds) with white body and black head, neck, and wings. There is a high knob on the forehead and the feet are half-webbed. A hundred years ago the goose occurred as far south as Melbourne, but destruction of habitat, a series of disastrous droughts and to some extent poisoning and shooting have eliminated it from the southern regions. Fortunately flocks of up to thirty thousand still concentrate annually on breeding grounds on the lower limits of the Adelaide and Alligator rivers. The breeding range, limited as it is to a strip within forty miles of the north coast is, however, very restricted.

Magpie geese recently came under criticism because of the destruction they wrought in ricefields that were being established on the flood plains of the Adelaide River. Research showed that the planting had been carried out in one of the traditional breeding areas, that there was a direct correlation between the birds' tendency to concentrate in the ricefields and the amount of water available elsewhere on the plains, and that the birds did not so much consume the newly planted seeds as disturb them. Efforts were initiated to kill all the geese in the cultivated areas. However, it was realized that the failure of the rice crop was due to improper leveling of the fields, young rice plants being just as susceptible to drowning as to drying out.

The geese breed at the end of the wet season, in the deeper and more densely vegetated parts of a few large swamps. Their nests are bulky structures made of trampled water plants. Four to fourteen eggs are laid; sometimes two females contribute to a single nest. Magpie geese feed on grass seeds obtained from the edge of the water, and especially wild rice; underground bulbs become the main food as the swamps recede. With the establishment of an efficient rice industry in the Northern Territory only a matter of time, authorities have set aside one of the main breeding areas of the magpie goose as a reserve. Accordingly, even if the birds must be removed from some of the agricultural areas in the future their survival as a species is assured.

TORTOISES, ARCHERFISH, AND BUFFALOES

Tortoises have been found as fossils in rocks estimated at one hundred and fifty million years old. There are thirteen different kinds in Australia (rather a smaller fauna than the thirty-odd species in North America), and they are of considerable interest because they belong to a group, the Chelyidae, that elsewhere occurs only in New Guinea and South America. The explanation for such a broken distribution is elusive, but one thing is certain: they must once have had a continuous distribution between the continents. Unlike North America, Australia has no true vegetarian tortoises; all subsist on a diet of worms, mussels, snails, shrimps, and insects. They occur throughout the fresh-water areas of the continent and fall into two main types, the "long-neck," whose head cannot be completely withdrawn into the shell and hence must be folded around the edge, and the "short-neck," whose neck can be folded straight back. Tortoises are common inhabitants of the northern lagoons and rivers and can be seen lying with their nostrils on the surface or sunning themselves on a log or bank. They go ashore only when forced to move from a drying waterhole to a new one, and when the time comes for the female to scoop out a hole on dry land and lay her twenty elongate, white eggs. The aborigines catch the tortoises, which they esteem as food, by wading through swamps or lagoons and groping for them with the hands.

The rifleman or archerfish *(Toxotes jaculator)* is one of the strangest inhabitants of the waters of northern Australia, for it obtains its food, insects and spiders, by shooting them down with jets of water. It does this from a position just under the surface of the water. So splendidly is the mouth modified for the role that the fish is said to score hits more often than

Long-necked tortoise (Chelodina longicollis), *one of the thirteen Australian tortoise species that occurs wherever there are rivers. (Vincent Serventy)*

Baobabs or bottle trees (Adansonia) *in an inlet near Derby, Western Australia. Famous for their strange shape they vary greatly in form. (E. S. Ross)*

misses, bringing down prey from a distance of several feet. Beyond Australia these fish extend through the tropical islands as far as India. The small crocodiles are their chief enemy in the lily ponds.

The Asian buffalo was introduced to the Northern Territory between 1825 and 1829. First there were thirty-four animals released, then another small group in 1838. Away from natural enemies, and remarkably free from disease, the buffaloes flourished, so that by 1885 the combined population of the mainland and Melville Island was estimated at sixty-eight thousand. These powerfully built buffaloes are some ten feet long and five feet tall and have large, curved horns. For the most part they stay near water, loving to wallow in the oozy mud. They do most of their feeding in the morning and late afternoon, resting among the trees by day. One calf is born each year. Hunting buffalo for their hides forms a minor industry, and a few years ago between six and eight thousand animals were killed per year, the skins bringing about twenty dollars each. It is controlled by permit because excessive shooting in former times threatened the animals with extermination.

ESTUARIES AND MANGROVES

For the most part, the coast of northern Australia is low, though in areas of eastern Arnhem Land there are cliffs ranging from thirty to two hundred fifty feet in height. Elsewhere, sandy beaches, dunes, wave-cut rock platforms, and raised coral beaches face the sea. Of the major inlets, Van Diemen Gulf is believed to have been formed by crustal sagging; the valley of the Fitzroy River in the Kimberleys and its outlet King Sound are defined by faults. Other inlets, including the Gulf of Carpentaria, had their origin as valleys and coastal lowlands flooded by the rising of the sea at the end of the last glacial period.

The wealth of silted river mouths, estuaries, quiet bays, and tidal mudflats in northern Australia has induced the development of extensive mangrove forests. "Mangrove" is a collective name for trees that are adapted to survival in saline, waterlogged soil in which the salt concentration fluctuates with the tides, and which is subject to alternate drying out and flooding. Mangrove seeds, which are able to withstand prolonged exposure, are borne about on the currents until washed up onto land. Mangrove forests are best developed in the tropics, where the greatest number of species occur. There are fourteen genera in northern Australia, compared with a mere seven species at Brisbane and two at Sydney.

Mangroves are generally able to flourish despite high tidal fluctuations (up to thirty and forty feet). Studies by botanist R. L. Specht, however, have shown that some species are specialized for life in one area and others in another, the critical factor in distribution apparently being the frequency of tidal flooding. Thus, the spectacular *Rhizophora mucronata,* a tall tree with roots like flying buttresses, is common only near river mouths. Other species occur farther up the estuaries, adjacent to the shore, or on slightly higher ground.

Mangroves are important in the distribution of vertebrate animal life. Flying foxes roost in them, making nocturnal sorties to find flowering eucalypts in the surrounding woodlands and to hunt for figs in the monsoon forests. Possums *(Trichosurus)* feed on their foliage. Half a dozen bird species are limited to mangrove areas. These include the mangrove bittern *(Butorides striata),* which stalks over the mudflats and takes to the mangroves for roosting and nesting, and the mangrove kingfisher *(Halcyon chloris),* which uses them as lookout posts from which to flutter down and snatch up crabs. Northeastern Australia has its mangrove warblers *(Gerygone cantator* and *G. levigaster)* and mangrove honeyeaters *(Meliphaga fasciogularis* and *M. versicolor).* In the northwest of the continent two thickheads, the white-breasted whistler *(Pachycephala lanioides)* and the brown whistler *(P. simplex),* live and feed among the mangrove branches and leaves. Other birds, such as the small red-headed honeyeater *(Myzomela erythrocephala)* and the shining flycatcher *(Piezorhynchus alecto),* occur both in mangroves and in the monsoon forests. Finally, the mangrove fringe down the dry western coast of Australia has permitted a few species that require fairly dense cover—such as the golden whistler *(Pachycephala pectoralis)* and gray fantail *(Rhipidura fuliginosa)*—to occur well beyond their usual range limits.

CROCODILES AND MUDSKIPPERS

Crocodiles are certainly the most spectacular inhabitants of the muddy estuaries of northern Australia, and traveling up one of these waterways, eyes peeled for a sight of one of these big lumbering brutes sun-bathing on a bank, is an interesting experience. My first such journey was up the Forrest River, which enters Cambridge Gulf in the Kimberleys. In its lower reaches this stream is broad; the banks, lined with somber mangroves, are broken here and there by small creeks coming in from the forests beyond. One minute the stream is wide and shallow, the next minute it has narrowed to sweep beneath a cliff or travel a serpentine course through a series of mudbanks. Each bend brought its series of surprises: groups of migratory godwits *(Limosa lapponica)* and curlews *(Numenius madagascariensis)* from Siberia; egrets stalking in the shallows; pelicans taking off in slow, labored flight; a stately jabiru *(Xenorhynchus asiaticus),* Australia's native stork, standing on its nest high in a riverside gum. In places I could see marks on the mud where crocodiles had slid into the water, but I was unsuccessful in catching a glimpse of one; that had to wait for a later occasion, when I sat on a streambank at dusk. How very like a drifting log the crocodile was, despite its protruding eyes, how effortlessly it floated, and how silently it slipped out of sight when it realized it was being watched.

There are two kinds of crocodile in Australia, the large estuarine crocodile *(Crocodilus porosus),* a species that has a wide range from India to the southwest Pacific and is said to grow to twenty-five feet in length, and the smaller, narrower-snouted Johnston's crocodile, an inhabitant of freshwater streams and billabongs. The latter reaches a maximum length of about eight feet, but is harmless to man. The estuarine crocodile inhabits the lower reaches of the Forrest and other coastal rivers, but when these are in flood it may penetrate the fresh water for distances of up to fifty miles or

Purple-flowering waterlilies on a billabong of the Finniss River, Northern Territory. (Australian News and Information Bureau)

more to snap up the livestock that come down to drink. On the other hand, they have been sighted as much as forty miles off the coast when moving from one place to another. Their main food is fish, but they vary this with snakes, lizards, water birds, and mammals. Birds are seized from beneath the surface. Mammals are sometimes captured when they come to the water's edge, the victim being dragged into the water and held under until it drowns.

Crocodiles lay their eggs in shallow holes in the soft earth of the riverbank in late spring (October to December). The holes are scratched with the forefeet, and the seventy or more eggs, each three inches long in the larger species, are then covered with soil and left to be hatched by the heat of the sun. The eggs take about two months to hatch. Well armed with rows of sharp teeth, the babies, ten inches long in the case of the estuarine crocodile and 9 1/2 in the Johnston's crocodile, take to the water to begin an independent existence.

Crocodiles are confined to the northern strip of Australia from about Derby to Cairns, though there are records of their appearance farther south. Tertiary and Pleistocene fossils are known both from the arid Lake Eyre basin and from the coastal areas of South Australia and Victoria—evidence that these areas supported good rivers and were much warmer in the not so distant past.

The estuaries and mangrove forests of northern Australia also harbor a strange little fish known as the mudskipper or goggle-eyed mangrove fish *(Periophthalmus)*, which has the curious habit of leaving the water to perch on the mud and even climb on the exposed roots of the trees. When disturbed, it skips away rapidly ahead of one. When moving over the mud, at its leisure, the fish "rows" along on its elbowlike pectoral fins. The body color is muddy gray, flecked with lighter and darker markings. There are five Australian species, all tropical, and they range in length from four to about ten inches. *Periophthalmus* is able to breathe by extracting air from the water it holds in its pouchlike gill chambers, and possibly also through the skin. Crabs, flies, and other small life constitute the food.

ROCKY GORGES AND BROAD GRASSLANDS

Much of the Northern Territory is part of an old plateau, the northern end of the Great Western Shield of the continent.

It is of variable height, seven hundred feet above sea level in the Darwin–Katherine area, nine hundred feet at the head of the Fitzmaurice River, and twelve hundred feet in Arnhem Land. Here and there ancient Precambrian metamorphic rocks protrude above the plateau as hills and ridges. For the most part, however, the mountainous appearance of Arnhem Land, the Kimberleys, and other sections, is due to streams, having carved gorges through the plateau over long periods of time. The rugged range country holds little water. Spindly, stunted gums exist precariously among the tumbled rock and on the steep hillsides. As in the desert ranges farther south, the white-trunked ghost gum *(Eucalyptus papuana)* and spinifex are conspicuous.

The large rivers of the Northern Territory have their headwaters in such broken terrain. It is difficult to traverse, either on foot or by vehicle, and a journey I made by vehicle through the upper Victoria River entailed a winding series of long, slow climbs—first gear was necessary for nearly forty miles. In their lower reaches the rivers run through broad alluviated valleys and flood plains of their own making; the Daly River flood plain is between twenty-five and fifty miles wide in places. These flood plains are sometimes not much easier to negotiate than the gorge country, for now the truck bogs down in the deep sand. The roads are mere tracks, deep wheel-ruts and a ridge in the middle. Bitter experience taught us to stay in second gear and maintain as much speed as possible. All might be well for fifty miles, then a sudden bend would force us to slow down. The truck would sink into the sand and we would jolt to a sudden stop, the wheels digging deeper the faster they were spun. Lengths of matting were carried to get us out of such predicaments—but first we would have to jack up the wheels to get the matting under them. On occasions extensive bad stretches were negotiated, forty feet at a time, in this way.

Southwards from the coastal woodlands and the rugged

Facing page: A clump of mangroves, with their characteristic tangle of roots, on the north Queensland coast. (Vincent Serventy)

The goggle-eyed mangrove fish (Periopthalmus) *has the curious habit of emerging from its mudhole (left below) to lie in mud or even on the low branches of a tree (below). (Both by Herbert Chargois)*

plateau country of Arnhem Land lies the Barkley Tableland, a broad belt of savanna grassland that stretches unbroken for a thousand miles from east to west, and includes some of the finest cattle country in Australia. Here and there are a few wide lagoons, but the watercourses are ephemeral and run only after rain. I spent some time on the Barkley in 1952 studying the effects of drought on the distribution and breeding of birds. It was a year of record drought, and nearly a million head of cattle perished. The country was dry and parched, the shrubs withered, and the great areas of former grassland lay bare in the warm winter sun. A survey of the bird life on the Alexandria Downs cattle station showed that only ten species of birds remained: it seemed unbelievable that, in the same area during a favorable year, the ornithologist Collingwood Ingram had recorded nearly one hundred different kinds of birds.

FRILL-NECKED LIZARDS AND GOANNAS

Lizards abound in the tropical north, and each section has its quota of small, swift-running skinks and dragon lizards that shoot across one's path. Often, also, one comes upon the larger, heavy-bodied and sluggish blue-tongues *(Tiligua)*. Geckos are equally common, though one has to pull the bark off dead trees to find them by day: they are nocturnal.

The most striking land reptiles of northern Australia are the frilled or frill-necked lizard *(Chlamydosaurus kingii)* and the large goannas. The former is one of the dragons (Agamidae), the group that includes the bearded dragon of the south and the spiny devil of the desert. The frill-neck, which is up to two feet long, is characterized by a great flap of skin that extends from the back of the head and ordinarily lies in neatly folded pleats along the side of the body. When the lizard is alarmed this opens like an umbrella and makes the animal appear to be several times its normal size. The patterns on the shieldlike frill, the distended pinkish mouth, a loud hissing, and the readiness with which the lizard makes small jumps toward the intruder are enough to make the most hardened bushman step back. The time thus gained gives the plucky animal the chance to turn tail and streak for cover.

Goannas (Varanidae) are large lizards with flattened heads, long, sharp teeth, somewhat flabby, leathery bodies, and forked tongues. The tail is long and compressed laterally and the claws are large. Some species are arboreal and at least one is semiaquatic. The largest Australian species is the perentie, of the drier parts of northern Australia and of central Australia, which reaches a length of seven to eight feet (the Komodo dragon of Indonesia reaches ten feet). *Megalania prisca,* an Australian fossil form from the Pleistocene, was fifteen to seventeen feet long! The smallest of the contemporary species are six to eight inches long. Eight species occur in northern Australia. The larger goannas are partly scavengers but also consume rodents, small birds, eggs, and nestlings. Of the commoner forms, Gould's goanna *(Varanus gouldi)* occurs in races of various colors but tends to be brownish in grassland areas, gray in forested and high rainfall areas, and reddish in the desert. It will be seen stalking over the ground, but it turns tail and flees for its burrow when frightened. Arboreal species like the eastern *V. varius* rapidly ascend the nearest tree, spiralling around to keep on the opposite side of the observer. A water goanna, *Varanus*

mertensi, inhabits the smaller Kimberleyan streams, propelling itself rapidly through the water weeds by means of its flattened tail. Goannas hide their eggs in hollows in trees or underground. All species are much esteemed as food by the natives; the flesh is whitish and not unlike that of chicken, though some people feel it has a fishy taste.

Northern Australia is also rich in snakes of various types and sizes, all but a few harmless to man. In rocky areas the aborigines sometimes catch rock pythons, a species that grows to perhaps ten feet and is esteemed as food. The large venomous snakes include the brown snake *(Demansia)* and the death adder *(Acanthophis).* One rarely sees the snakes, so astute are they at getting out of the way, but leggings will give a visitor peace of mind, as well as protection from the annoying grass seeds and undergrowth.

RUGGED GRANDEUR—THE KIMBERLEYS AND THE HAMERSLEY RANGES

The Kimberleys, in the northwest corner of the continent, constitute one of its most rugged sections. Much of the area is over two thousand feet high, with residual peaks like Mount Hann (2,800 feet) protruding from the plateaulike surface. The whole block is bounded by scarps to the east and west, suggesting that it might have been thrust upwards as a gigantic dome or horst. The two largest rivers of the region, the Ord to the north and Fitzroy to the south, partly encircle the mountains. The Kimberleyan coast is deeply indented, the gulfs being mostly ancient river valleys flooded by a rising sea.

My first view of the Kimberleys was from the east, at the end of a month-long expedition across the flat central deserts of the continent. Well before the first rocky outcrops were reached, the spinifex and scattered shrubs began to give way noticeably to trees and grasses. When the scarp became visible it took the form of a long, low, purple mass through the shimmering heat haze, an exciting and gratifying sight. A few hours later we entered a narrow belt of foothills and were soon following narrow cliff-enclosed valleys, refreshed by the green river gums that fringed the dry stream bed. The higher rainfall and protection of the ranges manifested itself in a grove of bananas and a clump of cerise bougainvillea by a settler's house. The bird life had changed noticeably: various honeyeaters, wood swallows, tree swallows, rock pigeons, and other new species were here.

The road through the mountains to Wyndham on the coast provided a vivid impression of this rugged country: valleys overhung by steep red scarps, gorges, flat-topped tablelands, broken ridges, and rough hills. The broad undulating valleys.

Right above: The yellow-flowering water plant Limnanthemum *covers Leila Lagoon near the Gulf of Carpentaria. Such colorful lagoons are a feature of the north. (G. M. Chippendale) Right: Brolga or native companion* (Grus rubicunda), *a native crane known for its spectacular courting dances, here stands by its nest in a marsh. (Rod Warnock) Far right: Black ducks* (Anas superciliosa), *many of which migrate annually between the coastal Northern Territory and southern Australia. (Douglass Baglin)*

The King Leopold Ranges in the southern Kimberleys, where weathering has created a series of parallel ridges separated by valleys. (West Australian Newspapers Ltd.)

included many areas of Mitchell and Flinders grasses, excellent cattle fodder. Since it was the dry season the sandy riverbeds held nothing but a series of broad pools, and footprints on the sandy margins of these provided an excellent record of the many kinds of animals that had come down to drink the previous night. Debris caught in the branches of the river gums and high up on the bank testified to abundant summer rains. Close to the sea, near Wyndham, the terrain changed to wide, parched flood plains covered with dry grasses.

The Kimberleys are composed largely of ancient Proterozoic rock laid down perhaps five hundred million years ago. The wildest and most spectacular scenery is in the King Leopold Ranges and along the Fitzroy River to the south, where the rock is Devonian limestone. The whole area is of great interest to botanist and zoologist alike. One of the most unusual plants is the bottle tree, trees whose huge, swollen trunks take a variety of shapes and forms. The name comes from their shape, not capacity to hold water, although the thirsty traveler can sometimes obtain small quantities of this from hollows at the bases of the branches. In the dry season the leaves turn yellow and fall off, exposing the large fruits, which the aborigines convert into a floury paste. Vying with them in color at this time are the yellow-flowering kapok trees. The bird life of the plateau country and gorges includes the plumed pigeon *(Lophophaps plumifera),* whose reddish coloring camouflages it excellently against the rocks, and the white-quilled rock pigeon *(Petrophassa albipennis),* a rare dark brown species. The shrike trush *(Colluricincla woodwardi),* one of the few bird species confined to the area, has an unusual habitat, the steep cliff faces and shrubbery clinging to them. Black-faced wood swallows *(Artamus cinereus)* and migratory tree martins *(Hylochelidon nigricans)* from the south flutter and hawk over the gorges.

The range country is the habitat of rock wallabies *(Petrogale penicillata brachyotis),* which emerge at dusk and may be seen, silhouetted against the skyline, in the failing light. Larger and much more prominent, however, are the euros or hill kangaroos *(Macropus robustus),* which frequent the spinifex-covered plateautops. The *Pandanus* thickets along the waterholes in the valley floors are the best places to see birds. Northern gems like the crimson finch *(Neochmia phaeton)* and the lovely wren *(Malurus amabilis)* compete for attention with the yellow silvereye *(Zosterops lutea),* white-gaped honeyeaters *(Stomiopora unicolor),* and the great bowerbirds *(Chlamydera nuchalis).* In the shallows among the water lilies are herons, teal, magpie geese, and an occasional darter *(Anhinga novae-hollandiae),* variously hunting for frogs, insects, and the water snake *Fordonia.* When the eucalypts are flowering they are alive with red-collared lorikeets *(Trichoglossus rubritorquatus),* silver-crowned friarbirds, and rufous-throated honeyeaters. The grasslands of the Kimberleys are one of the last places where the Australian bustard *(Eupodotis australis)* remains common. In the dry season these birds become so lean that shooters decline to hunt them, which is heartening for the naturalist to hear.

Once, while setting traps for the little native mice, *Pseudomys,* I had an interesting lesson on the productivity of the Kimberley pools. It came as I watched an old aborigine wading with a three-pronged fish spear in the waters of a drying pool. Since the water was then only three to four feet deep it was all too obvious—or so I thought—that he could not possibly get a fish of body length greater than six inches, and a distinct feeling of sorrow for the old fellow swept over me. Suddenly he lunged, the point of the spear disappeared into the water, and to my amazement he hoisted a large barramundi, weighing fully six pounds, onto the bank. In the ensuing hour half a dozen other fish of at least two pounds in weight were obtained, plus three large water goannas. As a final acknowledgement of my error I asked the old fellow for permission to take his picture complete with catch. Proud of his success, he was only too happy to oblige.

Southwards from the Kimberleys the coast of Western Australia bulges far out into the Indian Ocean. This sector, which the Western Australians call the "northwest" of their state, is also broken plateau country. Its backbone is the Hamersley Range, and it closely resembles the Kimberleys in its physical features. The flora and fauna, however, are much poorer; desert elements are prominent. A number of

The blue-winged kookaburra (Dacelo leachi) *with a snake that it has probably killed by banging it against a branch. Kookaburras do not kill as many snakes as is often thought. (Vincent Serventy)*

Kimberleyan species reach the area, some of them being confined to single river valleys. The most intriguing of these valleys is that of the Fortescue River, where there are several permanent pools. Here occur groves of tea tree or cadjeput *(Melaleuca leucodendron),* palms, and birds like the swamp pheasant or coucal *(Centropus phasianinus).* The interesting thing about these populations is that they are quite isolated from their relatives to the north, for a broad swath of sand desert cuts through to the sea between the two areas.

Sands and Mountains of the Desert

The Desert Center of Australia

9 The greater part of the vast interior of Australia is red desert, miles of flat terrain where the heat waves dance and relief is afforded only by stark, rocky outcrops, sand dunes and withered mulga trees. To many the searing sun, aridity and loneliness are terrifying. For the earliest explorers, travel in the Australian desert was an appalling experience. The first man to cross it—in the midsummer of 1844—Captain Charles Sturt, has left us a striking description of what his men faced:

> The mean of the thermometer for the months of December, January, and February had been 101°, 104°, and 101° respectively in the shade. Under its effects every screw in our boxes had been drawn, and the horn handles of our instruments, as well as our combs, were split into fine laminae. The lead dropped out of our pencils, our signal rockets were entirely spoilt; our hair, as well as the wool on the sheep, ceased to grow, and our nails had become as brittle as glass. The flour lost more than eight per cent of its original weight, and the other provisions in a still greater proportion.

But Sturt, who expected to find some kind of sea in the center of the continent, was poorly equipped for his undertaking. To the modern traveler it can be a delightful and fascinating place. There is exhilaration in the spaciousness, the cloudless skies, the star-filled nights, the varied pastel tones of the mountains, and the acres of yellow porcupine grass waving in the wind. The "red heart of Australia," as it has been called, is something to see, for, scenically, it ranks with the Great Barrier Reef, the tall gum forests, the Tasmania highlands, the volcanic luxuriance of Tahiti, and the snow-covered peaks and fiords of New Zealand. And one's destination should be Alice Springs and the Macdonnell Ranges, in the center of the continent.

Actually, the desert that covers one third of Australia (extending over a great part of the west and out from the center to cut the coast in the south, the Nullarbor Plain) is not true desert in the sense of an arid area devoid of life. There are few shifting sand dunes of the Sahara type and only rarely does it approach the degree of aridity seen in some of the mountains fringing the Red Sea. Everywhere it contains vegetation, and some climatologists accordingly refer to it simply as semi-arid land.

The center of Australia consists for the most part of endless plains of red sand. In the east, the so-called Simpson or Arunta Desert is largely made up of consolidated sand dunes, arranged in great parallel northwest-southeast and north-south ridges, more or less evenly spaced and following the direction of the prevailing winds. To cross these at right angles is tedious and slow, with a jeep or land rover engine groaning away at a mere five to ten miles per hour and with constant backtracking in search of harder ground or a low saddle. Much of the southern desert areas are stony or gibber desert, gently undulating surfaces so completely covered with flattened stones that in some places the scanty, ephemeral plants that spring up following rain are hard put to reach the surface. Most of this stone represents remnants of old rocky plateaux. Some of it is laterite. Lateritic concretions are believed to result when rain water seeps downward, dissolving out iron minerals; these are redeposited on the surface as the moisture is drawn up and evaporates, the nodules gradually increasing in size.

The central and western desert plateau is broken by mountain ranges rising from one thousand to two thousand feet above the peneplain. These are essentially linear ridges of massive red rock representing an ancient surface dissected through the ages by wind and water. In central Australia solitary prominences or tors loom up from a flat desert plain. A few of these resemble mesas (Mount Connor), while Ayers Rock looks like a huge rounded boulder dropped from above by some primordial titan and Mount Olga, a gigantic pile of pebbles. Each outstanding geological feature of central Australia is the basis of fascinating aboriginal legend. These are supposed to have originated in that hypothetical "dream time" when the ancestral spirits were forming the world. But to the scientist these desert mountains, bluffs and prominences, and the various bizarre outcrops, are "indurated residuals." Residuals are rocks that have withstood the weathering of wind and rain better than their surroundings, having been hardened at some time by compressive forces or the intrusion of gases or liquids from the center of the earth. Most of the Centralian plateau has been reduced to sand, but these sentinels protrude for a thousand feet and more into the desert sky.

Another feature of the Australian arid lands is the dry lakes. Some are mere depressions, others hundreds of square miles in extent. Many have shimmering surfaces that look tantalizingly like bodies of water in the distance. The effect is produced by the crystals of gypsum, which forms a fine layer over the surface; in one place, gypsum spreads over hundreds of acres. The illusion that one is approaching water persists until one is within yards from the shore. Mirages, in

Celebrated Ayers Rock, a residual mass of conglomerate, glows a vivid orange 1,100 feet above the sand plain. (Gordon de'Lisle)

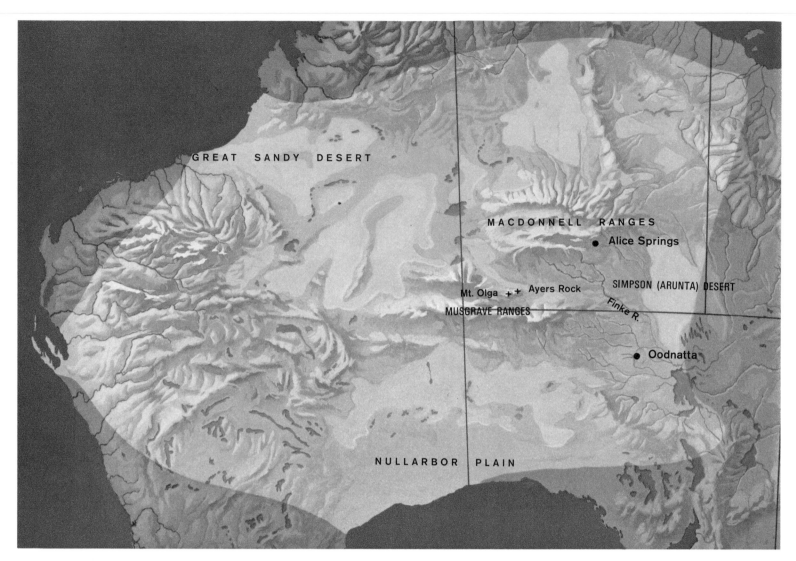

GREAT SANDY DESERT

MACDONNELL RANGES

• Alice Springs

Mt. Olga + + Ayers Rock

SIMPSON (ARUNTA) DESERT

MUSGRAVE RANGES

Finke R.

• Oodnatta

NULLARBOR PLAIN

The arid center of Australia, consisting of endless plains of red sand broken only by low rocky outcrops and mountain ranges, is in many ways the most colorful and picturesque part of the continent. Though popularly referred to as desert, it does not approach the extremes of aridity found in Arabia and southwest Africa.

which lakes appear where none exist at all, are also a feature. In early gold-prospecting days many an old miner was lured to his death by these fantasies of the desert. But in a modern vehicle, equipped with ample water and gasoline, one can be amused by them.

FROM ADELAIDE TO ALICE SPRINGS

Perhaps the best appreciation of the overwhelming vastness of central Australia comes in an air journey from Adelaide to Alice Springs. From the narrow coastal fringe of green the way is over the dry scrub country—sand desert liberally sprinkled with shrubs and bushes, many of them the mulga, *Acacia aneura,* a species of wattle that flourishes in the desert. Before long this scrub belt gives way to arid gibber country, rust-red and apparently quite bare, its colors dulled by the heat haze above it. From time to time some slight elevation throws a shadow, or a higher ridge in the lee side of the sun casts purple tones across the scene. And then the plane is over Lake Eyre, the largest of all the dead Australian lakes. Its broad shoreline is yellowish, its surface brown; here and

there muddy channels enter the lake or a darker streak indicates where a current once carried water out toward the center. South to north, Lake Eyre is sixty miles long and it is some time before the northern shoreline, with its clumps of porcupine grass and straggly bushes, appears. Then we move out over the true red sand country, a subdued rust-maroon carpet stretching in all directions, relieved only by an occasional line of hills, flung hard and low against a distant horizon.

The Centralian ranges stand out strikingly from the air. As we approach the airstrip at Alice Springs, almost in the center of Australia, the Macdonnells come into view. Our impression is of three or four huge parallel ridges of red rock extending from east to west. But they are quite unlike any normal mountains. The surface is cross-striated, cut by hundreds of transverse slashes; this is the bedding plane, but it is not the ordinary horizontal arrangement. An enormous twisting of this section of the earth's surface, probably over a great

Little clumps of saltbush (Atriplex) *send long shadows across a clayey section of the desert in northern South Australia.* *(Howard Hughes)*

160

period of time, has turned the bedding plane of these desert mountains so that it now points vertically to the sky. The mountain valleys are seen to have a richer vegetation than the plains. Bushes cover many of the hillsides and trees are scattered here and there. The creekbed in the valley is fringed by a meandering line of eucalypts.

An alternative way of obtaining an overall view of the Australian center is by making the rail journey of two or three days from Adelaide to Alice Springs. This way one catches glimpses of the animal life: a small mob of kangaroos hopping beside the train in the late afternoon, an emu stalking off across the plain, wedge-tailed eagles and various smaller hawks spiraling against the cloudless skies. And at some point there will be a mile or two where the scattered shrubs are green and there is a carpet of wildflowers, indicating where a cloudburst has fallen.

Another advantage of the rail journey is that at the few rather desolate railside towns or at sheep ranches, called sheep stations, one can get a glimpse of aborigines, the original inhabitants of the desert, now clad in the garb of the Australian drover or cowboy.

DESERT RAINS

To the climatologist the limits of the Australian desert are the ten-inch annual rainfall line in the south and the fifteen-inch line in the north. The latter applies because rain, due to evaporation, is less effective in the subtropics.

Australia is watered by two rainfall systems, a winter one that penetrates from the south (the so-called Antarctic System) and a summer one that comes down from the north (the Monsoonal System). The desert lies at or toward the limit of penetration of both systems. Rain in the Australian desert can thus come from either direction. A highly erratic rainfall characterizes all deserts. Some areas may go years without significant rain. One year there may be good winter rains and the next year all the rain will fall in summer. Again, most may be in a series of light falls that barely wet the surface. At Oodnadatta, for example, one-third to one-half of the annual rainfall of four to five inches falls in amounts of less than fifteen-hundredths of an inch. These light falls often induce plants to start growing but, if no other rains follow immediately, the plants die before they can seed. Others, like the little white everlasting daisies, are hardier. Though in a dry year they may only manage to produce stunted foliage and flowerheads one-quarter of an inch across, instead of the customary one-half inch, they usually manage to complete the cycle.

The irregularity of the desert rains is particularly tantalizing to the stockman: one year, or season, there will be ample food for the cattle, the next, none. Alternatively, a chance shower may initiate good plant growth on one ranch and miss the next: so that one man's stock will be fat, and

Left above: The introduced Mexican poppy (Argemone mexicana) is now established near Alice Springs. (H. Dacre Stubbs: J. Allen Cash) Left: Black or fork-tailed kite (Milvus migrans) at nest in a eucalypt in northern Australia. The commonest hawks of the desert, they circle above towns and cattle stations, looking for refuse. (John Warham)

another's thin and scraggly. Kangaroos know how to grapple with such vagaries of the climate: they are nomads and go wherever conditions happen to be best.

Every so often really heavy rains fall across a section of the Australian desert. The results are dramatic: a carpet of green blankets the red sand and within ten to fourteen days flowers turn the countryside into a riot of color. The *Acacia* and *Cassia* bushes burst into golden bloom. Birds appear by the hundreds and insects are everywhere. There may be flooding, so that torrents sweep down the old "dead" river channels and out across the plains. Such inundations, with their source in a distant range, can come so suddenly that persons camped in the soft sands of the riverbeds have been swept away during the night, or lost their belongings in the swirling waters. Such a flood will sometimes pierce the sand plain for as much as a hundred miles. Long before the water reaches the distant dry lake, however, high evaporation and porous soil reduce it to a trickle. The courses of "ghost" rivers, however, tell us that in former geological times the waters from the Macdonnell Ranges not only reached Lake Eyre, but the sea beyond.

HOT DAYS AND COLD NIGHTS

The temperatures of deserts are characteristically extreme. The days are cloudless and there is no protection from the withering force of the sun. The heat reflected by the sand makes the ground uncomfortable to walk upon, even with shoes. The glare sears the eyes and the face is burned. But, since there is no blanket of vegetation to prevent heat loss from the ground, with the coming of night the soil rapidly cools. Cold nights are therefore just as much a feature of the deserts as are hot days.

Most people visit the Australian desert during the winter months. The days are not then overhot. The nights are quite cold, but much of the time not uncomfortably so, and a sleeping bag together with some form of head cover are adequate. On such nights it is a pleasure to sit around a flickering log fire, beneath the cloudless sky. But when bitter winds begin to sweep through the dunes it is time to scoop out a trench for one's sleeping bag and "weather it out."

The winds of deserts result from the rapid fluctuation in temperatures on the desert surface and in the air above. Rising columns of air produce vortices—generally called whirlwinds in Australia—and these may bear masses of dust, grass, and other debris, spiraling aloft for hundreds of feet. As the winds advance across the plain, this captured material is borne along in the form of a revolving column. Sometimes the desert winds send great grass clumps rolling and bouncing across the landscape. The air is then filled with stinging particles of sand, and progress against the wind is extremely unpleasant. At these times the desert birds cower in the scant shrubby shelter or press themselves close to the ground, while rodents and lizards keep to the burrows that protect them from sun, sand, and the excessive temperature fluctuations.

ADAPTABLE PLANTS

The plants of the desert are interesting in that few of them occur elsewhere and the visitor, especially if he should come

Wedge-tailed eagles (Aquila audax), *Australia's largest hawk and a close relative of the golden eagle, are common in the desert. (Robin Smith)*

when they are flowering, finds himself in a whole new wonderland. The plants, moreover, show an interesting range of modifications and adaptations that permit them to thrive in this harsh environment. So specialized are many that they will not grow in a well-watered suburban garden.

The three main categories of plants are the ephemerals, the perennials, and species that function successfully above ground throughout the year. Speaking broadly the ephemerals, to which most of the wildflowers of central Australia belong, do not have special structural adaptations for desert life, other than drought-resistant seeds. They have, however, the capacity to grow and flower in a very short time. Perennials die back when conditions dry up but have underground roots and tubers that spring to life with the next rain. Two of the best-known wildflowers, the brilliant-red Sturt's desert pea *(Clianthus formosus)* and that dainty, creeping succulent with the rose-red blooms, Parakeelya *(Calandrinia),* which is an excellent camel food, are perennials.

The most important plants of central Australia are those

that function throughout the year: the trees and shrubs come into this category. Their leaf structure is modified to minimize water loss. The leaves of eucalypts here, as elsewhere, hang vertically so that the sun's rays strike them only at an angle and, in dry seasons, the leaves of most shrubs and trees of all kinds take on a withered, drooping look. A few kinds of trees shed their leaves during droughts. Acacias do not have leaves in the adult plant, replacing them by a leaf-stalk that is flattened into a small oval bract. Again, the leaves of many desert perennials are very tough and leathery, the cuticle being greatly thickened and the surface protected with wax, resins, densely matted hairs, or encrusted salts. An example of this is the saltbush *(Atriplex)*, which is such a feature of the low-lying clay areas in far-western New South Wales and in the southern desert areas. Succulents, characterized by thick waxy or juicy tissues also occur in Australia, though there is nothing to match the magnificent cactuses that dominate the Arizonan and Sonoran deserts of North America, or the euphorbias found widely in the medium and lower rainfall zones of Africa.

Thorniness is a characteristic of many desert plants in some parts of the world; for example, in Africa or Mexico the dominant small trees of the open country are often formidably thorny, the spines of African acacias often being two or three inches in length. Yet in Australia, only a minority of species have even short spines. Dr. W. L. Brown of Cornell University has offered a very interesting explanation of such differences among the acacias: in Africa they are heavily browsed by a number of large herbivores and hence some protection is needed, whereas in Australia no such protection is required. The herbivores of the Australian arid lands are essentially grazers, that is, grass eaters. As if to support this suggestion *Triodia,* the most widespread of all desert grasses, is very spiny, and quite formidable to push through. Cattle and sheep cannot eat it except when it is freshly sprouting. The large hill kangaroo or euro *(Macropus robustus)* that lives on the rocky plateau and outcrop country does, however, feed on it quite extensively.

TOUGH MULGA AND HARDY PORCUPINE GRASS

Porcupine grass and mulga dominate the arid and semi-arid areas of Australia, each occurring in tracts that extend over hundreds, and in some cases thousands, of square miles.

Porcupine grass, the name given to several species of *Triodia,* is a xerophytic spiny grass that occurs in clumps resembling giant pincushions. These are commonly a foot high and six feet across, though the Adelaide mammalogist, H. H. Finlayson, has recorded some in the Musgraves as much as six feet high and twenty feet across. The base of the clumps is hard and spiky, but it shows green shoots following rain. Yellow-flowering stalks grow out of the base and, when waving in the wind, are a beautiful sight. This is deceptive, however, for a man walking among porcupine grass finds his legs stinging from hundreds of minute spearlike wounds.

Mount Olga, like the other high features of central Australia, represents masses of rock that have withstood weathering better than their surroundings. In the background are the Petermann Ranges. (Bon Strange)

165

The robustness of the clumps depends on the nature of the soil and whether the area has been ravaged by fire. Often, the center of the plant will die so that, in place of a dense mass, only an outer ring of growth prevails around a low sandy mound. Porcupine grass is difficult to kill for the roots are deep. New clumps can be produced by underground runners. The aborigines obtain a resin from *Triodia* by beating the clumps on an anthill or rock and melting the dust at a low temperature. The resin is used to fix stone spear points on wooden shafts, or axe-heads on handles.

Porcupine grass forms the home of many species of small lizards, as well as cockroaches, crickets, grasshoppers, and other insects. When a clump is fired, the inhabitants burst forth in all directions. Small mammals, too, shelter in the porcupine grass. A few birds are dependent on porcupine grass, notably the rufous-crowned emu wren *(Stipiturus ruficeps)* and to an extent the grass wren *Amytornis striatus*. These birds wriggle through the dense clumps with the ease of mice.

Mulga *(Acacia aneura)* is a small tree that grows to thirty feet in height and may either be sparsely distributed over the sand country or occur in dense stands. Apart from the desert it is distributed widely through the drier grassland areas of New South Wales and Queensland, where its pendant blue-green foliage is a feature of the landscape. The wood of the mulga is hard, yellowish on the outside and dark red on the inside. In former times aborigines made boomerangs from it (though myall was much preferred for this); today this strikingly grained wood is used to make the ash trays and similar objects sold in souvenir shops all over Australia.

Adding an unworldly, if not melancholy, touch to the sand-hill areas of the desert is the curious desert oak *(Casuarina decaisneana)*. This tree, which reaches fifty to sixty feet in height, is commonly solitary but may occur in small clumps. Its blackish, drooping foliage of needles casts shimmering shadows on the sand. Botanically this casuarina stands somewhat apart from the other members of its genus, being best described as an "old desert" element. It is most striking when silhouetted against the sky and sand hills at dusk or dawn.

Many lesser perennials of the Australian interior are peculiar to one region. Some occur only in sand-hill belts, between knolls or ridges, on top of ridges, or on their slopes. Others are part of the scrub in mountain creekbeds or adjacent to rocky outcrops where partial shelter and some underground water is found. These plants include needlewoods, beefwoods, mallees, myall, didgee, and the very tough ironwood *(Acacia estrophiolata)*. The kurrajong is another widespread small tree that may occur in continuous tracts. Oddities are the so-called sand-hill poplar *(Codonocarpus)*, a spindly tree with pink bark, and the elegant native pine *(Callitris)*.

Among the smaller perennial shrubs, reaching a height of three feet or occasionally five feet, are two that figure prominently as cattle food in parts of their range, the saltbush *(Atriplex)* and the bluebush *(Kochia)*. Both are essentially southern, the true saltbush not occurring north of the Musgraves. Throughout its ranges the saltbush is found mainly on clay soils, many of which are saline, while the bluebush prefers lime hillocks, watercourses, and sandy flats. Grasses that are suitable as stock food have an irregular distribution, being mainly developed in valleys within the hills. Of them the mulga-grass *(Aristida arenaria)* is one of the best.

Unlike the acacias that extend widely through the desert, the eucalypts are, for the most part, confined to the ranges.

One species, however, is a striking feature, the river gum *(Eucalyptus camaldulensis)*. It fringes the dry rivers and larger watercourses so that from a hilltop, or from the air, the drainage patterns of the country can always be traced by following the line of growth of the river gums. They form a meandering course out across the plains. The river gum is a great, spreading tree, twisted in branch and gnarled in trunk, which has green foliage when all else is drab. It is the home of birds such as the little red-tipped pardalote *(Pardalotus substriatus)*, the white-plumed honeyeater *(Meliphaga penicillata)*, and the red-tailed black cockatoo *(Calyptorhynchus banksi)*. By day the gums provide shelter from the sun, by night a homely canopy above the sleeper. And from time to time the foliage is adorned with large white flowers and the air rings with the calls of honey-eating birds that have converged from far and near for the feast of nectar.

HAWKS, FINCHES AND PIGEONS

A visitor to central Australia is sure to see a good cross-section of bird life, especially in the mountain ranges. The desert sky always contains several species of hawks, from the wedge-tailed eagle, Australia's largest eagle, down to the diminutive mouse- and insect-eating kestrel *(Falco centroides)*. One is most likely to see eagles perched on the tops of dead trees, or soaring on air currents high above the Macdonnell Ranges or Ayers Rock. A close relative of the palearctic golden eagle, this species is characterized by a long wedge-shaped tail and a plumage that is brown in younger birds and turns to blackish-brown about the sixth year. These eagle-hawks, as they are also called, place their large stick nest, which they return to year after year, in the top of an isolated tree, from which they can obtain a good view of the country around about. They are part hunter, taking small kangaroos, rabbits, and such, and part scavenger, even descending from time to time to pick up animals killed by cars. In some places the wedge-tail comes in for criticism as a killer of sheep. Much controversy surrounds the issue, however, many landowners maintaining that it will only consume a sheep that is dying or already dead, and that its value as a scavenger and rabbit killer far outweighs any harm it may do.

A very common large hawk is the fork-tailed kite *(Milvus migrans)*, a rather scraggly bird that is seen constantly in the air above the town of Alice Springs and around ranches, where it gleans the discarded animal parts from the slaughter-houses. The same species found in the streets of Indian villages, these kites generally fly singly or in pairs, but sometimes in larger groups, and are given to roosting in aggregations. Their flight consists of a leisurely flapping action. Occasionally the swift, bird-hunting black falcon *(Falco niger)* will be seen. Somewhat rarer are such birds as the gray falcon *(Falco hypoleucus)* and the square-tailed kite *(Lophoictinia isura)*, the latter usually being observed so high in the air that identification is difficult.

A good place to observe desert bird life is among thickets or, better still, beside one of the rare water holes. The noisy

A "dust devil" or "whirly-whirly" carries a column of dust and sand high into the air in the Australian interior. (Vincent Serventy)

red-breasted babblers *(Pomatostomus rubeculus),* are slim-bodied brown birds with long bills and tails, and ground feeders that continuously squabble among themselves; when approached they stream away to the nearest saplings and there chase each other upward through the branches. Black-faced wood swallows *(Artamus cinereus)* are aerial feeders, using an exposed branch to sortie forth after insects. Here also will be the pied butcherbird *(Cracticus nigrogularis),* shaped like a small crow but black and white in color and belonging to the Australian family of Cracticidae. Butcher-birds have the curious shrikelike habit of impaling the bodies of their prey on thorns or wedging them into forks in shrubs so that they can feed on them at leisure. The pied butcherbird is one of the most beautiful songsters of the Australian bush, its caroling often enlivening the dawn. The notes have a distant, ethereal quality about them, and they carry so well through the morning air that it may be some time before one can locate the bird itself, perched high on a dead branch. The inhabitants of the thickets and trees include many of the species familiar in other parts of the continent along with a proportion restricted to the desert. Among the wide-ranging species are the willie wagtail *(Rhipidura leucophrys),* peewee *(Grallina cyanoleuca),* the hooded robin *(Melanodryas cucullata),* and red-capped robin *(Petroica goodenovii).* Of the honeyeaters the white-plumed *(Meliphaga penicillata)* and spiny-cheeked *(Acanthagenys rufogularis)* have almost an Australia-wide range, while the gray-headed *(Meliphaga keartlandi)* and white-fronted *(Phylidonyris albifrons)* are true arid country species.

Possibly the most numerous bird of the desert is the little zebra finch *(Taeniopygia castanotis),* well-known to aviculturists throughout the world. Its general body color is brown, the bill is orange, and the tail is banded black-and-white. The male, in addition, has a bright orange cheek-patch, and orange-brown flanks spotted with white. Zebra finches occur in flocks of from about a dozen to fifty and feed on the ground, hopping over it in search of grass seeds. Like the other desert seed-eaters, they drink frequently, and the installation of watering places for cattle has permitted a great increase in numbers. The zebra finch, which also occurs in the grassland and woodland sections of the continent, constructs its spherical nest of fine grasses in a low shrub. Four to eight white eggs are laid. These birds breed freely in captivity and may have several broods in the course of a year.

There is a second species of finch in central Australia, the rare painted finch *(Emblema picta),* which is strikingly patterned in red, brown, black, and white. I have only seen it adjacent to water in the rugged mountain-range country.

Parrots and pigeons are common in the desert, and many of the more interesting birds belong to these groups. All must drink frequently, and a water hole is the place to see them. The most common parrot is the galah *(Kakatoe roseicapilla),* silver-gray above and pink below, and somewhat larger than

Left: The spectacular Devils Marbles on the main north-south road near Tennants Creek. (Robin Smith) Right: The arid Parsons Range in Arnhem Land north of the Roper River Mission is typical of many desert mountains. (Frank Hurley: Rapho-Guillumette)

the domesticated pigeon. It lives in the river gums and goes out onto the plains to feed. Flocks drink at about eight o'clock in the morning, after their dawn period of feeding, and again in the late afternoon. The pink cockatoo *(K. leadbeateri)* has somewhat similar habits but is much rarer. I once had a delightful view of a group of these birds by an isolated rock hole at Tanami in the middle of the northwestern desert. They came in at dusk and were so indignant at finding an intruder at their drinking spot that they fluttered low over my head, screeching loudly, in an obvious effort to drive me away. They then took up a position on the top of the nearest tree and, with long crests raised and wings outstretched, made the evening air ring with their shrill protests.

Other Centralian parrots include the rare pink-colored Bourke parrot *(Neophema bourki)* and the magnificent, long-tailed princess parakeet *(Polytelis alexandrae),* in which the upper parts are greenish-yellow and the throat a beautiful rose red in color. Both are confined to the arid regions. Another parrot of this area, the red-tailed black cockatoo *(Calyptorhynchus banksi),* is widespread in the mountains.

The rarest and most mysterious bird in Australia is also a desert dweller, the night parrot *(Geopsittacus occidentalis).* This species inhabits the porcupine-grass country, mountain ranges, and shrubby samphire country. Never seen by day, it comes out to feed on grass seeds after dark. About the turn of the century they were not uncommon and pet cats living on cattle properties in the Macdonnell Ranges frequently brought in dead specimens. In recent years two other species of Australian birds that have long been presumed extinct have been rediscovered, the noisy scrub bird *(Atricornis clamosus)* in southwestern Australia and the Eyrean grass wren *(Amytornis goyderi)* on the northern shores of Lake Eyre. The night parrot has been sought in vain, however, though rumors of its existence still persist. On my trips into the desert I have frequently sat up late at night beside a water hole hoping that the species might come in to drink. The effort was in vain, only bronze-wing pigeons *(Phaps chalcoptera)* coming to share the lonely vigil.

BIRDS AND DROUGHTS

The outstanding feature of the bird life of central Australia is its relative unpredictability. Nature bestows mobility upon birds and those of the Australian interior make full use of this power, hence there will be a marked difference in the number of species present in a good season and a bad one. I witnessed interesting examples of this when I was in central Australia during the drought of 1952. Little surface water remained anywhere and native tribesmen from hundreds of miles away were converging on places of white settlement. At Ayers Rock, where I carried out field work in May, only thirty species of birds were present. In July an inch of rain fell, followed by another in August; by the end of that month the count jumped to over sixty different species, and most were preparing to breed. It goes without saying, accordingly, that visitors going to central Australia to study birds should take rainfall into account in planning the time of their visit!

Nomadism is the birds' main defense against droughts. On occasions, however, a drought, or a heat wave, has been so widespread that it led to catastrophic loss of bird life. A heat wave swept northern South Australia in February, 1932;

the temperature exceeded 116 degrees Fahrenheit for sixteen consecutive days in one area and did not drop below one hundred degrees for two months in another. Birds converged on small dams and at drinking places beside railway stations in hundreds of thousands. So great was their frenzy to get to water that great numbers plunged in and drowned. Sixty thousand budgerigars *(Melopsittacus undulatus)* were recovered from one small dam, and a forty-gallon petrol drum filled with bodies in a single afternoon. All told, members of twenty species of birds perished, most of them budgerigars and zebra finches. The budgerigar, so well known as a household pet in North America and Europe, is highly nomadic in the wild and is normally more than capable of looking after itself. The seasonal movements of the flocks take them to the south and north of the continent and, in good seasons, into the desert.

Normally, observers are too few and far between in the drier parts of Australia to get any sort of balanced picture of the destructive effects of droughts on bird life. The veteran ornithologist H. G. Barnard, who lived in the Duaringa district of central Queensland for over fifty years, records that the droughts of 1902, 1915, 1919, 1922, and 1926 were each responsible for a marked extermination. That of 1902 was the most severe in recorded memory. Australia's sheep population was reduced by more than half, large areas of Queensland were stripped of every vestige of grass, and trees died over hundreds of square miles of country. It took a long time for the bird populations to recover. Red-backed wrens *(Malurus melanocephalus)* were not seen for three years, the laughing kookaburra *(Dacelo novae-guineae)* took over five years to regain its former numbers and, after thirty years, the beautiful little paradise parrot *(Psephotus pulcherrimus)* has still not returned.

KANGAROOS AND DINGOS

Sixty years ago Professor Baldwin Spencer made a remarkable pioneer study of the mammal life of central Australia and showed it to be both diverse and interesting. It would be pleasant to report that there has been a great increase in knowledge of the desert mammals since then, however, rather the contrary is the case. Expeditions since that time have collected only a fraction of the species he found. The reasons are not easy to pinpoint though undoubtedly the presence of the introduced fox, cat, and rabbit throughout much of the desert has a great deal to do with it.

Most prominent mammals today are the red or plains kangaroo *(Macropus rufus),* the dingo *(Canis dingo),* and the little rodent mice *(Notomys* or *Pseudomys),* which are undoubtedly the most numerous of the mammals. This can be appreciated if one is able to be abroad before the morning winds stir the sand—in places the ground between the clumps of porcupine grass is patterned by their footprints.

It takes diligence and patience to study the smaller mammals of the desert. The most beautiful, by far, is the rabbit

Relict grove of palms (Livistona mariae) *in the bed of the Finke River, one of the curiosities of central Australia since their nearest relatives are on the north coast seven hundred miles away. (Douglass Baglin)*

bandicoot *(Macrotis lagotis)*, round-bodied, about the size of a small rabbit, with a long snout and ears, and soft, gray silky fur. Like all bandicoots, of which there are two other species in the desert, it has strong claws and obtains its insect food mostly underground, sending the earth out behind it in showers as it digs. Rabbit bandicoots once ranged widely over the southern half of the continent, but in recent years have been found in only a few scattered localities. Insectivorous and carnivorous marsupials include the dainty little *Antechinomys spenceri,* which moves with a hopping gait, and the mouse-eater *Dasyuroides byrnei.* The smaller members of the kangaroo tribe (Macropodidae) included the hare-wallabies *(Lagorchestes conspicillatus)* and the rat kangaroo *(Caloprymnus campestris),* but these are now almost extinct.

The red kangaroo, which is discussed in detail in an earlier chapter, is numerous in the shallow valleys of the mountain ranges, where Mitchell grass and other prime herbage grow extensively. They occur also, however, on the sand plains. Kangaroos shelter in the mulga by day, coming out at dusk to graze. They require surface water but apparently drink less regularly than the emu. When the writer was camped near Maggie's Spring at the base of Ayers Rock, in 1952, it was possible to make a study of the frequency of the different animals' visits to the water by the tracks they left behind. Those of kangaroos appeared only every third day.

The dingo is a true dog and resembles a small alsatian in its erect ears, somewhat broad forehead, and brushy tail. Most individuals are reddish-yellow, though the body color can be quite variable. The dingo does not bark, only howls, and its melancholy serenading is a familiar sound of the desert night. Just how Australia came to have a wild dog was long debated. Archaeological studies have now proven that it was introduced by the aborigines, and subsequently became feral: the bones of dogs are not found in the camp sites of the earlier aborigines, only in deposits less than five thousand years old.

The dingo ranges widely over Australia today. In the desert a visitor may see one or two, or, rarely, small packs slinking along a dry riverbed. Dingos mostly pup in the winter months, selecting a remote cave for the lair.

THE AMAZING MARSUPIAL MOLE

The marsupial mole *(Notoryctes typhlops)* is certainly the most remarkable mammal in central Australia for, though a marsupial, its body form resembles that of the true moles of the northern continents and, especially, the African golden moles. It is a small, mouse-sized animal, with silky, iridescent fur. It varies in color from a drab yellowish-white to reddish-gold. The snout consists of a horny shield, the nostrils are small and slitlike, while the eye, represented by a pigment spot in the embryo, almost completely degenerates by adulthood. If the hair of the sides of the head is pushed aside, the external openings of the ears will be found. The mouth is small and is situated on the underside of the head. Enormous digging claws are developed on the third and fourth digits of the forelimb, while the second, third and fourth of the hindlimb have somewhat smaller claws. This mole inhabits the more arid parts of the desert, burrowing in search of subterranean insects, and coming to the surface only during

rain or overcast weather. When captured and kept in a box they are said to exhibit a feverish restlessness, to consume their food very quickly, and shuffle along by means of strangely fluid and sinuous movements. Though the marsupial mole has a wide range from the Nullarbor Plain to Ninety-Mile Beach near Broome, very few have been seen alive. Few details of its breeding, beyond the fact that it apparently has only one young in the pouch at a time, are known.

ROCK PYTHONS, SPINY DEVILS AND OTHERS

The desert is apparently habitat *par excellence* for small reptiles and the visitor is more aware of them there than in any other region. Swift-running little dragon-lizards (Agamidae) and skinks (Scincidae) dart over the rocks and between clumps of porcupine grass with the speed of lightning. Snakes (Elapidae) sun themselves on the sand, wriggling quickly away when disturbed. Most are small and harmless to man but from time to time a mulga snake *(Pseudechis australis),* or other alarmingly large species, will be seen. If a log be rolled over a blind snake (Typhlopidae), or one of the little legless lizards (Pygopodidae) with long snake-like body and vestigial hindlimbs, a group that has forsaken surface living for subterranean life, will be found. After dark the geckos come out from their hiding places beneath the bark of trees, under rocks and among the porcupine grass. All have soft flabby skin and large eyes but, among the ten species occurring in the desert, there is a wide range of diverse types from *Nephrurus,* with a heavy, bony skull, to the long-legged barking geckos. Several families of reptiles, notably the goannas (Varanidae), dragon lizards (Agamidae), and geckos (Gekkonidae), have more species in the desert than in any other region. There are seven species of goannas, for example, compared with only two and three respectively on the eastern and western coasts at the same latitude.

The most striking reptiles of central Australia are the rock python *(Liasis),* the perentie or giant goanna *(Varanus giganteus),* and the little spiny devil lizard *(Moloch horridus).* The rock python grows to about ten feet in length and lives in the mountains rather than on the sand plain. It lies coiled up by day, but in the late afternoon it may sometimes be seen sliding over the rocks adjacent to a water hole, waiting for suitable prey. It is a great boon to the aborigines, being one of their favorite foods. The perentie, also about ten feet in length when mature, is the largest of Australian lizards and the largest goanna except the famous Komodo dragon. It is richly patterned in reds and blacks, grays and browns, the markings varying with individuals and the area. The flattened head bears a formidable array of sharp, pointed teeth, so that when the throat is inflated with air and the animal hisses and waves its powerful tail from side to side, the effect is most alarming. Perenties are scavengers, eating anything from eggs and smaller reptiles to carrion. The tail is very powerful and is said to be able to knock an aboriginal woman off her feet.

The spiny devil lizard is completely covered with spines,

Standley Chasm, a tall cleft or crack in the rock wall, cut by running water. A flannel flower is among the plants clinging to the vertical surface. (Bon Strange)

An Australian aborigine cooking a goanna lizard. The aborigines are nomadic hunters whose whole economy is ecologically integrated with the land. (David Beal)

with larger protuberances on top of the forehead and back of the neck. It is marked with red, brown, and yellow blotches—perfect camouflage in the desert. It has a wide distribution even though its diet, consisting of small black ants, is specialized. In appearance it resembles the American horned toad although they belong to different groups. So unusual a creature has, of course, attracted much attention, and for a long time visitors bought specimens from the natives. Little was known of its life history until a few years ago, when naturalist C. C. Sporn described its egg laying. The spiny devil spends two or three days digging a slanting tunnel eighteen to twenty inches long and ten to eleven inches deep. At the bottom of the tunnel, six or seven eggs are laid, and then the lizard spends a day filling in the tunnel again on top of the eggs. The hatching period was found to be thirteen to eighteen days, or less when the weather was warm and dry; this is a long period for so small a lizard.

Another unusual dragon or agamid lizard, one that has a very strange habitat, is *Tympanocryptis maculosa* of Lake Eyre. Attention was recently drawn to this species by John Mitchell of the South Australian Museum. It inhabits part of the shimmering dry salt surface of the lake (which covers four thousand square miles), getting shelter under the salt crust, or in the shadow of the nests of the small black ants that constitute its food. Its color is almost as white as the salt. The eyes are small and deeply sunken and the eyelids have serrated edges, additional protection from the intense glare, wind-blown particles, and drying atmosphere. Even the nostrils help it survive in its inhospitable habitat, being narrowed to small slits and directed forward and downward.

FROGS THAT STORE WATER

One does not normally associate amphibians with arid places for not only must they maintain a moist skin for respiration—frogs breathe largely through the skin and moist tissues of the mouth, and only partly with the lungs—but they are dependent on surface water for the hatching of eggs. Central Australia, with its almost complete absence of surface water, is all too obviously the complete opposite of frog habitat. It is amazing then to find, after heavy rain falls, that the temporary pools may contain numerous frogs and the nights are enlivened by their croaking.

The secret is that the desert frogs of Australia, of which there are half a dozen species, have developed a mechanism for thriving in their inhospitable habitat, that of spending the dry periods in a kind of suspended animation (estivation) deep underground or at the base of hollow trees, and restricting their active life to the few weeks in the year when there is surface water.

The most interesting of all is the water-holding frog (*Chironectes platycephalus*). This species has the extraordinary habit of storing water in its urinary bladder and body cavity, distending itself like a tennis ball, prior to going underground. A foot to eighteen inches below the drying mud at the bottom of the pond it secretes a capsule of mucus about itself and this provides additional protection against desiccation. In this way it can apparently withstand droughts of a year or more. As soon as the land is flooded again it comes to the surface. Breeding follows immediately, the tadpole stage possibly being as short as two weeks. Metamorphosis has to be completed before the pond dries up; those individuals that have been lucky enough not to have fallen prey to the herons, which arrive with the rains, will become air-breathing frogs and be able to take shelter underground. Aborigines eagerly seek the water-holding frog both as a source of water, and of food. They search out their burial places with a pointed stick.

SURVIVAL IN THE DESERT

The adaptations that permit the various kinds of animals to thrive in the harsh and unpredictable environment of the

Mount Olga as seen from Ayers Rock, about thirty miles away across sand plains covered with mulga and porcupine grass. (Robin Smith)

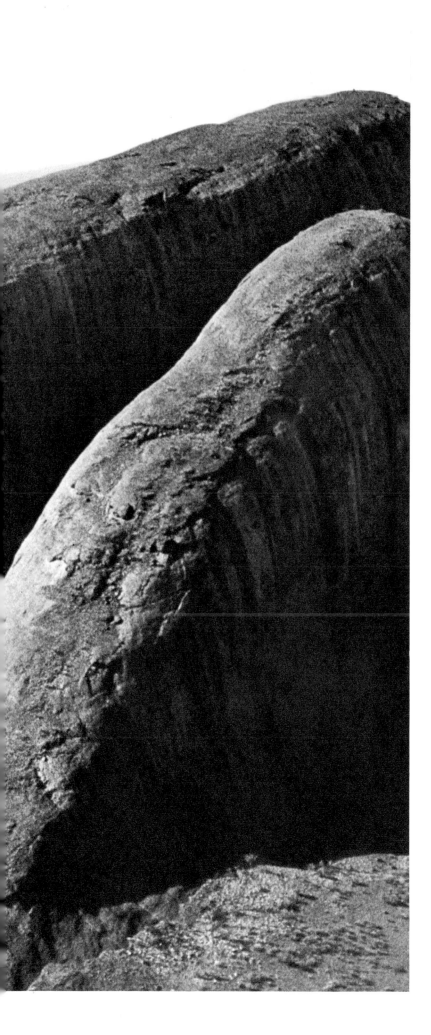

desert are both diverse and interesting. In contrast to the better-watered regions the time of abundant life, when animals make good their numerical losses, is not the spring but the period following the rains. This is strikingly evident even to the casual visitor. Insects of all kinds abound: bees, mantids, grasshoppers, and butterflies, while, at night, the lights of a vehicle may be darkened by swarming moths. Termites emerge as winged forms and go spiraling into the sky to found new colonies, invariably attended by enthusiastic parties of insect-eating birds. An unusually good rain may produce insect species not seen in years. One of the most interesting observations of this type was made by H. H. Finlayson in the Musgraves in December, 1933, when the air was found to be literally vibrating with the song of a cicada, *Thopha colorata.* Although the aborigines had a name for the insect, the young men of the tribe had never seen it before! The insect probably is a parallel to the American seventeen-year cicada, in which winged forms appear only every seventeen, or in another form, thirteen years. Apart from frogs, the filling of the clay pans and rock pools produces swarming masses of *Apus* and other shrimps. The breeding of the birds is timed to the rain, and there is evidence that they, and some of the small mammals, bear more young in good seasons than in ordinary ones.

The subterranean way of life is more common in the desert than any other area, since only the insulating capacity of the soil can give protection against excessive heat and cold, and dryness. Most lizards are able to withstand the hot sun, but a few are said to die if kept in it for more than a few minutes. This is also true of many small mammals. In addition to burrows, stones, caves, and logs provide protection for reptiles and insects. Most desert forms are nocturnal, emerging only after sundown when conditions are cooler and predators find it hard to detect them. Many visit the water holes only at dusk. A few species satisfy their water requirements by drinking dew. Others are apparently able to do without water altogether. The physiologist K. Schmidt-Nielson has shown that, in the American desert, the kangaroo rat *(Dipodomys)* has achieved a means of retaining body fluids and of manufacturing water from the fatty seeds of the plants on which it lives. Presumably, some Australian desert species have similar adaptations. The ability of the camel to do without water for days on end is proverbial.

Storing food underground is characteristic of various animal species, including the termites and honey ants. In the latter nectar is stored in the abdomens of the so-called workers, which become distended until they are as large as a pea and unable to walk. The aborigines consider honey ants a delicacy. A few Australian reptiles and small mammals store food as fat in their tails, and the thickness of the tail is then an indication of the condition of the animal. The alternative to storing food and water is to reduce the need for it. Estivation thus characterizes many animals besides frogs: the crab *Telphusa,* the crayfish *Asacopsis,* and various gudgeon fishes. Snails withstand droughts by sealing their shell off with a plug of mucus.

As indicated, in the desert the more mobile birds and

Great rounded domes on the western side of Mount Olga. Mount Olga and Ayers Rock are isolated prominences about 250 miles southwest of Alice Springs. (Janet Finch)

177

The water-holding frog (Chironectes platycephalus) *burrows some eighteen inches underground when temporary pools dry up, distending itself like a tennis ball and going into estivation until the next rains. (Harry Frauca)*

kangaroos, and aboriginal man, are nomadic or seminomadic, seeking new living areas when conditions become unfavorable. Unfortunately, we do not know much about the ecology of those animals that stay behind and remain active throughout all conditions. Some foods are obviously available in the desert all year, for example seeds for the rodents and certain insects, and ants for the spiny devil lizard and marsupial mole. A few scavenging hawks are always to be seen in the sky, and the presence of various insectivorous birds in the undergrowth and porcupine grass is proof that the pickings are always there for these animals too, even if slim.

Some desert animals show structural adaptations for walking on sand, including flattened toes in certain lizards. Locomotion by hopping has been acquired independently by desert animals in all continents, perhaps because an erratic gait makes the animal more difficult to catch. Color also plays a part. While there are very many exceptions to the rule, it is common for desert races of animal species, or even desert species, to have a paler, redder color than those of higher rainfall areas. This is evident in many lizards as well as in birds such as the Australian emu-wrens *(Stipiturus ruficeps)* and whitefaces *(Aphelocephala nigrocincta* and *A. pectoralis),* the lighter color apparently serving to reflect the heat. Camouflage considerations must also play a part.

THE ECOLOGY OF ABORIGINAL MAN

A chapter on the Australian desert would be incomplete without a section on the aborigines, for, in contrast to most races of *Homo sapiens,* they function ecologically as an omnivorous species that "crops" the food resources of their environment without interfering unduly with its basic balance. This is indeed rare since mankind functions almost universally as a major force in degrading the natural habitat. In the desert the Australian aborigine is a nomadic hunter, moving about with the changing food resources but practising no agriculture; by means of religiously applied social rules and conventions, he maintains a population level that is fairly constant and also within the carrying capacity of the country.

The Australoids, as they are called, are slim-bodied, wavy-haired people with velvety, chocolate-brown skins, prominent eyebrow ridges that protect deeply sunken eyes from the desert sun, and somewhat broad noses. The men stand five-and-a-half to six feet in height. When the tribe is moving from one area to another, the men lead, unburdened save for spears and boomerangs, for they must be ready to seize the chance to secure game; the women, carrying the children and the tribe's few possessions—digging sticks, water-carriers, and string bags—bring up the rear. A well-defined division of labor marks aboriginal society, the killing of large game being the lot of the men, whereas the gathering of bulbs, yams, grass seeds, honey ants, grasshoppers, lizards, and the other smaller items, is the role of the women. Desert life demands considerable mobility, and the stalking of game on the open plain, stamina and resourcefulness.

In his early teens the aboriginal boy becomes heir to a long heritage of knowledge about survival in the desert. He learns to stalk game, secure arboreal phalangers from their hiding places in the hollows of trees, obtain wood-boring grubs (witchety grubs) from the roots, and catch goannas and pythons. Knowledge of the whereabouts of the various water holes in the tribal territory, and of where water can be found by digging, are handed down from generation to generation. The initiate learns to withstand hardship and subjugate his wishes to the needs of the tribe.

Conservation is appreciated by the aborigines, who identify themselves with animal species on the basis of a supposed ancestral relationship. Thus they see themselves as integral components of the countryside, not detached from it as does modern man. A new-born child is admitted to a totem named after one of the major food animals: this confers upon it the obligation not to eat that kind of animal, or else only under special circumstances. This, and certain other cultural restrictions (e.g., a few kinds of food can be eaten only by women), must function to prevent the overharvesting of a particular resource and can only have evolved over centuries of trial and error.

MOUNTAINS OF THE GREAT WESTERN PLATEAU

The desert mountains are of great interest to the biologist, for though the flora and fauna have much in common with those of the surrounding desert, they function as refuges, supporting a wide range of forms that otherwise would be unable to exist in the center of Australia. Thus, half a dozen species of eucalypts grace their irregular slopes and broad valleys, including the magnificent white-trunked ghost gum *(Eucalyptus papuana).* The largest range, the Macdonnells, contains a stand of living palms *(Livistona mariae)* thriving in a desert gorge nearly seven hundred miles from the nearest relatives on the coast. The palms, together with cycads

(*Macrozamia macdonnelli*) and a variety of other plant forms, are leftovers from a time when the sand desert was well-watered and they ranged widely through the interior country. Similarly, the ranges have permanent rock holes, containing a half a dozen species of fresh-water fish, a species of crayfish, and a whole host of aquatic insects not found in the surrounding sand desert. When droughts descend on the plains country, and there is widespread loss of life, it is from the mountain populations that the country is colonized again. Many bird species are always present in the ranges and appear in the plains country only in favorable seasons. The ranges are also the haven of the euros or hill kangaroos, the dainty little rock wallabies (*Petrogale penicillata lateralis*), and of the echidna. Lastly, when all the water holes of the desert have dried up, it is to the ranges that the aboriginal tribes retire as a last resort.

The ranges of the desert, in terms of geology, are relatively minor features. They are only fifty to one hundred and fifty miles in length and vary in width from perhaps ten to fifty miles—bare, rocky chains with shallow valleys in between. The average height is one thousand to fifteen hundred feet above the plateau, higher peaks rising to about three thousand feet. As scenic spectacles, however, these mountains of central Australia are not easily forgotten. It is most exciting, after traveling for days across the flat country, to see a low purple range appear on the horizon. As one comes closer, the wild contours, jagged and arresting, the rounded domes alternating with cliffs, and the deep chasms carved by eons of stream action, show up in all their vividness. With the morning sun full on them the desert mountains are a flaming orange-red. The mood and tones change with the hour. As the sun mounts to the zenith and the rock walls are thrown into shadow, their color changes to a deep red and, finally, to purple. In the late afternoon they become a misty blue, the last rays of the sun bathing the tips of the crags in gold until, with the coming of the night, the mountains are but inky silhouettes against the sky. Other effects are created by storm clouds, on the rare occasions when they hang over the ranges, and by rain wetting the rock surfaces or turning sections of the cliffs into miniature waterfalls.

Apart from the rocks, the vegetation of the ranges produces its own spectacular effects. The magnificent white trunks and bright green foliage of the ghost gums against the backdrop of red rock or vivid blue sky are a striking sight. Gnarled and twisted corkwoods (*Hakea*) with needlelike foliage and, in season, masses of pale yellow flowerheads, are scattered here and there at the foot of the cliffs and on the slopes. Gorges may be filled with dense undergrowth or, as where the old watercourse broadens out below Standley Chasm in the Macdonnells, by small parklike expanses of eucalypts. Porcupine grass covers the tops of the mountains, while in the valleys there may be broad meadows of waving yellow grass. From a hilltop at any hour of the day the whole mosaic of brilliant pastel tones lies before one: brilliant blue sky, red rocks, yellow grass, white tree trunks and then, beyond the ranges, the meandering green lines of river gums extending out into the endless haze of the cinnabar plain.

Best known of central Australia's mountain ranges are the Macdonnells for the delightful little town of Alice Springs nestles within them. The railway from the south enters the ranges through a deep V-shaped cleft, Emily Gap, carved in ancient times by a river. From Alice Springs a network of roads leads out to many of the spectacular features of the ranges. These include Standley Chasm, a deep cleft above which tower high cliffs of brilliantly red rock, and Simpson Gap, a wider opening guarded by a high, rounded headland on each side. At the bottom of Simpson Gap is a pool at which many of the small desert birds come to drink, all that is left of the mighty river that must have cut this deep passage through the ranges. Further afield is Ormiston Gorge, its chain of small pools ending in a deep, wide, permanent water hole. Though the gorge is rather hard to reach, the spectacular colors of its cliffs, white-trunked gums overhanging the water, areas of sand, purple mint bushes, and tall yellow daisies, are well worth the two-day journey in a jeep or land rover.

The highest peaks of the Macdonnells are Conroy (4,100 feet), Sonder (4,400 feet), and Ziel (4,950 feet). The ranges are a composite of ancient rocks, the youngest of them being of Ordovician age, that is, approximately 400 million years old, for the Great Western Shield of Australia has been dry land almost since the time when the first back-boned animals appeared on the planet. The main rock types are hardened gneisses, coarse-grained rocks with an irregularly foliated appearance, fine-grained quartzites, superficially like sandstone but much harder, and coarse-grained conglomerates, with some shales. Scientists are uncertain about the history of the ranges but it is generally believed that the initial elevation took place in Ordovician times, nearly five hundred million years ago, when heights of ten thousand to fifteen thousand feet were reached. Then, during a long period of erosion, the rocks were worn down almost to sea level. About seventy million years ago a gentle but protracted period of uplift began so that by the late Tertiary period, perhaps ten million years ago, the plateau was five thousand feet in height. Since then, erosion has reduced the area to its present height of a little over two thousand feet. It is from this period that outcrops, larger ranges, and isolated tors, of today stem. The rivers of central Australia have, of course, played a significant part in erosion processes, especially during long periods when the areas were much better watered than they are now. One can see their contribution in the many deep gorges and channels that dissect the Macdonnells today.

The Musgrave Ranges, about one hundred and fifty miles to the south of the Macdonnells and constituting an aboriginal reserve, are outside the tourist track. Fifty miles long and ten miles wide, and the chief range of northern South Australia, the Musgraves form a labyrinth of rounded rocky tors, grassy mounds and conical peaks, and present, especially along the southern front, precipitous flanks, rugged ravines and gorges, and stark contours broken only by an occasional tree. Grassy plains and valleys with little scrub growth are a feature here. The red rocks of the Musgraves are gneiss of a very ancient Archaeozoic age—probably as old as any rocks in the world. Various semipermanent rock holes occur in these ranges, so that long before the establishment of the mission station they were a gathering place of the aborigines.

Other ranges in central Australia, rarely visited except by scientists, include the Everards, near the Musgraves, the Petermanns and the Rawlinsons, the latter in Western Australia. Within Western Australia are the Warburtons, where the government of that state maintains an outpost to provide medical care and other help for the dwindling groups of aborigines that come there in times of drought.

Above: Sparse mulga (Acacia aneura) scrub near Angus Downs, typical of great areas of central Australia. (G. M. Chippendale) Right: Pink mulla mulla (Trichinium manglesii), with curiously fluffy flowers, is a plant that springs up soon after rain. (Albert Tasker)

Right above: Pink-flowering parakeelya (Ca-landrinia) brings beauty to the sandhills after rain. (Winifred Hilliard) Right: Dainty crested pigeons (Ocyphaps lophotes) *drink from a desert waterhole. The digging of wells and bores for cattle has favored many species of parrots and pigeons. (Eric Lind-gren)*

ISOLATED MONOLITHS AND DESERT SHRIMPS

The most striking solitary features of central Australia are Mount Connor, Mount Olga, and Ayers Rock, all lying within about a hundred mile radius of each other between the Musgraves and the Macdonnells, and the Devil's Marbles near Tennants Creek, on the south-north road between Alice Springs and Darwin.

Mount Connor is a flat-topped, mesalike structure, perfectly bedded horizontally, capped by a hard conglomerate, and with lower reaches of fine silicious sandstone that erodes slowly. It is the undermining of the sandstone by wind and rain that keeps the cliffs vertical, or overhanging in a most threatening manner. Deep crevices and honeycombing into caves and rock shelters are commonplace. Mount Connor is about three miles wide from east to west and a mile from north to south. It rises about one thousand feet above the plain and the vertical cliffs are from three hundred and fifty to four hundred feet in height. The peak can be scaled in the southwest corner and is sparsely vegetated.

Mount Olga is a series of thirty or so enormous monoliths, the highest rising directly from the plain to fifteen hundred feet, and each having a rounded summit and almost sheer, smooth sides. Viewed from the top of Ayers Rock, twenty miles to the north, Mount Olga looks like a pile of giant pebbles or huge eggs. Between the monoliths are chasms that provide a habitat for a variety of plant species and, though there are no permanent water holes, the runoff from the rocks and shelter are a boon to all living things. A most striking sight is sunset on the domes of Mount Olga—orange-red silhouettes against the blue haze.

Ayers Rock is a huge red dome, eleven hundred feet high, some six miles in circumference and two miles across at the widest point. Its lower slopes are steep and precipitous. It is composed of fine conglomerate, now nearly vertically bedded, which contrasts with the coarse-grained conglomerate of Mount Olga. The surface of the rock is seen to be weathering in flat sheets, so that a climber must take care lest a slab come free. Crevices, furrows, and honeycombing show prolonged wear by wind and water. Around these openings the wind whines and whistles on certain nights, so that the aborigines believe the area to be haunted and refuse to camp near it. In rare times of heavy rain the water is said to cascade off the slopes of Ayers Rock with a roar like that of the ocean. Certainly the effects of this are seen in the plants, an attractive parkland of eucalypts, acacias, and other shrubs surrounding the base of the rock.

Ayers Rock has a permanent water hole, Nelly's Hole or, in the aboriginal language, *Mutiguluna*. This makes the area a haven and therefore excellent for studying the life of the surrounding desert. Emus and kangaroos come there to drink as do the many smaller birds living in the vicinity: these include black-faced cuckoo shrikes (*Coracina novae-hollandiae*), white-plumed honeyeaters (*Meliphaga penicillata*), and Keartland's honeyeaters (*M. keartlandi*). Large goanna lizards (*Varanus gouldi*) frequent the rocks at the base of the cliffs while marsupial mice (*Pseudantechinus macdonnellensis*) and, astonishing as it may seem, the introduced house mouse (*Mus musculus*), the caves. The updrafts provided by the near vertical surfaces are much appreciated by the larger hawks and a pair of wedge-tailed eagles is frequently seen soaring overhead. Caves on the side of Ayers Rock are adorned with aboriginal paintings, now unfortunately getting rather faint, that tell the story of famous hunts in bygone times or seek to portray some mythical spirit ancestor. Ayers Rock is rich in associations. Almost every precipice, cave, and mark was found by anthropologist Charles Mountford to commemorate some exploit or adventure of the aborigines' "creation times." The gutters and weather stains exhibit the tracks of warring snakes, the innumerable potholes record the work of marsupial moles, and the caves are the camping places of the ancestral marsupial rats.

One of the most interesting discoveries made during my visit to Ayers Rock in 1952 was the presence of shrimps in shallow pools eight hundred feet up the sides of the monolith. In one place on the west face, water had etched out a shallow drainage channel that here and there enlarged to form depressions. Though there had been no rain for some time, this chain of pools contained water of varying depths. Some five species of shrimp were present, ranging from the size of a pin head to the shield shrimps (*Apus*) a couple of inches long. Chief types were the shield shrimps, so named because of their broad, flattened carapace from the end of which a long, segmented tail projects; fairy shrimps (*Branchinella*), with long narrow bodies and multiple legs and gills; and ostracods, tiny animals that resemble bivalve shells. All these desert crustaceans have drought-resistant eggs that are swept about freely by the wind. *Apus* in particular crops up again and again in areas in which it has never previously been seen. It must nevertheless be considered highly unusual for them to establish themselves some eight hundred feet above the ground, though once the eggs were lodged in cracks in the rock they could probably reappear after every rain.

RELICTS OF THE PAST

Relicts, that is, populations of animals and plants that once ranged widely but now survive in only a few "pockets," occur in the Macdonnell Ranges of central Australia. They tell an interesting story about past climates.

Based on a variety of evidence, it is known that the aridity of the interior of the Australian continent is comparatively recent. In fact, up to the end of the Miocene, twenty million years ago, the southern interior region was covered with broad-leafed trees, dominated by such types as *Cinnamomum* and *Nothofagus,* which must have given it a lushness rivaling rain forest. In the early Pliocene, however, the fossil record indicates that *Eucalyptus* and *Acacia* rose to dominance on the Australian continent, indicating a widespread change to drier conditions, and the earlier types vanished.

Right above: Sandhills cover great areas of the Simpson (Arunta) and Great Sandy deserts. Rain has induced the flowering of some small plants but their ultimate fate is emphasized by the dead shrub on the ridge top. (Janet Finch) Right: The knob-tailed gecko (Nephrurus laevis), a nocturnal inhabitant of sandhills, avoids both heat and predators by hiding underground by day. (F. J. Mitchell) Far right: Thorny devil lizard (Moloch horridus), a small species that subsists on black ants. It bears a resemblance to American "horned toads" (Phrynosoma), but the two are unrelated. (Norman Chaffer)

Subsequently, in the Pleistocene era, great climatic changes swept the earth. In the northern hemisphere four glacial periods occurred, ice caps moving southward to cover vast areas. Alternating with these were the warmer interglacial periods, when the ice cap retreated toward the poles. One widespread effect of the interglacial periods was that a vast amount of water was released by melting ice and the sea level rose two hundred fifty to three hundred feet. The result of this is seen in Australia's drowned coastlands and estuaries.

Since the southern continents are farther from the South Pole than the northern continents are from the North Pole, glacial effects were less severe in them: in Australia glaciation was important only in Tasmania and the Kosciusko region. The Pleistocene was, nonetheless, associated with marked climatic shifts. In essence, the most widely accepted theory is that rainfall belts moved north in the glacial periods, so that the arid region was not in the middle of the continent but farther north; the central position of the desert today is thought to be typical of interglacial periods. The alternative theory, recently suggested by the botanist Nancy Burbidge, is that during the glacial periods both southern and northern rainfall belts may have moved farther toward the center of the continent, thereby compressing the desert into a smaller area.

Whatever happened, there can be no doubt that up until the end of the Miocene and on several occasions during the more recent Pleistocene, central Australia experienced wetter conditions than it does today. The aridity is, in fact, relatively recent. The evidence for this is multiple: central Australia is now patterned with "dead" lakes and "ghost" rivers that never, or seldom, hold water. Secondly, many deductions can be made from fossils. Crocodiles, for example, require permanent rivers and lakes. Today they occur only in the far north of the continent, but fossil crocodiles are known from the arid Lake Eyre region, coastal Victoria and South Australia, indicating also higher temperatures in former times. The crocodile fossils are apparently both of Tertiary and Pleistocene age. The fossil remains of several giant herbivorous marsupials are known from central Australia. These are now extinct. Pre-eminent among these are *Diprotodon,* a huge four-footed herbivore with the bulk of a rhinoceros, and *Nototherium,* which had the bulk of a bullock. The long-dry Lake Callabonna in the most arid region of South Australia is a giant graveyard of *Diprotodon,* the bones of dozens of animals having been found there, where presumably they had sought the last available water. While fossil stomach remains indicate that *Diprotodon* probably consumed plants not very different from those found in the region today, it and the other large herbivores could have lived only in country having ample drinking water. Radio carbon dating of *Diprotodon* bones indicate that the last individuals died no longer than 6,700 (plus or minus 250) years ago, and they may have survived until more recently.

There is another very interesting source of evidence that fertile conditions existed in the Australian desert until relatively recently, and that is the distribution of living plants and animals. Here we will review only the evidence supplied by the organisms of the mountain ranges of central Australia, which, as indicated previously, contain many relict forms.

Some years ago, the writer journeyed to the Macdonnell Ranges to try to determine just how common were the relict populations of animals. As a guide there was the grove of palms, *Livistona mariae,* discovered by the explorer Ernest Giles in 1872 along a tributary of the Finke River. Palms have a strictly peripheral distribution in Australia, occurring in pockets along the west, north and east coasts from the Fortescue to about New South Wales—the border of Victoria. A parallel case is that of the cycad *Macrozamia,* which also has a relict population in the Macdonnells. Both these plants have heavy seeds so that they could not have been carried into the Macdonnells by water or birds. They could have reached there, in fact, only if they once occupied the intermediate territory.

The trip to the Macdonnells was inspired by the discovery made by a Lutheran missionary, E. Rieschieck, of a series of fern clusters clinging to the damp walls of a narrow and deep cleft (Talipota Gorge) at the western end of the Macdonnells; eventually specimens of five fern species and two moss species were sent to the National Herbarium of Victoria in Melbourne. They included a Victorian and a New Guinea species. Ferns and mosses are, of course, spread by spores and are wind-blown, so that their occurrence does *not* indicate that these plants once lived in the intermediate areas. But the discovery merited further studies. The party decided to concentrate on water holes, as it was felt that these would be the best places to find relict species.

Among many others, we found five species of fresh-water fish in Ormiston Gorge. These proved to be species now found in northern Australia, except one, *Fluvialosa,* which elsewhere occurs in the Murray–Darling system. A specimen of an earthworm (possibly the first taken in central Australia since the Horn expedition in 1899), found in the tiny cul-de-sac canyon containing the ferns, belonged to a species that occurs elsewhere only along the east and south coasts. Our search also turned up a fresh-water snail *(Stimulator consetti)* previously known only from the Harding Ranges of northwestern Australia; it may of course have been conveyed into the area by a bird. In addition, we collected various fresh-water insects with coastal relationships. But we were not successful in finding *Bothriembryon,* a genus of snails belonging to southwestern Australia that has a species on Eyre Peninsula and one in the Macdonnells.

All in all, the animal species we found could not have reached the Macdonnell Ranges by chance over the waterless desert. They must, accordingly, be relics from days when the intervening areas were less arid.

The western Macdonnell Ranges viewed from the plain. Small gums line the dry watercourse in the middle distance, and the dark green shrubs beyond are mulga. (Robin Smith)

Volcanic Spires, Palms, and White Beaches

The Volcanic Islands

10

The Pacific Ocean is the earth's largest physical feature, covering a third of its surface. It measures eight thousand by twelve thousand miles, and its area, sixty-eight million square miles, is greater than that of all six continents. It averages fourteen thousand feet in depth, and the Mariana Trench, 35,800 feet deep, is the greatest chasm on earth.

Right: Part of the seven-mile long caldera of dormant Halea-kala volcano on Maui, Hawaiian Islands. Its desolation and spatter cones suggest a lunar landscape. (Ray Atkeson) Below: Ferns are the first plants to recolonize after an eruption: this picture was taken in March, 1964, four years after the forest was killed by hot ash from the cinder cone of Kilauea Iki. (Allen Keast)

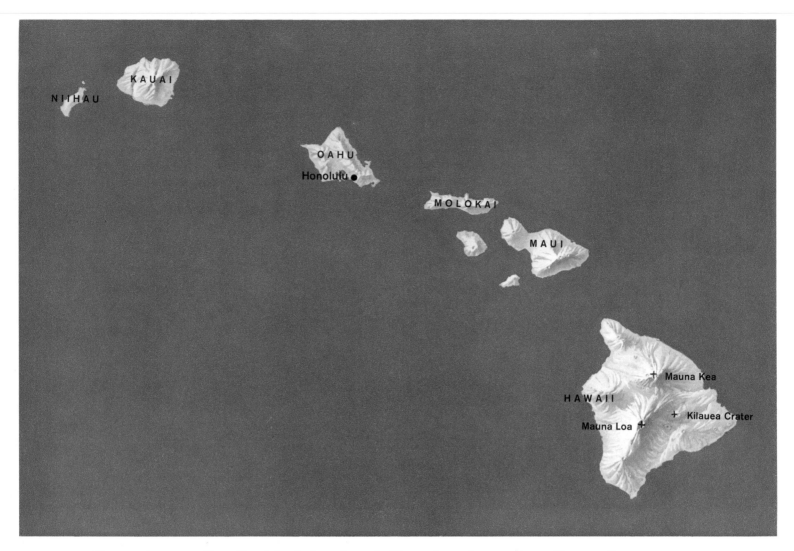

The southernmost Hawaiian Islands have been built up by volcanoes from the sea floor over many millions of years. The Hawaiian group extends northwestward from Kauai, as a chain of low coral islands and reefs, for 1,660 nautical miles to Midway and Kure.

But the Pacific is much more than a vast expanse of water. It is festooned with low, palm-covered atolls and high volcanic islands containing misty canyons, tree ferns, waterfalls, and sometimes fiery, lava-spewing volcanoes. It is the muffled roar of the surf against a reef and it is marine gardens where fishes and corals vie with each other in beauty of color. Here the beach sands shimmer in the midday sun, and the nights are cool, clear, and star-studded. Flying fish burst from the surface of the water in erratic gliding flight. Sea birds in the thousands cram tiny islets. Huge, grotesque turtles struggle up beyond the tide line to lay their eggs. Tranquillity is embodied in the word Pacific, but its potential for violence is enormous. Tropical storms are explosive in their suddenness, frightening in their ferocity. Violent hurricanes scatter the coconuts from the palms and send huge waves sweeping over reef and beach. Occasionally tsunamis, or tidal waves, overwhelm whole islands.

The Pacific has always fascinated man. For most of his history, however, he restricted himself to hesitant voyages around its rim. Then, perhaps about A.D. 500, came a hardier people, the Polynesians. The Vikings of the Pacific, they ventured far out on its waters in their double canoes to colonize distant islands. They were expert navigators and

mariners, but depended strongly on gods and good omens to help them through storms and around reefs. It was not until 1513 that Basco Nunez de Balboa crossed the Panamanian isthmus and became the first European to see the Pacific. He was awed by its vastness. Then, in 1520, Ferdinand Magellan approached it from the south. Delighted with its calmness after his terrible journey around Cape Horn, he named the new ocean "the Pacific."

With the rediscovery of Tahiti by Samuel Wallace in 1767, Europe was introduced to a new concept of paradise on earth, the Pacific island with its white beaches, precipitous volcanic peaks framed by waving palm fronds, and azure seas, and a race of people that were as innocent as they were beautiful. Small wonder, then, that the crews of European ships mutinied rather than leave for home. Down through the generations since then, idealists and adventurers have made Tahiti their goal.

Fountains and rivers of molten lava pour from erupting Kilauea Iki on Hawaii in November, 1959. (Werner Stoy: Camera Hawaii)

THE ORIGIN OF THE PACIFIC

Authorities hold that the oceans are nearly as old as the earth itself and that they began when the cooling of the planet permitted its vaporous envelope to turn to rain. Some attempt to explain their distribution in terms of an early sorting out of lighter granitic rock, of which the continents are mostly composed, from the heavier basalts that underlie the oceans. The former, it is suggested, rose as land while the latter clung to the earth's core. No one, however, knows why there is any land at all: there is so much water that if all the irregularities of our planet's surface were smoothed out, the globe would be covered with water to a depth of twelve thousand feet!

A fascinating, and in some ways more plausible, theory has been advanced to account specifically for the Pacific: that in primordial time, the moon was torn, by some vast cosmic force, from where the Pacific basin now lies. This would have occurred when the earth's crust had already begun to harden. The moon's density, the proponents of this theory argue, is only 3.3 as against 5.5 for the earth. This means that it could well have come from the lighter, more superficial, rocks of the planet. A catastrophe of this nature would obviously have had effects far beyond the Pacific basin, including compensatory contractions in other parts of the earth's crust, which would explain the existence of the other oceans.

Recent research has taught us a great deal about oceans. We now know that the crust of the planet is thinner under the sea than on the continents. This is why scientists engaged on "Project Mohole," the attempt to get a sample of earth's inner core by boring, are trying to do so through the ocean bottom. The real study of the ocean bottom could be said to have started when World War II brought the development of continuous and precise depth recorders based on the echo-sounder principle. Now we find that in the depths of the abyssal sea, there are huge canyons and winding valleys that rival anything on land. Great mountain ranges, sometimes fringed by cliffs half a mile high, extend for thousands of miles over the ocean floor. Since there are no strong erosion forces under the sea, some of these features are undoubtedly very old.

The ocean bottom also varies from region to region. The part of the Pacific that lies northeast of an imaginary diagonal drawn between Japan and Chile is of fairly uniform depth, Hawaii notwithstanding. To the west of this, however, the ocean floor is fissured, distorted and elevated. These features are directly or indirectly associated with island groups. Thus the Tuscarora Trench, east of Japan, is made up of a series of deep fissures that border the convex outer arc of the Bonin, Mariana, and Palau islands.

Man has long been interested in the nature of the material lining the deep trenches or basins of the sea: one reason, among many others, is that such information might throw light on legends of sunken continents. Dredging and boring have shown that the Atlantic floor is covered with the accumulated skeletons of minute marine organisms called radiolaria and globigerina, which live near the surface but fall to the bottom when they die. The bottom of the Pacific, by contrast, is mostly fine red ooze. The reasons for the peculiarities of the Pacific are unknown. We do know, however, that there are no such things as sunken continents there.

CONTINENTAL, VOLCANIC, AND CORAL ISLANDS

The islands of the Pacific fall into three types: continental remnants, volcanic islands, and coral islands. Continental remnants are thought to have once been part of larger land masses. The mechanisms whereby they became islands are not known. It has been variously suggested that these pieces of land, after breaking off from the continent, drifted to their present positions; and alternatively, that subsidence drowned the intermediate areas. Both theories have their advocates and dissenters but paleomagnetic studies in recent years have made drifting sound the more plausible explanation. On the other hand, at various times, New Zealand has been larger, and rather different in shape, than what it is now. Most of the continental islands, interestingly enough, are connected to the nearest continent by submarine ridges a thousand or more fathoms beneath the surface.

Volcanic and coral islands are concentrated in the central

Silversword (Argyroxiphium sandwicense) *in blossom near the summit of Haleakala, on the island of Maui. These curiosities, with their silvery, dagger-shaped leaves, flower between the ages of seven and twenty years, and then die. (Werner Stoy: Camera Hawaii)*

The lava fountain of Hawaii's Kilauea Iki during the eruption of December, 1959. (Camera Hawaii)

areas of the Pacific. The former are built up from undersea volcanoes, the result of thousands upon thousands of lava flows. Coral islands, many of them the circular lagoon islands or atolls, are also true children of the sea—the creation of countless billions of coral polyps working over untold eons.

Vulcanism has figured very importantly in the history of the Pacific. The ocean's borders today are fringed by a line of volcanoes, the Pacific's "girdle of fire," as it has been called. In the western part are the volcanoes of New Zealand, New Guinea, New Britain, the Philippines, Japan, the Aleutians, and Alaska. Volcanoes, active or not long extinct, extend along the western seaboard of the Americas. Inland from the volcanoes of the Pacific is an extensive zone of instability, which is frequently shaken by earthquakes.

Geologists use the term "andesite line" to separate the areas that have continental volcanoes, which are characterized by acid lavas (andesites), from the areas of oceanic volcanoes, characterized by basic lavas (basalts). In the eastern Pacific the line of demarcation closely coincides with the edge of the continental shelf. In the southwest Pacific, however, the zone of continental volcanoes extends far seaward to embrace New Zealand, Fiji, the New Hebrides, New Caledonia, the Solomons, New Guinea and New Britain—islands containing sedimentary rocks, the so-called "continental remnants."

THE BIRTH OF VOLCANIC ISLANDS

It is presumed that the primordial Pacific had no islands. Since lines of structural weakness occur all over the globe, it is equally certain that it could not have been long before volcanic lavas burst forth on the bottom of the sea. Eruptions of submarine volcanoes are common occurrences. Not only do our seismographs record them, but ships in volcanic zones suddenly find themselves tossed to and fro in violent turbulence and dwarfed by huge waterspouts and gas clouds that rise into the air. Black pumice, ash, and the bodies of deep-water fishes come to the surface. And far away a tidal wave may rush toward a distant shore at speeds up to ninety miles an hour. Sometimes, of course, the seeping of molten rock from a subterranean fissure is so gentle that only sensitive instruments can detect it.

The bottom of the Pacific is studded with volcanic peaks, some mere ripples on the bottom, others hundreds or even thousands of feet high. Some of these peaks are now dead, their energies spent. A few are old islands sinking back into the depths. But many are active and growing, spewing forth rock in violent explosion, or sending cascades of molten lava down their sides. At what rate such peaks are rising upward none can say, but some of them do reach the surface. Then begins the endless struggle with the waves, the mountain exploding, hissing, and gushing forth tons of lava and ash, the forces of attrition and erosion wearing and carving away at the emerging giant. Sometimes an island is formed only to be destroyed by the sea or by its own internal explosions. One such appeared in the Mediterranean between Sicily and the coast of Africa in 1830, a two-hundred-foot-high cinder pile. But no further volcanic activity followed, and within a few years waves and storms had reduced it to a shoal. Far out in the Pacific, two thousand miles east of Australia, a little volcanic island suddenly appeared in 1913.

It had a career of perhaps twenty years before explosions from its own cone shattered it; Falcon Island, as it was named, is now only a shoal.

In the Pacific today there are some two thousand volcanic islands. Greatest of all is the island of Hawaii. Its twin colossi, Moana Loa and Moana Kea, rise 13,675 and 13,805 feet above sea level, from a base fifteen thousand feet below the surface of the Pacific. Two of Hawaii's volcanoes, Moana Loa and Kilauea, erupt regularly, so that the island is still growing.

Sometimes volcanic islands are built up around a single giant crater. Others have come from the junction of two volcanoes. More often, a whole series are involved, as in Tahiti, for example. Tahiti consists of a large land mass, Tahiti proper, joined, by a low saddle, to a smaller one, Tahiti Iki: two separate clusters of volcanoes are responsible for this island. Maui, in the Hawaiian Islands, is another such "double island" formed by two clusters of volcanoes; the caldera in Maui's major peak, Haleakala, is seven miles across. On Oahu, where Honolulu is located, two clusters of volcanoes lie side by side, separated by a wide saddle. These were active at different times; Oahu, accordingly, is made up of an older and a younger section, and these differ somewhat in their vegetation and land snail fauna.

HOW LIFE COMES TO NEW ISLANDS

We can only guess how long oceanic islands remain uninhabited after their emergence from the sea. Life cannot survive on barren lava rock. Yet from the very beginning the spores of fungi and ferns, swept through the air on high-altitude jet streams or by hurricanes, drop on the island. Perhaps some forms of life start their tenuous careers when the island is just a few years old; others begin only after centuries have gone by. Gradually volcanic ash accumulates along with the lava, and strong winds and drenching rain begin to weather and pulverize the rock. Sea birds, resting from a storm, leave their phosphate-rich droppings. Once established, lichens and fungi do their bit to create soil. Driftwood and old coconuts cast up on the shore help make organic debris.

Eventually a time comes when the colonization process quickens. Ferns appear. Airborne seeds of larger plants, such as the thistledown of daisies, drop on the island and take root. "Aerial plankton," tiny insects and spiders—which Dr. Linsley Gressitt of the Bishop Museum of Hawaii has found are carried by winds all over the Pacific—now have a place in which to live. The development of the island as a habitat is cumulative, each new colonizer improving conditions for the others: plants support insects, insects support spiders, and spiders, the birds. Coconuts and other seaborne seeds now find sand or soil in which to grow. And sooner or later a few land birds, blown far off course, find the island and establish themselves there.

No study has yet been made of the development of life on a new island in mid-ocean, but the recolonization of Krakatoa, in the Sunda Strait between Java and Sumatra, destroyed by volcanic explosion in 1883, does provide us with an insight into the process. Not one plant or insect remained on the island after the holocaust. Nine months later, investigators found a single spider tending a web, but there was of course nothing to catch. A quarter of a century later the island bore

White Island, an island volcano off the northeastern coast of the North Island of New Zealand, has the look of a newborn volcanic island. (Robin Smith)

only a few scattered clumps of grass. Then the tempo of colonization began to quicken. Each year a few new plants took root. By 1908 insects, lizards, mollusks, snakes, land birds, and even a few mammals, inhabited the island. Dutch scientists noted that 90 per cent of the new inhabitants were forms that could be distributed by air.

An organism's reaching a remote oceanic island alive is obviously a matter of the merest chance. Capacity for dispersion, ability to float on air or water, and to remain viable for long periods in the sea, are all-important. Even marine forms have their problems: many species can live only in the shallows around islands. The capacity to colonize varies with the length of larval life and the stamina of the larvae; in many species this is the dispersive phase of the life cycle.

Charles Darwin was fascinated by the subject of dispersal. He tested the role of birds in plant distribution by cultivating mud taken from the plumage of migratory species. To his surprise, eighty-two plants belonging to five species resulted from one test. But over longer distances birds are probably of only limited significance as dispersive agents. The writer once attempted to find out why there is neither mistletoe nor the mistletoe bird *(Dicaeum)*—the little bird that lives on the fleshy seeds and is the main agent in distributing them—on Tasmania. He fed captive birds the seeds and found that it took only half an hour for them to pass through the digestive tract. Tasmania lies nearly one hundred miles from Australia, which would probably be a flight of about an hour and a half for the bird. For this bird to become an agent in establishing mistletoe in Tasmania, accordingly, a chance seed would have to stick to its feathers (rather than be sheltered in the alimentary canal), and the bird would then have to be swept well out over the sea against its will, and happen to brush off the seed on a suitable host tree in Tasmania. The mistletoe bird, however, takes great care to keep the sticky seeds from its plumage, and it is a sufficiently strong flyer to prevent itself from being swept out of sight of land. Hence, the odds against mistletoe reaching Tasmania with the help of its friend are great indeed.

Despite such difficulties, remote oceanic islands do, in the course of time, acquire a flora and fauna. But the length of time necessary to build up a comprehensive series of life forms is obviously immense. Dr. F. R. Fosberg, the famous plant geographer, once set himself the task of estimating how long it took to establish and develop the Hawaiian flora, which consists of about four hundred basic types. If the islands are between five million and ten million years old, he reasoned that the flora could perhaps be accounted for by a successful colonization once every twenty to thirty thousand years.

SINKING ISLANDS

Only a handful of the thousands of volcanoes in the Pacific Ocean are active today. In the Hawaiian group, eruptions have occurred in historic times only on Hawaii and Maui; the cones of the others are now so eroded that they are barely recognizable. There are no active volcanoes either in the Society Islands or the Marquesas. Both groups, however, are well endowed with basaltic spires—grotesque, jagged projections—the hardened throat-plugs of old volcanoes. Vulcanism has long since died out in the Cook Islands, Rapa, the Carolines, and Fiji. But Samoa, Tonga, New Guinea, New Britain, the Solomons (Bougainville), the New Hebrides, Indonesia, the Philippines and the Marianas have active craters.

Charles Darwin was the first to draw attention to the very interesting fact that in some groups of Pacific volcanoes, activity progresses linearly along the island chain. Characteristically the direction is from northwest to southeast, although in Samoa it is reversed. The relative age of one island in a group can be determined without much difficulty. New islands have perfect cones, and their lava beds are black and hard. Old islands, as a result of protracted weathering, lose their upper parts and have broken outlines; their contours are rounded, their lavas are fragmented and decaying into rich soil. And, surprisingly, these old, worn-down islands start to shrink back into the sea. The reason for this sinking is not known, but it is commonly attributed to the withdrawal of the magma from beneath them or the collapse of the sea bed in the region. But the barrier reef around these islands does not disappear. It is a living unit and can offset the subsidence by growing upward. Slowly the island becomes separated from its reef by a lagoon of increasing dimensions. The ultimate step in the process is, of course, the complete disappearance of the island and its replacement by an atoll or a shoal.

I was recently able to follow in the steps of Charles Darwin and study the structure of the Society Islands. At the southeasterly end of the group is the lovely little volcanic island of Mehelia, which must have been active until quite recently. It has perfectly conical contours. To the north of it are the ruggedly beautiful islands of Tahiti and Moorea, the former dominated by a 7,339-foot peak, and the latter by some of the most striking volcanic spires in the world. But I was

The black sand beach of Kalapana on the island of Hawaii results from volcanic ash and eroded lava. (Werner Stoy: Camera Hawaii)

195

quite unprepared for the view of Bora Bora at the northern end of the chain. Here was an old mountainous island within an atoll-like reef. Bora Bora squats in the middle of a wide, greenish-blue lagoon that is fringed by a palm-capped reef of sand. The reddish-black volcanic rock, green slopes, sands, palms, lagoon, reef, and deep blue sea, give Bora Bora claim to being the most beautiful island in the world. But there is no doubt that it has reached an advanced stage of evolution. A long, low rectangular ridge and an adjacent conical one constitute the backbone of the island—all that remains of an immense crater rim. The island measures a mere five and one-half by three miles, while the reef that once nestled under its slopes is nine by six miles. Bora Bora is a sinking island. In a few hundred thousand years it will be reduced to an atoll.

The Hawaiian Islands show a similar series of evolutionary stages. The southernmost island, Hawaii, reaches a high point of 13,805 feet and has an area of 4,030 square miles. It has two active volcanoes; if this giant is not still growing, it is at least holding its own. Maui, twenty-nine miles to the northwest, 10,025 feet high and 728 square miles in area, has a volcano, but it has not erupted since 1750. Oahu, another twenty-eight miles away, has a maximum elevation of 4,025 feet and an area of 604 square miles. Though a majestic formation, with high contours and deep canyons, its volcanoes have long been inactive. The same applies to Kauai, seventy-three miles beyond, and still older and more eroded.

One hundred and seventy-five miles northwest of Kauai is a much weathered old rocky fragment called Nihoa, 895 feet high and 156 acres in area. Nihoa rests on a wide, shallow bank, all that is left of a once majestic and high island many square miles in extent. Some three hundred miles farther along the chain, at French Frigate Shoal, two very curious rocks thrust up out of the sea. One is a pinnacle 122 feet high, called La Perouse Rock; the other is a mere ten feet high. Inspection shows that they are composed of lava rock, and surrounded by an immense, shallow platform, fifteen miles in diameter. La Perouse Rock, which must have been quite an island in its prime, is today only the merest vestige of its former self.

Beyond the volcanic remnants, the Hawaiian Archipelago stretches 1,660 nautical miles to the northwest as a complex series of low coral islands, reefs, and shoals. Included in the chain are Laysan Island and, terminally, Midway and Kure, which are atolls. The volcanic islands are thus restricted to the southernmost third of this series. But who can say that the islands beyond were not all, at one time or another, proud, high islands.

CANYONS AND WAVE-SWEPT HEADLANDS

The Hawaiian Islands today are of great interest to both the biologist and the geologist. The islands have been greatly changed by settlement, especially densely populated Oahu. But Hawaii and Maui have national parks and Kauai a state park that are a tribute to the administration. Kauai and Hawaii still have excellent virgin forest, where the endemic birds and insects may be studied. The parks in Hawaii and Maui safeguard centers of volcanic activity, and a variety of unique plants.

Kauai, the northernmost of the inhabited islands, is re-garded by many as the most beautiful of the group. The air journey to it from Honolulu is over an ocean area that is ten thousand feet deep. But long before it comes into view, Kauai's position is indicated by one of the characteristic features of oceanic islands, the long cloudbank that over-hangs it. The ancient sea-going Polynesians relied heavily on such cloudbanks to help them locate islands. Migratory birds are believed also to use them, especially the Pacific golden plover *(Pluvialis dominicus),* which annually undertakes a nonstop two-thousand-mile ocean flight from Alaska. On close approach one sees that Kauai's cloudbank is much longer than the island itself, which makes it even more help-ful as a marker.

Kauai is famous for its magnificent seascapes and striking mountain canyons and valleys. On the north coast are high, rounded headlands of red volcanic rock, which drop pre-cipitously down into the sea. Because there is little develop-ment of reef offshore here, deep water, capped by white-capped waves, swirls and crashes against the bases of the cliffs. At Kilauea lighthouse, cliffs extend in both directions as far as the eye can see.

Westward and eastward from the lighthouse, the cliffs give way to low hills and beaches. The coastal plain widens, and small rivers cut paths across it from mountains to sea. Some of these are navigable for a few miles; one can travel up them to the point where waterfalls burst out of the precipices and dense grottoes of ferns crowd the water. In their lower reaches these streams are fringed by cane fields or, of more interest to the naturalist, by small marshes.

At one of these marshes I stopped to watch long-legged Hawaiian stilts *(Himantopus himantopus)* feeding in the shallows and the native gallinules *(Gallinula chloropus)* pad-dling around the edges of reedbeds. It was late afternoon, and all was still and peaceful. Then, to my delight, out from a dense clump of undergrowth on the far bank flew one of the birds I had come to Hawaii hoping to see, the short-eared owl *(Asio flammeus).* It was a dark-brown bird with a buoyant and comparatively rapid flight. The owl systemati-cally patrolled the far shore of the stream, hovered momen-tarily over a clear area, then sailed out over the marsh. Instantly bedlam broke loose among the feeding waterfowl. The stilts yelped, and quickly scattered in all directions. The gallinules made a mad dash for the reeds, half running, half flying. Tranquillity had turned to chaos. The owl, gliding now, made a low pass over the spot where the gallinules had disappeared, then returned to the bank, and flew off upstream. The short-eared owl occurs in many parts of the northern hemisphere and was presumably blown across to Hawaii from the American mainland. The study of its drop-pings and pellets show it to be almost entirely a rodent feeder here.

Where there is coastal plain, Kauai's coastline consists of low knolls, many of which are adorned with the magnificent crimson-flowing ohia or *Metrosideros,* and white beaches fringed by *Pandanus, Casuarina,* and young coconut palms. Black volcanic rocks protrude here and there from the surf and beaches.

Hoary Head Range area of Kauai, Hawaii, with the Pacific surging against black lava cliffs. (Ray Atkeson)

THE BOOBIES OF KILAUEA LIGHT

Red-footed boobies *(Sula sula)* are common inhabitants of reefs and cays in the tropical Pacific, where they form nesting colonies hundreds of birds strong. The birds are close relatives of the gannets of temperate regions. Unlike these relatives, they rarely nest on headlands. Hawaii, however, has two such colonies, one on the grounds of a naval station on Oahu, and another at the Kilauea Light on Kauai. The latter colony is easily accessible to tourists, for a road goes to within a few feet of it. The authorities have put a fence at the bottom of the road, both to safeguard the birds and to prevent visitors from falling the several hundred feet to the ocean below. The boobies take all this in good part. They are oblivious of man and his clicking cameras.

Red-footed boobies are pure white except for the wings, which are black. The beak is pale blue, with a pink base, and there is a blue fleshy area around the eye. The legs are a deep coral-red. These birds look very sedate in profile, perched on their nests, but when they turn head-on, the position of the eyes gives them a puzzled expression.

"Booby Point" protrudes farther into the sea than any of the nearby headlands, and the stiff breezes on it assure the birds a ready takeoff. The birds are masters of air currents, and it is a delight to see them swooping up over the point, one after the other. When a bird is above its nest it suddenly banks, hovers, then drops onto the rim of the crude saucer of sticks. Only in a high wind do they lose their composure and have difficulty making a landing.

Most of the nests had eggs in them when I visited the colony in March. In a few cases, the young were just hatching. About forty pairs nest on the point and, silhouetted against the sea, they made the most attractive colony I have visited. The birds did much of their fishing just offshore. They were, however, constantly being molested by frigate birds that sought to steal their catch before they could return to land.

WAIMEA CANYON AND THE HAWAIIAN DUCK

The road from the southern seaboard to the state park at Kokee, on the crown of Kauai, passes several very interesting physical features. Outstanding among these are Hanapepe Valley and Waimea Canyon. Hanapepe extends inland as a deep cleft in the hills. It has high, green headlands and steep cliffs of red volcanic rock. Dense undergrowth clings to the base of the slopes, and crowds the valley floor so that its little stream of clear water is barely visible. The upper parts of the valley are lost in misty haze. The scene is rendered doubly arresting by the purplish *Bougainvillaea* and yellow-flowering *Cassia,* both introduced plants, that cover the foreground.

Westward along the coast, the road passes Waimea Bay, Captain Cook's landing place in 1778, then sweeps inland on a twisting course up towering ridges. Magnificent vistas of the coast unfold behind one. The road parallels Kauai's most spectacular gorge, Waimea Canyon. Presently, at a height of 3,657 feet at Puu Ka Pele, the full canyon comes into view. Precipitous cliffs and great, rounded promontories overhang knife-ridged slopes and eroded hills in the valley floor. Far up the valley, a silver stream may be seen. Waimea

is memorable as much for its misty purples, reds, greens, and blues as for its grandeur. The slopes and plateaus are a mosaic of tones. Sunlight, mist, and rain combine to produce ever-changing effects.

The mountain streams of Waimea and other gorges on Kauai are among the few remaining habitats of the rare Hawaiian duck *(Anas wyvilliana),* a small, brown species with a blackish head. It is a relative of the mallard of North America and Europe, and at one time had a wide distribution on Oahu as well as Kauai and Niihau. The draining of marshes, hunters, and possibly the introduction of the mongoose, have all helped to kill it off.

Kalalau Lookout, where Kauai's western rim drops spectacularly down to the sea, is one of Hawaii's most impressive natural features. It overhangs a gigantic valley with sides so steep that it has only rarely been entered from the land side. This is the so-called "Valley of the Lost Tribe," where a group of islanders is said to have once lived in complete seclusion.

The almost perpetual fog adds to the sense of mystery surrounding Kalalau Valley. One may visit the top of the plateau many times without ever getting a view of the surrounding country. Then, once, just before sunset, the fog will lift, and the visitor's patience is well rewarded. The far wall of the valley is seen to be a cliff of breath-taking immensity, its face scalloped by a series of great vertical knife-edges that extend from rim to valley floor. Vegetation clings to fissures and little platforms in the rock. As the mist clears the visitor finds himself on a vertical precipice, perhaps fifteen hundred feet high. The valley floor far below is covered with dark green scrub. The wide mouth of the valley terminates in the blue sea. Puffs of mist roll up the walls, obscuring first one part of the valley, then another. As the sun sinks, the clifftop glows gold against the sky and the vertical edges of the precipice appear as gold striations on a purple backdrop. The miracle remains for just a few moments. Then the mist billows in from the sea and all is gone.

THE FORESTS OF KAUAI

Some distance before one reaches the precipice of Kalalau, a section of primeval forest has been set aside as the Kokee State Park. This gives us a glimpse of what Kauai must have been like originally. The trees grow sixty feet tall and are moderately diverse, with small-leaved forms predominating. Ferns of all kinds are abundant. Lichens cover the trunks, and fallen logs are soft with mosses. The fairly open canopy permits a dense undergrowth. There are no vines, or lianas, however, to impede one's progress.

Bird song rings through the air. After a while it becomes apparent that most of the song is coming from only four types of birds. Conspicuous among them is a bantam-sized feral rooster that crows constantly. It is not a native, and is probably a descendant of the fowls brought by the early Polynesian colonizers of Hawaii. Indian mynahs *(Acridotheres tristis),* loud and melodious singers, have invaded the forests from the lowlands, where they are ·very plentiful. The delicate songs issuing from the foliage are coming, it turns out, from the white-eye *(Zosterops palpebrosa),* an import from Japan. Only one native species, the scarlet apapane *(Himatione sanguinea),* contributes materially to the chorus. But it is the most joyous and versatile of all. It utters many

Surf and lava cliffs at Napoli on Kauai. (Ray Atkeson)

different calls as it hunts for insects in the treetops, feeds from the red pompoms of the *Metrosideros,* or passes in flight. This combination of foreign and native species characterizes the state of bird life throughout Hawaii today. Years ago an acclimatization society, which still exists, established all manner of exotic birds; such an approach is the very opposite of the conservation practices of today.

Birds are the most prominent form of Hawaiian wildlife. One of the first of the less conspicuous local species I came upon in the forest was a small, short-bodied bird, olive-yellow above and on the chest, with a grayish-white abdomen, a somewhat long and downcurved bill, and a short tail. It hopped along a lichen-covered branch, poking underneath the bark and into dead curled leaves, occasionally uttering a single call note. Then it flew to a vine of the banana passion-fruit and pushed its beak into one of the green fruits. It was the amakihi *(Loxops virens),* an insect-eating member of that exclusively Hawaiian family, the Drepaniidae. Later, I found that the amakihi was quite common.

A small bird that proved to be a feature of the Kokee forests was a dainty little native flycatcher known as the elepaio *(Chasiempis sandwichensis).* It had a somewhat

stocky body and upturned tail. The coloring was brown flecked with white on the back, chestnut over the head and shoulders, and white on the underside with a black smudge on the breast. The beak was somewhat long and black, the eye large and bright. The elepaio proved to be very trusting, evincing as much interest in me as I did in it. The first individual I saw was feeding low in the undergrowth, hopping among the leaves and stems and over the ground beneath. But no sooner had I become convinced that it was an inhabitant of the lower reaches of the forest than it flew up into the tree canopy and commenced to feed just as assiduously at a height of fifty feet. A common feature of island birds was thus demonstrated. In a well-stocked continental forest, each of the many kinds of insect-eating birds will be specialized in a different zone, one on the forest floor, another in the undergrowth, another the branches, others the foliage. They thus reduce competition among themselves. On islands, however, with their relatively few species, this tendency is much less clear-cut, and some species feed equally at all levels.

The longer one remains in the forests of a remote oceanic island the more one comes to realize its paucity of species.

199

Only very few of the basic groups of birds are represented. Thus, in Hawaii, one listens in vain for the familiar "rat-tat-tat" of a woodpecker, the screeching of parrots, and the melodious songs of orioles. No doves, hummingbirds, or kingfishers frequent the forest, nor wrens or warblers the forest floor. There are no finches or sparrows in the clearings, and no swifts or swallows flutter above the trees. Hawaii has only one hawk and one crow, and these are rare and confined to the largest island. If the visitor has any doubt about the difference between this and a normal forest, he need only wait for the night. Neither the hooting of owls nor the stridulating of tree crickets is to be heard. The silence is complete.

THE HONEY CREEPERS

When Charles Darwin did his famous researches on the Galapagos Islands, a group of volcanic islands about the same distance from South America as the Hawaiian Islands are from North America, he was fascinated to find that one group of birds had been particularly successful on the islands. This group, the Geospizinae, or, as they are called, Darwin's finches, had produced species with a wide range of bill forms; the various species mimicked the ecology of warblers, the ecology of orioles, of sparrows, or of grosbeaks. Darwin rightly concluded that only a few families of birds had been able to colonize the island, and that in the ensuing ecological vacuum, one versatile family had developed species to fill niches it would not otherwise have occupied.

Darwin never reached Hawaii, so he was unaware that a group of birds there demonstrated this phenomenon even more strikingly than the Geospizinae. These are the Drepaniidae, honey creepers. At some time in the remote past the ancestral drepanid, which is believed to have been either a member of the Coerebidae (American honey creepers) or Thraupidae (tanagers), came to Hawaii from North America. It found few other land birds present, and possibly none. In time it developed species specialized for all the wonderful ways of life it found available. At the time of European settlement there were already twenty-two species and many more races of drepanids in the Hawaiian Islands. In their beaks and in their feeding behavior these species resembled warblers, flycatchers, creepers, sparrows, finches, grosbeaks, parrots, hummingbirds, and honeyeaters. Dr. Dean Amadon, head of the Department of Birds at the American Museum of Natural History, has shown that such extreme radiation of forms is without parallel in the bird world.

It is very sad to have to report that apparently all but perhaps ten of the drepanids are now extinct. Wholesale clearing of the forest and the introduction of bird species from elsewhere have taken an irretrievable toll.

SPECTACULAR HONEY CREEPERS

The plateau of Kauai between the forests and Kokee and Kalalau, dominated by the red-flowering *Metrosideros,*

Wailua Falls of Haua, Maui, amid luxuriant tropical forest. On the left, the plant with the feathery leaves is breadfruit. (Werner Stoy: F. P. G.)

is a wonderful place to find honey creepers. Here I saw three species, in addition to the amakihi of the forest. Two are among the most spectacular in the whole group, the scarlet apapane and the vivid flame-colored iiwi *(Vestiaria coccinea).* These two predominantly nectar-feeding species search out the ohia where it is flowering, at low or high altitudes. They are two of the few species that have been seen at sea and hence ornithologists believe may move from island to island.

I had first seen the apapane in the interior of Oahu many years before. Here, now, it was the same joyous and vivacious bird I remembered so well. Apapanes love to perch on the topmost branches, where their brilliant coloring glows like a tiny torch. Their flight is rapid but marked by a fluttering action. Ceaselessly active, all the birds in the community

Red-footed boobies (Sula sula) *have a colony of about thirty to forty pairs on a promontory near Kilauea Light on Kauai. (Alfred M. Bailey)*

seem to be in motion at once. And all the time the air is ringing with the calls of the birds, melodious notes that are sufficiently diverse to suggest half a dozen species. The apapane would grace the avifauna of any continent.

The iiwi is about the same size as the apapane, but differs from it in that the coloring is flame-red and the wings jet-black. The orange bill is very long and downcurving, making the forepart of the head look like an attenuated sickle. Iiwis are not so common as apapanes. They are equally mobile, but their calls are somewhat harsher and less diverse.

The third drepanid I saw on the Kauai Plateau was the smallest of the group, the aniniau or lesser amakihi *(Loxops parva)*. Its body is a mere four and one-half inches long. The aniniau's entire upper surface is bright yellowish-green, with a rich yellow below; the female is somewhat duller. The bill is relatively short and straight. These birds spent much of their time searching for insects among the outer leaves of the trees. From time to time, however, a male flew to a crimson ohia flower and drank from the nectar, the aniniau's yellow contrasting brilliantly with the blossom. The aniniau is more lively than the amakihi, and in my own mind I categorized it as a "foliage-feeding warbler with a sweet tooth."

The other honey creeper I had hoped to see, the so-called Hawaiian creeper *(Loxops maculata)*, which occupies the creeper or nuthatch niche in the fauna, I saw when I visited the island of Hawaii. This small, greenish bird with the dagger-shaped bill hops over trunks and branches, clinging to their vertical surfaces or hanging upside down, busily

Hawaiian teal (Anas wyvilliana), *a small brownish duck with a blackish head, were formerly widespread, but as a result of the draining of marshes, are now rare. (Alfred M. Bailey)*

poking its bill into their cracks and fissures. The creeper feeds almost entirely on bark insects and spiders.

The honey creepers of Hawaii are all very similar in their breeding. They build rather loosely constructed, open, cup-shaped nests in trees or bushes. The eggs are white with lilac-color and grayish spotting and marking around the larger end. They breed in the spring, but the season may be rather protracted. Though some species are relatively solitary, most seem to be social or semisocial in their behavior. Some of the species were found on only one island; presumably those species evolved there. Probably some were mainly lowland species, but we can never be sure of this because the rich lowland forests are gone forever.

THE FIERY CAULDRONS OF KILAUEA

The island of Hawaii tapers gradually upward to form a pair of great rounded domes, Moana Loa and Moana Kea, which are snow-capped for part of the year. But so gradual is the slope, a mere twelve degrees, that it seems incredible that they reach a height of thirteen thousand feet. Nevertheless, from across the sea at Maui, or framed by the feathery fronds of tree ferns near their base, these colossi are among the great sights of the Pacific.

Hawaii has five volcanoes. The small Kohala, in the north, is very old and long extinct. Hualalai has erupted only once in historic times, in 1801. Moana Kea has not been active since the Polynesian people have been on Hawaii—perhaps seven hundred years. Moana Loa, and the smaller Kilauea on its slopes, are very active. The former has erupted thirty-seven times since 1832 and the latter thirty times since 1800, an average of once every 3.6 and 5.5 years respectively. Their activity is, however, quite irregular. It is calculated that in the last hundred years Moana Loa has poured out $3\frac{1}{2}$ billion cubic yards of lava, some of it from the crown, but much from secondary vents on the side. Individual flows are about ten feet deep.

Partly because of the frequency with which they erupt, the activity of the Hawaiian volcanoes is the best documented in the world. They are also gentle, and permit close approach. The eruptions are seldom violent explosions, the magma having a greater fluidity and less gas content than in most volcanoes. Each eruption has, however, its memorable features. Occasionally small towns and villages have been destroyed but only rarely has there been loss of life.

The most spectacular eruption of recent years was that of Kilauea in 1959. It had its beginnings in early October when the Volcano Research Station on the rim of the great summit caldera, which measures $2\frac{1}{2}$ by 2 miles, recorded the first of a series of earthquakes. The quakes increased steadily in frequency until, by early November, they were occurring at the rate of fifteen hundred a day. On November 14, at about eight P.M., with a deafening roar, a line of flaming lava fountains burst forth from Kilauea Iki, the smaller of the two craters and the one that had not erupted for nearly a century. The molten rock rose high in the air and fell back onto the inside wall of the crater, running down the slopes in a hundred streams. These converged near the bottom in a great glowing river. Slowly this spread out in the floor of the pit, covering the old 1868 lava there. By now the acrid, sulphurous fumes had spread from the lava up over the crater rim and had been carried all over the island by the winds. Veteran volcano watchers converged by plane and boat to witness this, the greatest of all firework displays.

By the afternoon of November 15, the line of fountains had been reduced to a single one. All the force of the volcano was concentrated in this fountain. Within a few days it reached a height of nineteen hundred feet, the highest ever recorded in Hawaii. Driven by the wind, cinders were now falling over a wide area at the top of the crater. Trees flickered and glowed like jewels as they caught fire. Much of the debris fell on the crater rim, and a cinder hill started to build up. By December 21, when the eruption ended, this hill was one hundred and fifty feet high, a considerable area of forest had been laid waste, and cinders covered the ground—to a depth of five feet—for half a mile back from the vent.

The major crater of Kilauea is Halemaumau, which is seven hundred and fifty feet deep and has a diameter of three thousand feet. This pit was famous during much of the nineteenth century and up until about 1921 as an almost continuously active lava lake. Then an eruption apparently changed the distribution of the underlying molten mass, and the bed of Halemaumau dropped. Today the crater is being plugged by a steadily cooling mass of blackened lava, a process that, it is estimated, will take at least forty years to complete. Halemaumau, in Polynesian mythology, is the traditional home of Pele, the fire goddess. As one stands on the lava desert about the crater's rim, surveying the great cracks in the walls and utter desolation of the floor of the crater, it is easy to understand why uneducated people once tried to explain Halemaumau in terms of supernatural powers.

Halemaumau and Kilauea Iki are assumed to be the places where the area's main lava conduits reach the surface from an estimated depth of thirty-five to forty miles underground. From these conduits, the rifts, or lines of weakness, extend to the southwest for more than ten miles, and to the east.

PEKING NIGHTINGALES, EUROPEAN SKYLARKS, AND NATIVE GEESE

Hawaii's Volcano National Park is not only one of the best places for seeing a great diversity of volcanic features in a small area but also for observing native Hawaiian plants and birds. One might go to the park planning to concentrate on ferns or Hawaiian geese but come away equally impressed by immense lava flows, craters, rift zones, cinder and splatter cones, steam vents, and lava tubes.

It is not easy to divorce biology from geology in Hawaii. In the first place, the volcanoes created the islands. Here one can see barren lava beds being colonized by the first hardy species—for example, such ferns as the amaumau (Sadleria). By 1964 the ash pile left by the 1959 Kilauea eruption was already dotted with the first little clumps of light-green herringbone fern, virtually glowing against the black cinders. Hawaii has developed many kinds of plants, and a goose, that live only on the old lava beds of the volcanoes. And lastly, in this era of destruction by man of the native flora, good growths of certain Hawaiian plants remain only in the inaccessible walls and bottoms of some of the old pit craters.

My first morning in the Hawaiian Volcano Park was misty and wet. The stark, black walls of Kilauea Iki were seen through a rainbow, and about its floor played a hundred

The nene or Hawaiian goose (Branta sandwicensis), *a rare and striking native bird, is an inhabitant primarily of the broken rock and stunted vegetation of the lava fields. (Alfred M. Bailey)*

little columns of steam, the result of rain's seeping into the surface cracks. The tree ferns around the rim glistened with moisture. But the dampness had little effect on the irrepressible apapanes that were feeding on the flowering ohias. A particularly rich area for plants and birds occurs around the Thurston Lava Tube, a long tunnel through which a river of lava once drained. Much of the rock has now weathered to fertile soil. Four or five species of tree fern occur here, the trunks of the ohias and other trees are covered with lichens, and the fallen logs and rocks are matted with mosses. Elepaeo, apapane, iiwi, and amakihi are here, plus the introduced white-eye. Also present is the Peking nightingale, or red-billed leiothrix (Leiothrix lutea), a noisy species brought from the Orient in 1911. They are green above and yellow below, and have a bright-crimson bill. They live in groups that move to and fro in the forest, warbling, scolding and squeaking.

The lava fields themselves are mostly barren and hence not good for birds. Where there are grassy patches, however, introduced European skylarks *(Alauda arvensis)*, first brought over from England in 1865, occur. Their aerial songs lend enchantment to an otherwise drab area. Sometimes skylarks incorporate strands of "Pele's hair," fine-spun strands of volcanic glass, into their nests. Golden plover, too, occur in the lava areas. By April they have begun to acquire the first traces of their breeding colors, gold spotting on the back and black feathers on the breast. They feed mainly on insects and berries. Where the grass is longer, the California quail *(Lophortyx californica)* may be seen, as well as pheasants *(Phasianus)* that are hybrids between two introduced species, the ring-neck and the Japanese blue.

The lower slopes of Moana Loa are covered partly by forest and partly by old lava fields, the latter taking over entirely at about the six-thousand-foot level. The forest is the habitat of the Hawaiian hawk *(Buteo solitarius)*, a large-bodied, somewhat slow species that feeds chiefly on rats, mice, and insects. It shares the habitat with various native and introduced birds, including the creeper *(Loxops maculatus)*.

The lava fields between six and eight thousand feet, now largely covered with shrubbery and rank grass, are the retreat of one of Hawaii's most unusual birds, the nene or wild goose *(Branta sandwicensis)*. Nenes are striking birds, with mottled, brownish bodies, black faces and heads, and creamy-white necks, but among the broken rock and stunted vegetation of a lava field, they are nearly invisible. Unfortunately, there are very few left in Hawaii: by 1940 hunting, and the introduction of rats, mongooses, and pigs had reduced them from thousands to an estimated thirty to fifty individuals. Others survive in reserves such as that of Peter Scott on the Severn River in England. In recent decades the State of Hawaii has been carrying on a vigorous campaign to restore the Hawaiian goose, raising them in captivity and releasing them on the slopes of Moana Loa and of Haleakala on Maui. Since their natural foods, grasses, herbs, and berries, remain abundant, it is hoped that the birds will build up in numbers.

THE UBIQUITOUS FERNS

One is never out of sight of ferns in Hawaii. In the wetter areas they grow in such luxuriance that the trunks of the tree ferns and the waist-deep growth of smaller species make travel over the forest floor a slow and exhausting business. Most of the seventy species found in the islands grow in the park. They range in size from the rock-clinging film fern, only an inch long, to giants that tower forty feet above the ground. There are herringbone ferns and lance ferns, adder's tongues and bird's nest ferns, false staghorns and maidenhair ferns. Many are terrestrial but a considerable number in the forest are epiphytes, growing on the trunks of trees and of larger ferns.

Other ferns grow in the dry places, including the dry hillsides of Moana Loa and Haleakala. They even appear on the walls of the pit craters, where they find sheltered, damp, and well-lit surroundings. The bottoms of some of the larger of these craters, which may be as much as nine hundred feet across and three hundred and fifty feet deep, are often jungles of ohia and fern.

The abundance of ferns on volcanic islands is largely due to the ease with which they disperse, the small, light spores being carried great distances by the wind.

A LUNAR LANDSCAPE

At the eastern end of Maui stands Haleakala, ten thousand feet high—the House of the Sun, according to Polynesian legend. The third largest volcano in the Hawaiian Islands, it is crowned by a huge depression, seven miles long by 2 1/2 miles wide—long thought to be the world's largest caldera.

From the road the view is of sugar cane and pineapple fields, long sandy beaches and rolling surf and, beyond, half lost in bluish mist, the mountains and gorges of the western end of the island. Eventually the visitor reaches the top of the mountain and the rim of Haleakala's caldera. Looking down into the crater, the sight is awesome—a lunar landscape. Jagged cliffs and volcanic rocks fall away to a vast amphitheater of blackened lava flows, cinder cones, and sand dunes nearly three thousand feet below. Not a shrub nor patch of grass enlivens the scene. Beyond, the far wall rises precipitously to a jagged silhouette, except for two low sections over which the sea mist rolls. The immensity, desolation, and barrenness of it all is profoundly oppressive.

Polynesian legend has it that Haleakala last erupted in 1750, when vents formed on the side at altitudes of 575 and twelve hundred feet, and lava flowed down into the sea. Geological studies show that Haleakala had two protracted periods of activity, separated by a time of quietness and erosion. Today it is presumed extinct.

Plant life on Haleakala is very interesting for many species are not known outside this area. Included here are several high-altitude plants plus many that are found in the dense jungles of Koolau gap, on the seaward side of the crater. A curious-looking crater plant is a tree lobelia *(Clermontia haleakalensis)*, one of the most primitive of its group; it has a robust trunk, stubby branches, and long, straplike leaves. Also here are tree geraniums with flowers like violets, shrubby buttercups, begonias, two of the three species of native orchids that occur in the islands, a native raspberry *(Rubus hawaiiensis)*, and various ferns.

Most famous of the crater species is the silversword *(Argyroxiphium sandwicense)*, which has become the symbol of Haleakala. This curiosity has a short, woody stem, crowded with lustrous, silvery, dagger-shaped leaves. After a growth period of seven to twenty years, during which it has reached a height of three to five feet, the silversword flowers. Between one hundred and four hundred reddish-purple flowerheads issue from the top of the plant, and it then dies. On Haleakala, silverswords are confined to the region between seven thousand and nine thousand feet; they are also seen on the high peaks of Hawaii. Silverswords and other rare and fascinating plants of Haleakala have been reduced to a fraction

Right above: The lushness of Tahiti is expressed in the dense tropical foliage, crimson flower and gushing waterfall. (Elizabeth Horner) Right: Tree ferns form a wall in the Hawaiian National Park, Hawaii. About seventy species of ferns occur on the islands. (Allen Keast)

of their former numbers by grazing animals, especially goats.

Of the mysteries surrounding the Hawaiian flora, none is so tantalizing as how the high-altitude plants came to the islands. Most of them cannot survive at sea level; many of them must have developed where they are found.

The cliffs of Haleakala adjacent to the Koolau and Kaupo gaps are the nesting place of a small black-and-white sea bird, the dark-rumped petrel *(Pterodroma phaeopygia)*. These creatures of the night come ashore only after dark, when their barking calls betray their presence. Their nests are as much as six feet deep in the rocks.

MOKU MANU, ISLAND OF BIRDS

A mile or so off the eastern coast of Oahu, two tall volcanic pillars thrust out of the sea, the waves washing and swirling around their bases with unceasing vigor. These sentinels are the home of millions of sea birds: boobies, terns, noddies, and shearwaters. The birds are as safe as they can possibly be from man's intrusions. No boat can land on the rocks without being dashed to pieces.

A group of Hawaiian ornithologists try to get onto Moku Manu every year to check the species. They have to be strong swimmers; anchor their boat on the lee side, then swim through the rolling surf and scramble up onto the rocks when there is a lull. When I was in Hawaii in March 1964, I expressed a desire to visit the island and it was agreed to attempt a landing although previous trips so far that year had failed. Accordingly one Saturday morning found us on the clifftop nearest the island studying the sea through field glasses. The possibilities seemed reasonable; an hour later we were in a launch on our way from the outer harbor.

Moku Manu is a good five miles along the coast from the nearest launching place. Nevertheless, in due course we approached the towering monoliths and gazed in awe at the myriads of birds swarming about their slopes. The peaks rose hundreds of feet above the sea. One had precipitous sides, and was obviously unapproachable; the other, closer to the land, had grassy slopes and a somewhat flat plateau. It was toward this that we maneuvered, coming in as close to the lee side as safety permitted. Eventually a landing spot was selected, a flat rock that was exposed between swells. One after another, cameras sealed in biscuit tins and towed in air-inflated bags, we plunged into the water and made for the land. I found the swim no mean feat, for the swell first swept me in toward the rocks, then sucked me out again. In due course I was dumped among the rocks, scratched and bleeding.

A few feet in from the rocky foreshore, the island sloped upward at an angle of about thirty degrees, broken only by a few low ridges. It was covered with rank grasses and small bushes, and over all of it birds fluttered and yelped in countless thousands. Most common was the sooty tern *(Sterna fuscata)*, a dainty species, white in the body and black on the crown and back. Their single eggs were scattered over the ground. Some were on bare areas; others were on rocks, in

The imposing shoreline of Akapa Bay, Nuku Hiva, in the Marquesas. The jagged spires represent the throat plugs of old volcanoes. (E. Aubert de La Rue)

the grass, or under bushes. Here and there, guarding their eggs, were groups of the common noddy *(Anous stolidus)*. They were distinguishable by their sooty-brown coloring and grayish-white cap. Somewhat rarer were white-capped noddies *(A. tenuirostris)*, which are a rich chocolate brown with clear white crowns. Moving through the colony without stepping on eggs was most difficult. Our intrusion created bedlam, the birds taking to the air as we approached and dropping back onto the eggs as we passed: our progress was marked by a rolling mass of fluttering birds. I did my best to train my telephoto lens on suitable birds, but finding a single individual by itself proved no easy task.

Interspersed with the terns were the larger red-footed boobies and the brown boobies *(Sula leucogaster)*, big chocolate-brown birds with white breasts and yellow bills. Their nests were either on low bushes or on elevated rocks. These too took to the air when we approached too close.

Because of the risk of a rising sea, our time ashore was limited to about an hour, and I was unable to search a series of small burrows on the upper slopes for their shearwater inhabitants. The return journey to the boat was accomplished by jumping off the rocks and swimming through the surf. As he left, one member of the group looked at me and said: "You've got the most scratched legs. You had better go last. Sharks follow the scent of blood."

BIZARRE INSECTS

A study of Hawaiian insects made a few years ago by Dr. E. C. Zimmerman of the Bishop Museum in Honolulu shows that 3,722 species have been described for the islands. Today about five thousand are known. Dr. Linsley Gressitt informs me, however, that the original total may have been ten thousand species, for organized collecting was not started until after the insects had been drastically affected by settlement. The insect fauna is just as unbalanced as is the avifauna. There are no native cockroaches (although 15 species have arrived since settlement), mantids, phasmids, springtails, earwigs (12 since settlement), stoneflies, mayflies, caddis flies, fleas (7 immigrants), suckling lice, or termites. Sixty-three per cent of the insect orders are thus not represented here. At present the numbers of species of grasshoppers and their kin is 45; dragonflies and damsel flies, 29; bugs, 223; lacewings, 60; moths, over 1,000; beetles, over 1,600; wasps and bees, over 1,000. Recent studies have shown that the islands have a few hundred species of *Drosophila* flies. From 10 to 20 per cent of the moths, beetles, and wasps of Hawaii are not true natives.

Among the peculiarities of Hawaiian insect life are damsel flies that do not require streams in which to breed, the larvae living in little pockets of water at the base of leaves. The larvae of one species is the only terrestrial damsel fly in the world; it inhabits damp places on the forest floor. Many groups of insects have produced flightless forms in Hawaii, including grasshoppers, bugs, lacewings, beetles, wasps, and flies. Entomologists believe that under continental conditions, these would be at such a competitive disadvantage that few would survive. Another characteristic of the insect fauna is that within the different groups some genera have been abundant on one island, and others on another island. This indicates that each island was colonized individually. Some species of insects are extremely local, being confined to one valley only. Others, like insects elsewhere, are restricted to one food plant or a few such plants. Several species have been found living within and feeding on the silversword, and nowhere else.

A study of Hawaii's insect fauna on the basis of origins shows that about 95 per cent have Pacific affinities, and only 5 per cent American. This contrasts somewhat with the birds, where many of the most important species—goose, hawk, waterhen, stilt, and thrushes—are obviously of American origin.

TAHITI AND THE SOCIETY ISLANDS

The Society Islands lie as far to the south of the Equator as Hawaii is to the north. They are much more remote from the nearest continent: Australia is approximately four thousand and South America 4,800 miles away. Their area is a mere six hundred square miles, whereas that of the Hawaiian Islands is 6,435 square miles, these islands being approximately 4,200 miles from San Francisco. These factors have had a great influence on the development of the fauna and flora: there are, for example, only seventeen species of native land and fresh-water birds; there are seventy in Hawaii. No recent list of the number of plants is available, but an old one names six hundred. Even if the final total were twice as large it would still be much smaller than the seventeen hundred that occur in the Hawaiian Islands. What the Society Islands lack in plants and animals, however, they make up for in beauty.

Tahiti seen from the sea is a wild, rugged, untamed island, with volcanic peaks towering high into the sky. Once safely across the reef into the blue-green lagoon the voyager

Right: Bora Bora, Society Islands, looking out across the lagoon to the rim of the reef. (Jerome Schweitzer) Below: A red-tailed tropic-bird, its curious tail-feathers streaming out behind, rides the air currents. These birds nest in the cliffs of many Pacific Islands. (John Warham)

approaches a palm-lined foreshore. Only then does the luxuriant vegetation of the lower level become visible. Then, too, the deep, jagged valleys, the precipices that rise for a thousand feet, the fine white lines of the waterfalls and cataracts, and the green, forested ramparts of the mountainsides, can be distinguished.

Tahiti, which is only thirty-seven miles long, was born when two series of volcanoes emerged from the abyss of the Pacific, touched each other at their edges and then cooled. The result was a double island made up of a larger part, Tahiti, and a smaller part, Tahiti-iki, or little Tahiti. Today the islanders live on the narrow strip of coastal flatland. The bulk of the island is a precipitous hinterland: in the larger segment there are the peaks of Orohena, 7,352 feet, and Aorai, 6,778 feet, and in the smaller segment, Roniu, 6,370 feet. Although there are tracks across the island, the only times the Tahitians go inland is when they wish to catch fish and shrimp in the clear mountain streams.

Early voyagers to Tahiti noted that the huts of the inhabitants were scattered across the flat country, and there was little attempt to form villages. This tendency doubtless accounts for the vegetation of the lowlands—patches of coconuts, bananas, breadfruit, and papayas alternate with areas of thick scrub and original forest. There is a small but interesting segment of gnarled old Tahitian chestnut trees and twisted banyan figs in Tahiti's Botanic Gardens. Along the foreshore the casuarina, with its long, pendant foliage, and *Pandanus* are interspersed with the coconut palms. Additions to the flora in European times include frangipani from South America, but the crimson-flowering *Hibiscus,* which the Tahitian girls are so fond of wearing in their hair, was probably imported by the Polynesians themselves.

Back from the narrow coastal strip Tahiti rises sharply. The outermost mountains are smooth and rounded, though steep. Precipitous ravines cut through the old volcanic rock. Coarse grass and dwarfed ferns are prominent, with dense vegetation, penetrable only with a machete, clogging the slopes and creek bottoms. Several hours of climbing bring one only a little way into the interior of the island, which rises ahead in its mist-shrouded vastness.

Proper penetration of the hinterland of Tahiti requires a guide. One can then follow one of the swift-flowing rivers until it is blocked by high waterfalls or, better still, head for Lake Vaihiria.

The Vaihiria River is a typical mountain stream: somewhat broad in its lower reaches, it very soon enters a narrow ravine with nearly vertical walls. To walk, one must go along the streambed, alternating between the two banks. A few hours of climbing bring one deep into the mountains. Vegetation springs from every ledge, and the water is overhung by ferns and branches. Gnarled buttress roots make progress difficult, and the stream gurgles and races over large stones that sink under one's feet. There is little air movement in this sheltered gorge, and it seems stifling. Mosquitoes are in attendance, especially in the patches of sunlight. Now, though, one comes upon true Tahitian luxuriance: giant tree ferns, wild bananas, and magnificent chestnuts. Trunks are festooned with "Spanish moss", a fibrous hanging plant, and epiphytic ferns. Mosses form a green carpet over the stones. A pause is made by a wide pool while the guide spears some of the little shrimps and small fish about six inches long. Finally, late in the day, one emerges at Lake Vaihiria, around whose dark

water the mountains rise almost vertically on all sides. The old crater is forbidding, its bottom covered with black ooze and strewn with sunken trees and boulders. Fifteen hundred feet above sea level, Vaihiria is the only high volcanic lake in the South Pacific. Legend and mystery surround Vaihiria, for the Polynesians regard its black waters as bottomless. It is in these waters that the "big-eared" eels live, big blackish creatures with dark, bluish eyes. The species is characterized by large pectoral fins. Some of the eels are nearly four feet long, and as thick as a man's leg.

VOLCANIC SPIRES AND WHITE TERNS

Moorea, ten miles from Tahiti—one can see its outlines clearly across the sea—is only about one-third of the size of Tahiti. Its coastal fringe is similar but the beaches tend to be white, a welcome relief after the black sands on much of Tahiti. It has several magnificent features, including the view of a series of tall volcanic spires across the waters of Baie de Cook, a palm-fringed shoreline that is without parallel in the world.

Bird life is not well developed in the Society Islands. In Moorea, however, tropic birds *(Phaëthon lepturus),* a long-winged white bird the size of a large pigeon, glides and spirals in magnificent solitude against the backdrop of the mountains. Tropic birds are exceptional among sea birds in that they nest inland in ralley precipices. The palm trees along the foreshore of Moorea are a favorite place for the little white or fairy tern *(Gygis alba),* a dainty bird, thirteen inches long, with black eye, bill and feet, and deeply forked tail. Terns love to perch high on the fronds above the water's edge. They, too, have peculiar nesting habits, placing the single egg in a knothole on the horizontal branch of a tree. Frigate birds, large, long-winged sea birds with deeply forked tails, are another feature of the shoreline; they are often seen hovering on the air currents that sweep down from the mountain ridges.

The conspicuous land birds of the Society Islands today are mostly introduced species. Pre-eminent among them are white-eyes *(Zosterops lateralis)* from Australia, and little finches from Australia and Africa. The finches, greenish above, grayish below, and with bright scarlet bills, rise in flocks from the grasses beneath the coconut palms. The most common of the native birds are the little green pigeon *(Ptilinopus),* which can frequently be seen flying among the clumps of trees along the foreshore, and a kingfisher *(Halcyon),* a drab-colored species that skulks in the forest. In quite atypical style, it apparently gets much of its insect food from the branches of the trees. Most of the time, however, it seems to sit silently on a shaded branch, only uttering its chattering call note when another kingfisher happens to fly into view. The loveliest of the native birds of the Societies was a little blue parrot. It was abundant in former times, Bora Bora at the northern end of the chain having a distinctive race, while the Marquesas to the north had a separate species. I sought the bird in vain. Possibly, however, it still exists in the mountainous interior.

Coconut palms (Cocos nucifera) *form the tropical shoreline of Tahiti. Across the bay is Tahiti Iki. (Werner Stoy: Camera Hawaii)*

Like Hawaii, the Society Islands have no native mammals and no frogs, and the only reptiles are a few small lizards. Land snails, however, are widespread in all the islands. Those of Moorea and Tahiti were used in an important evolutionary study some years ago by Dr. H. E. Crampton. It was found that nearly every one of the narrow canyons had evolved its own form.

THE MARQUESAS, SAMOA, AND TONGA

There is space here for only a brief reference to the other major volcanic groups in the Pacific. Chief of these are the Marquesas, the Cook Islands, Samoa, Tonga, and the Marianas.

The Marquesas, some eight hundred miles northeast of Tahiti, are a series of eleven fairly large, high islands that are both fertile and very beautiful. The group is famous for its dramatic ruggedness and striking spires. Hiva-oa, the largest island, measuring twenty-three miles by ten miles, is guarded by a forbidding rocky coast. The highest peak, Mount Pout-tai-nui, on Ua-Pou, is 4,040 feet in height. In early days the Polynesian inhabitants of the islands suffered sorely from the introduction of European diseases and other abuses, and the population dropped from an estimated fourteen thousand to one thousand or less. As might be expected from the isolation of the group, the number of animal species is very low: there are only eleven species of land birds and five kinds of lizards in the Marquesas, and no mammals or frogs occur.

Far to the east of the Society Islands is precipitous, heavily-wooded Pitcairn Island, haven for the *Bounty* mutineers, and beyond that is Easter Island, only sixty-four square miles in size. Easter, 2,300 miles from South America, 2,800 from Tahiti, and 2,300 from the Marquesas, is one of the most isolated islands in the world. It is an old, worn-down volcanic island that has been treeless as far back as records go. It is most famous for its monuments in the form of giant human heads carved from the volcanic rocks of one of the craters by people, and for reasons, unknown.

The Cook Islands, to the west of Tahiti, fall into two series, the southern Cooks, which are volcanic islands, and the northern ones, which are atolls. Rarotonga, with its rugged volcanic hills and bold precipices, is particularly beautiful. Vegetation extends almost to the summit of the highest peak, Te Manga, 2,140 feet high.

Tonga, two hundred miles east of Fiji (which lies seventeen hundred miles east-northeast of Australia), combines weathered volcanic islands and coral islands. It has, however, only fifteen species of native land birds, compared to the sixty-five on Fiji.

The Samoan Islands, four hundred to five hundred miles northeast of Fiji, fall into an eastern group and a western one. The largest of the Samoans, Tutuila, where Pago Pago is located, is twenty-five miles long; the crest of the island is a broken mountain range with numerous deep valleys. Matafao, 2,140 feet high, near the center of the island, is the highest peak. Western Samoa is made up of two large islands, Savaii and Upolu. Savaii reaches a height of 6,094 feet and was the site of a volcanic eruption in 1902; there has, however, been no activity there since 1911. Upolu, with a maximum height of 3,608 feet, has an extinct volcano, Tofua. The Samoan Islands, which were undoubtedly the starting point of many of the long voyages of the Polynesian peoples, have about thirty resident species of birds; they are mostly of kinds widespread in the southwest Pacific, but one species, the tooth-billed pigeon *(Didunculus strigirostris)*, which has a powerful, curved, owl-like bill, is confined to these islands. Also of interest is the fact that three groups of insects, mayflies, caddis flies, and termites, all common in Australia and New Guinea, penetrate to Samoa but no farther east.

To the north of New Guinea, the Marianas and Caroline Islands in Micronesia are composed largely of volcanic islands, the former group having active craters. The islands are remote and their faunas are poor. The number of native bird species in the Marianas is twenty-one, while in the Carolines, Ponape has eighteen and Palau has thirty-two species. Both island groups show the poverty in mammals and reptiles that is so characteristic of the many islands of the eastern Pacific.

Shoreline of Tahiti Iki, with coconut palms silhouetted against the evening sky. Tahiti is in the background. (Werner Stoy: Camera Hawaii)

Coral Necklaces in Azure Seas

The Atolls

11

Strung out through the deep, tropical waters of the Pacific Ocean are festoons of islands of a type that seemed very strange to early navigators. Narrow rings capped by white beaches and green coconut palms, they lay so low in the water that a ship would be almost upon them before they were sighted. Their outer reefs were like stone, and against this the sea crashed with a roar, threatening to tear apart any ship that approached. The mariners found that some of these lagoon islands, or atolls, were so large that it took a day to sail around them. Many, however, had channels that led through the outer reefs, the coral barrier, into the quiet waters of a lagoon. If a ship could find one of these passes, as they are called, it could reach safety.

When the early sailors landed they found coconuts in great abundance, affording a cool, sweet drink. Land crabs swarmed everywhere, providing a succulent change in diet, and fish were numerous in the lagoon. On some of the islands, at the right time of the year, the eggs of sea birds were scattered all over the ground. But altogether there were probably only two dozen species of land plants and one or two kinds of land birds. Fresh water was lacking, but brackish water could be obtained by digging. Perhaps a few observant sailors noted the great contrast between the amazing diversity of life in the sea and the lack of variety ashore.

These ring-shaped islands, or atolls, were composed of coral. Some voyagers suggested that the coral-building animals had instinctively built up the great circles to afford themselves protection in the inner parts. A few believed that the islands were the rims of gigantic, ancient volcanic craters. But most were content just to marvel.

THE DISTRIBUTION OF CORAL ISLANDS

Atolls occur widely in the Pacific and Indian Oceans. The greatest complex is the Maldive Archipelago, south of India. In the eastern Pacific, however, the Tuamotus, composed of seventy-eight atolls and innumerable reefs, extend through a belt of ocean twelve hundred miles long and five hundred across. The most heavily populated of these, Rangiroa, which is two hundred miles from Tahiti, has a lagoon forty-two miles long and fourteen wide. West of Tahiti the northern Cook Islands are all atolls, and Tonga, near Fiji, is made up mostly of coral islands. North of Fiji are four great groups of atolls, the Ellice, Phoenix, Gilbert, and Marshall islands. Canton Island, in the Phoenix group, was for a long time an important airfield, since it is about halfway between Honolulu and New Caledonia. It is nine miles long, but seldom more than six hundred yards wide, and encloses a chop-shaped lagoon. The Ellice Islands are composed of nine small atolls, and the Gilberts of sixteen islands. The Marshalls are a double chain of atolls, some 130 miles apart, consisting of thirty-four islands and 870 reefs. None rise to more than a few feet above sea level. The group, however, includes the world's largest atoll, Kwajalein, consisting of ninety islets scattered around a reef that encloses a 650 square mile lagoon. The Carolines, west of the Marshalls, include both coral and volcanic islands.

Nauru and Ocean Island, between the Gilbert Islands and the Solomons, are the famous phosphate islands of the southwest Pacific. So deep is the guano dropped by the birds on these islands that a million tons of the substance is exported per year. Nauru is an oval-shaped atoll, twelve miles in circumference, with only a small lagoon in the center. The lagoon is not connected to the sea and its waters are brackish. Nauru and Ocean Island are not typical atolls, for both are raised islands, a result of a warping of the ocean floor below. Nauru rises to 220 feet above sea level, and Ocean Island is three hundred feet high.

Other atolls, including Palmyra, Fanning, and Christmas islands, lie directly south of Hawaii, and because they straddle the Equator are known as the Line Islands. In the northern Pacific are Midway, Wake, and Johnston islands, all of strategic importance in these days of air travel. Midway Island, a relatively small island, near which occurred one of the most significant battles of World War Two, is some twelve hundred miles west of Hawaii.

All the atolls of the Pacific are confined to the region within thirty degrees of the Equator, since the calcareous structure of the coral reef can be produced only in waters above 69° F. There are no atolls in the eastern section of the Pacific: cold waters from the Antarctic well up there.

THE ORIGIN OF ATOLLS AND BARRIER REEFS

It is to Charles Darwin, who circled the globe in the *Beagle* between 1831 and 1836, that we owe our first scientific study of atolls. Darwin initiated soundings around Keeling Atoll in the Indian Ocean and found that the prepared tallow at the bottom of the lead came up with the impressions of living corals down to a depth of ten fathoms. As the depth increased, the living coral became sparser until, between twenty and thirty fathoms, there were only dead skeletal fragments. This

Bora Bora, the island "within an atoll," was in bygone ages a cluster of volcanoes. It is now eroded and steadily sinking, withdrawing from the barrier reef that marks its former limits. (Eliot Elisofon)

indicated to him that the coral islands could not have been built up from the bottom of the sea—there must have been, originally, some intermediate structure which had been sinking gradually through the years. Volcanoes were the obvious answer; many atolls, however, were far too large to be mere mountaintops. The ultimate clue was provided by Bora Bora and other islands encircled by a wide barrier reef. The large atolls, Darwin postulated, are the end result of a process that began as a fringing reef close inshore to a volcanic island and then went through the stage of being a barrier reef as the central land mass subsided. The reef survives because of its continued upward growth. Many archipelagos, Darwin noted, consist of large atolls at one end and more recent volcanic islands at the other.

Darwin was, of course, unable to produce evidence that old volcanic islands do sink, and various alternative theories were advanced. It was not until 1896 that a deep bore was put down through an atoll to find whether or not coral extended below thirty fathoms. The work was carried out on Funafuti in the Ellice Islands. A core 1,140 feet long was obtained. It proved to contain coral, or coral remains, throughout its length. Fossils found even in the lower core were mostly those of shallow-water species. Funafuti had obviously been sinking steadily for a considerable period of time. Darwin was vindicated.

Subsequent deep bores have confirmed these results. Between 1934 and 1936, Japanese scientists drilled a hole on North Borodino to a depth of 1,416 feet. In 1947 an American team drilled six holes on Bikini Atoll, one reaching 1,346 and another 2,556 feet. Finally, in 1951, cores were obtained on Eniwetok Atoll in the Marshall Islands 4,222 and 4,610 feet long. In each case, coral, or limestone derivatives, extended the length of the cores. At the bottom of the Eniwetok cores, however, was basaltic rock: the Marshall Islands, at least, were built up on old volcanic islands. Fossils obtained in these cores were at least of Miocene age, showing that sinking had been occurring for at least twenty million years. The coral bases of these islands may be even older than that. A few years ago several specimens of fossil coral were obtained from guyots, those curious, flat-topped mountains that lie deep in the ocean basins, and some of these have been found to be of Cretaceous age, seventy million years old. If, as argued, the truncated peaks are the result of wave action at a time when these mountains were on the surface, and their coral was deposited shortly after, sinking must have been going on for a long time.

The evidence is fairly conclusive that atolls are the remains of old high islands, though that is not to say that they can be formed only under conditions of subsidence. In recent years, biologists have realized that these old islands may have been the steppingstones along which animals and plants were able to establish themselves in a few of the more remote parts of the ocean. Hence, atolls could provide a clue to some curious aspects of the distribution of island life.

LIFE ON RANGIROA

The modern air traveler gets a view of atolls that Darwin would have envied. In March 1964, I was able to carry out field work on Rangiroa, in the Tuamotu Archipelago. During the air journey from Bora Bora, the visitor obtains a fine view of Tikahaou, an atoll sufficiently small to be seen almost in its entirety at one time. In the distance it appears as a faint smudge with the white line of the outer reef defining its circular outline. Closer, it is seen to be mostly bare, with only scattered clumps of palms.

Rangiroa is much more impressive. It is so large that only part of its curved rim is visible from the air at a time. The reef is broad, its surface dissected by surge channels and surmounted here and there by squarish, palm-covered islets of varying sizes. The plane follows the line of white-capped waves fringing the reef, and from the air it is possible to see clearly how precipitous the seaward sides are, contrasting with the shallows of the lagoon side. As we descend we see that the channels across the reef rim are of varying sizes and that many widen out into depressions and shallow pools. When a large wave hits the reef, the water surges through some of these and spills over into the lagoon. In some places, an unbroken crescent of palms extends along the surface of the reef for hundreds of yards. Elsewhere they are broken into little clumps by the shallow channels. The greenish lagoon surface is patterned with many reefs, yellowish, brownish, and purplish. These are the so-called patch reefs, and some are hundreds of yards across, while others are columns of coral only a few yards wide. Patch reefs are composed of corals that require still water.

The plane lands outside the reef and one sees the atoll—as did the early mariners—as a long, low line of palms. A launch puts out from shore, and one is carried over the broad rollers to the ship pass and into the lagoon. The lagoon front is a wide, sweeping curve of water. Ashore, dozens of brown-skinned Polynesians, clad in the brightest colors, gather around the landing place, eager to welcome the visitors.

Coconut palms completely dominate Rangiroa. Tall and stately, they rise to heights of fifty feet before spreading out as graceful, waving fronds. The ground is composed of fine white coral sand. Old nuts litter the parklike avenues between the palms. Here and there are broad, shady breadfruit trees (Artocarpus altilis). In places the gentle washing of the waves of the lagoon has undermined the palms, and they lean out over the water at angles of sixty degrees. Some of the trees have attempted to compensate by twisting the crown so as to get a maximum of sun. Where the roots are exposed, they form a dense and tangled net. This is obviously an adaptation for holding and absorbing as much as possible of the scant rain that falls.

Farther along the shore is an open area where the beach morning glory (Ipomoea), a creeper with a wide range over the Pacific, forms a carpet. Inland, here, the bases of the palms are crowded with a dense undergrowth of ferns and shrubs. The latter, mostly broad-leaved species such as Scaevola and Barringtonia, are in all stages of growth. The larger ones harbor a leafless vine, Cassytha filiformis, brownish-yellow in color and resembling a tangle of fine insulating wire. It hangs like a thick curtain over the foliage, almost obscuring it. The visitor finds himself stumbling over sprouting coconuts that are trying to fight their way through to the light. Conditions are hot and stifling among the trees. It is a relief to reach the fringe of the islet.

A small palm-covered islet on the surface of the reef. (Paul Popper Ltd.)

A surge channel cuts across the atoll rim here. It is shallow and the tide is coming in, the little rushes of water making the coarse coral fragments tinkle as they sweep over each other. A reef heron *(Demigretta sacra)* stalks the shallows for unwary crabs. Presently its neck shoots forward, and it takes a few quick steps and seizes its victim, lifting it high into the air; there is a writhing of legs, a gulp, and the bird is ready for fresh prey.

HERMIT, LAND, AND COCONUT CRABS

The ground here is swarming with little hermit crabs, dragging their bulky shell homes about with them. They are the "ants" of the atoll—continuously active, ever ready to feast on any item of food. There are a variety of sizes, but the tiny ones are by far the most common. A sudden movement causes them to stop in their tracks and withdraw within the shell so that the occupied shells become indistinguishable from the hundreds of empty ones lying around. If a hermit crab is picked up it will be seen that the claws fold neatly over the opening to form a perfect lid.

A study of the hermit crabs on the Tuamotus was made by L. G. Seurat in 1903. He found that in their very young stages they were aquatic and had to be sought on the outer reef or under stones along the lagoon shore. The larger ones spend their time on land, but their gills must be kept wet, so every day at sundown they return to the water for a short period, refilling the gill cavity. Hermit crabs drag their adopted, lopsided homes around with them throughout life. As they grow, they must find shells of increasing size, but there is a shortage of these—this is one reason for there being thousands of small crabs but few of the large ones. A hooked tip on the soft abdomen provides the necessary grip within the shell. To get an animal out, a twisting movement must be used, but the crab will shed the shell itself if warmed over a flame. It also leaves the shell to defecate. The eggs are laid in the shallows of the lagoon. Most atolls have no more than half a dozen species. They are invaluable scavengers; in places, however, they are said to have an adverse effect on the plant life by decimating seedlings.

Two of the most familiar crabs of atolls were rare on Rangiroa: the land crab and the coconut crab. The former live in burrows and may so honeycomb the friable ground that a human will fall through the surface. Some burrows are eighteen inches deep. Land crabs are nocturnal, coming out only after dark to scavenge and feed. A large individual will be up to a foot across, and they are highly esteemed as food by the Polynesians. On Ifaliuk Atoll the land crabs make an unusual spawning journey at times of full moon in May, June, and July, going down to the water's edge to shed their eggs. The crabs are then caught in large numbers. Their egg masses are particularly prized, their flavor being likened to shad roe.

The coconut crab *(Birgus latro),* one of the most widespread of all the atoll inhabitants, has a wide distribution through the tropical regions of both the Pacific and Indian Oceans. It is the giant of its tribe, mature adults reaching weights of from five to six pounds in places. A large individual will have a carapace six inches across and an extreme span of three feet between front and hind legs when it walks. The general body color is reddish-brown and black, but there is some individual variability. The crab's overall appearance is thickset, and it has considerable strength. Darwin learned this when he imprisoned one specimen overnight in a tin and found next morning that it had torn open the rim and escaped. Coconut crabs climb well and may frequently be found in the tops of the palms. There is, however, disagreement as to whether or not they actually tear down the growing nuts. Various observers have seen them opening nuts on the ground, pulling off strips of fiber with their formidable claws. It is said that they then use a finger of the claw to pierce the soft eye and break open the shell to reach the coconut meat inside.

So eagerly do the Polynesians seek the coconut crab as food that it has become rare on the settled islands. It is best eating during its estivation period underground (July-October on some islands), when the tail is very fat. After the female returns from spawning in the lagoon in December, the flesh is poor for some months. Coconut crabs are omnivorous, and are said to retain the flavor of the latest food they have taken.

RATS, LIZARDS, AND LAND BIRDS

Most atolls have a population of the small, brown Polynesian rat *(Rattus exulans)*. This animal is believed to have been transported accidentally in canoes during the great Polynesian migrations. Rodents are also known to be capable of traveling some distance across water on floating logs. They swarm on many of the islands and in places they wait around villages for food. They climb well and can often be seen at night among the fronds, where they may also make their nests. Their diet is diverse: pandanus fruit, birds' eggs, newly hatched turtles, coconut blossoms, and coconut meat. In places these rats are used by the Polynesians as food.

European house rats *(Rattus rattus)* have got ashore on many of the Pacific islands and are very destructive of coconuts, so much so that metal stockings have to be fitted around the trunks to keep them out of the palms. When they become abundant they are very destructive of the population of ground-nesting birds. An observer in 1854 on Howland Island, north of the Phoenix group, described how hordes of them lived in the sea bird colonies and subsisted on the eggs and fledglings. Occasionally, the birds would seize some of the younger rats and tear them to pieces, or fly up with them and drop them into the surf. The rats were quite unafraid of human beings and bit and squealed when they were trodden on. Eventually, it was reported, the rats exterminated the terns.

Gecko and skink lizards are the only terrestrial reptiles on atolls. The little skinks may be seen sun-bathing on the trunks of the palms, or in open spaces on the ground. Their swift movement is their protection. Geckos, by contrast, are largely nocturnal, emerging from hiding places in native huts or palm trunks to catch their insect food. The lizards, most of which have a wide range in the Pacific, were also probably distributed by canoe and log.

Part of the circular rim of a typical south Pacific atoll in the Low Archipelago. The surf surges through low points on the reef, creating small, palm-covered islets. (Eliot Elisofon)

Above: Maupiti is a high volcanic island in the Society Group with an outer reef about three miles across.   Right: Two atolls (about three miles in diameter) clearly show characteristic circular form and unbroken rims. Tuanake and Hiti (foreground), Tuamotu Archipelago, are viewed towards the west. (Both by N. D. Newell, American Museum of Natural History)

TURTLES

The green turtle *(Chelonia mydas)* has a wide range throughout the tropical Pacific. In the Tuamotus it is still common on some of the outlying islands, but so esteemed is its meat that its numbers have been steadily reduced by hunters. On Raroia, the "Kon Tiki island," it is said that from fifteen to twenty turtles are obtained each year, and the number taken on Rangiroa is probably about the same. Where they are not unduly persecuted, the female turtles come ashore between June and September to lay their eggs on the sand. Just before this period, when the turtles mate in the sea beyond the reef, both sexes can be captured. As many as two hundred eggs, round, and about the size of ping-pong balls, may be deposited by a female at a time, with successive layings perhaps two weeks apart. The weak link in the turtle's life history is undoubtedly the hatchling stage: the babies have to run the gauntlet of crabs and birds on land and sharks and fish at the water's edge. Studies in Sarawak showed that the number of hatchlings emerging from unmolested nests averages 46 per cent. This gives an ample margin for their increase, but it has been suggested that the turtles might be helped by gathering the young and depositing them in deeper water where there is more protection or, alternatively, by raising them in pens for a few weeks.

J. R. Hendrickson calculated that if each female, in six or seven trips to land per year for three years, deposited eighteen hundred eggs, the population would remain stable if only slightly more than one-tenth of one per cent of the turtles lived out their lives. He also calculated that the amount of high-quality protein obtained from an adult turtle was equal to that of a three-year supply of eggs. Since most females have a laying life of longer than three years, exploitation of the eggs is more profitable than killing the adults.

THE COCONUT PALM AND THE BREADFRUIT

I was able to count only fifteen common plant species on Rangiroa; the total number, allowing for introductions, is possibly two or three times that. I was struck not only by the small number of species but by the fact that most of them were well known to me from the Great Barrier Reef, 4,200 miles to the west. I had also seen a number of them some weeks before in Hawaii, 2,500 miles to the north. The strandline plants that characterize atolls are, in fact, known for their wide distribution.

Various observers have commented upon the paucity of plant species occurring on atolls, the total for individual islands ranging from seven to about 125. Various factors are, of course, involved, especially distance from high islands and the amount of rainfall. Nevertheless, the sterility of atoll soils, which are only finely fragmented coral, imposes severe limitations on plant life. Plants must have rather special tolerances to survive under these conditions.

Seeds can be distributed from atoll to atoll only by floating on the sea or riding on floating logs, by being blown by winds, carried by birds, or transported by man. A high proportion of them undoubtedly are dispersed through the first of these agencies. *Pisonia,* a broad-leaved tree that forms dense stands on some islands, is, however, largely transported by birds, for its seeds are very sticky and adhere readily to feathers. Of the three food plants used by man, two, the breadfruit and the coconut, have definitely been distributed by man himself, though some coconuts may have drifted ashore on their own and taken root. *Pandanus* may also have been transported from island to island to some extent.

The coconut *(Cocos nucifera)* is one of the wonder plants of the world. No other supplies such a high proportion of human wants. The wood makes furniture, spars, rafters, posts,

Above: Algal ridge at the rim of a reef flat serving as an intertidal platform. Right: Gravel ridge and lagoon across a channel on the windward shore between the volcanic island of Huahine an the small islet of Tomagagie, north of Garumaoa islet. (Both by N. D. Newell, American Museum of Natural History)

and fences. It can be burned for fuel. The leaves are used for thatching and basket weaving, hats and slippers. The small flowers can be fermented to make coconut brandy. The husk provides material for rope and matting. The shell is used as a drinking utensil or a bailer. Long before it is ripe the nut can contribute a pint of delicious juice. The tissues of the coconut, the meat, are a staple food of people throughout the tropics. The economy of the Pacific islands is largely based on dried coconut, copra, which is used in the manufacture of oil, margarine, and soap.

It is generally agreed that the coconut originated in Asia. One or two anthropologists, however, have suggested an American origin for it. Despite experimentation, botanists are still not agreed on how long coconuts drifting on the open sea retain their viability. Sir Peter Buck, the great student of Polynesian migration, asserts that when the first Polynesians reached their new homes in the Pacific all that was edible was the *Portulaca,* the roots of *Boerhavia,* seaweed, and *Pandanus.* The voyagers themselves introduced, besides coconut and breadfruit, the banana, taro, arrowroot, and sweet potato. Breadfruit and banana, it is noted, can be propagated only from the young shoots on the roots of the parental trees. The *Pandanus,* by contrast, occurs in many species and varieties in the Pacific, evidence of its spread and evolution before the advent of man.

Almost all of the Polynesian plants are of western origin, including the food plants. One notable exception, it is generally agreed, is the sweet potato *(Ipomoea batatas),* which apparently came from South America. Anthropologists, with the notable exception of Thor Heyerdahl of *Kon Tiki* fame, and a few others, believe that the Polynesian people originated in Asia. There is great uncertainty about how much, if any, contact these islanders had with South America. It might, however, be noted that in the shallow craters of remote

Easter Island grow two water plants of undoubted Andean origin. These are *Scirpus riparius,* used for making reed boats by both the Easter Islanders and the Peruvians, and *Polygonum acuminatum,* to which certain medicinal properties are ascribed.

CORAL REEFS

The atoll can be said to be the place where land and sea are truly integrated. The island itself is a creation of the sea and is occupied only by those plants and animals that can withstand its rigors. Here sea creatures like crabs have become adapted to land, but they must go back to the sea to breed. Turtles and sea birds have their domain in the oceans but must come to the atolls to reproduce their kind. Man is truly integrated with his environment here, getting sustenance equally from land and water.

Underlying all aspects of atoll life and ecology is the reef. This is the vast manufacturing complex that made the land possible. It teems with a diversity of creatures and ways of life exceeding that in any other life zone on the planet, with the possible exception of the tropical rain forest and certain rocky reefs. Here are the corals, in their multitudinous shapes, forms, and colors, sea urchins and sea stars, a variety of mollusks, sponges, worms with brilliantly patterned feeding tentacles, crustaceans and fish, breathtaking in their beauty.

For the successful establishment and growth of reef-building coral, the water must move neither too rapidly nor too slowly. This is why the most vigorous colonies are usually found on the sides of the reef and at lagoon entrances. The depth at which corals can occur is linked to the penetration of light: embedded in the tissues and moving freely in the

221

Courting dance of black-footed albatrosses (Diomedea nigripes) *on Midway Atoll in 1949. (Alfred M. Bailey and Robert J. Niedrach)*

Brown gannet (Sula leucogaster plotus), *breeding on both isolated atolls and volcanic islets, has a wide range through the tropical seas. (Keith Gillett)*

interior of the coral polyps are large numbers of symbiotic alga-like flagellates; the flagellates are known as zooxanthellae. These apparently provide the major part of the oxygen needs of the corals by synthesizing the gas and they also contribute some foodstuffs. In return they get carbon dioxide and nitrogenous wastes from the polyps. Zooxanthellae are responsible for some of the brighter colors of the polyps, particularly the yellows and reds. Deep-water corals have colorless polyps but they fluoresce.

Corals reproduce by shedding free-swimming larvae into the water, the result of a sexual process, and by budding. The rate at which reefs grow varies with their location; although much study still remains to be done a general figure would appear to be one inch per year, or just over three feet every forty to fifty years. Contrasting with this, however, are recorded cases of very rapid growth. One of these concerns a channel through coral in the Andaman Islands in the Indian Ocean. A chart prepared in 1887 showed a depth of six fathoms (about thirty-six feet) of water, but forty years later the water was only a foot deep. This would mean an average growth rate of coral of a foot a year, or one hundred feet a century.

Reefs show a well-developed zonation, with the different coral species and their associated organisms confined to distinct areas. Norman Newell of the American Museum of Natural History found that the Raroia reef could be divided into a front zone where great flagellate growths of *Acropora* and robust staghorn corals *(Pocillopora)* predominated, a strip from fifty to one hundred yards wide, which, because of its deep channels, he called the groove and spur zone; the channels themselves, a rich area for life; an algal ridge zone; and a reef flat or rock pavement zone. The algal ridge, which was at the outer margin of the reef flat, was made up of a dense encrustation of coralline algae such as *Porolithon*. The reef pavement, from thirty to fifty yards wide, was differentiated into life zones according to the occurrence of pits, depressions, and broad pools, with degree of exposure at low tide obviously having a marked influence on the distribution and kinds of animals that occurred.

On the Rangiroa reef I found the reef pools, which were fed by channels and surges and always contained water, particularly interesting. Many delicate kinds of coral occurred there, plus colorful seastars, the large, brown, slate-pencil sea urchins, and the long-spined urchins. Sponges grew on the sides of the pools, and a wide diversity of mollusks and crustaceans frequented the crevices within the coral colonies. There were also many small fish.

There is also a great range of animal habitats within the lagoons of atolls, which range to depths of thirty fathoms and more. Patch reefs can be looked upon as a complex series of apartments with a different fauna occupying each level. Some of the most magnificent of the branching corals grow in lagoons. A face mask and an air pipe will enable one to get a good view of the wonderful world of the lagoon and its bountiful life. On Rangiroa I saw thirty or forty species of fish in about fifteen minutes, no two having the same color, combination of colors, or patterning. Some moved

A female green turtle (Chelonia mydas) *laboriously "rows" her way back to the sea after having deposited her eggs ashore. (Keith Gillette)*

through the coral branches in schools; others were solitary. A few were bold, coming close to the observer, but the majority just went about their business of scraping algae and small animals off the coral, or picking up minute forms of life from the water. In former times the lagoons of the Tuamotu atolls were among the famous pearl-shell areas of the world, native divers going down without diving apparatus to depths of 120 feet. Today much of the best shell is gone and few atolls still retain considerable quantities.

The number of animal species inhabiting coral reefs is very great, for the reefs provide a wide range of water depths, degrees of turbulence and exposure, temperature and chemical conditions, and kinds of cover. The Rangiroa reef seemed very rich to me. Marine biologists agree, however, that the more remote eastern Pacific islands have a much poorer animal life than the continental fringe to the west. This occurs because reef organisms are rarely able to survive a journey across vast expanses of open sea. Hence, it is as much a barrier to them as to land organisms. Years ago a survey of the rich coral reefs of the Philippines showed that they had about 120 species of coral, seventy of marine worms, two hundred crustaceans, and three hundred mollusks. No comparable survey has been carried out on Tahiti or the Tuamotus. It might be noted, however, that the number of fish species recorded for Raroia is four hundred, quite a creditable figure.

THE RARE BIRDS OF LAYSAN ISLAND

The coral islands of the Pacific contain some of the world's largest nesting colonies of sea birds. The most interesting of the islands in this respect are two northwesterly members of the Hawaiian chain, Laysan and Midway, for here two species of albatross have huge colonies. Laysan, eight hundred miles west of Honolulu, is of particular interest because it also had a fauna of five unique land birds; a teal, a rail, two honey creepers, and a reed warbler. In association with these the history of Laysan, over the last sixty years, makes interesting, though tragic, reading.

Laysan was probably discovered about 1800 but details are not available. Captain John Paty, who annexed it to the Hawaiian Kingdom in 1857, described it as a low sand island twenty-five to thirty feet high, three miles long and one and a half broad. A lagoon a mile long and half a mile across occupied the center of the island. Beach grass was the dominant vegetation, together with half a dozen types of fan palms. Nesting birds, estimated at eight hundred thousand in number, virtually covered the island. A later visitor, Captain N. C. Brooks, spoke of a luxuriant growth of shrubs in places and declared that he collected twenty-five species of plants. Seals also occurred. The subsequent history of Laysan has been described by Alfred M. Bailey in his book *The Birds of Laysan Island.* The island was leased to guano diggers in 1890, and active digging went on from 1892 to 1904. With so many ships calling and men coming ashore, great changes took place on the island. Far worse was to come: in 1903 a Captain Schlemmer introduced rabbits to Laysan as a business venture. In no time they overran the island, destroyed practically every plant and started the sand drifting. The habitat of the native land birds became a desert, and three of the five species became extinct.

The sea birds did not fare much better. In the early part of this century feathers were much in demand for the millinery trade. Most active in this trade were the Japanese. Many thousand birds were killed on Midway, some three hundred thousand albatrosses and other species were killed on nearby Lisianski Island, and, notwithstanding a United States presidential order making the islands sanctuaries, two hundred thousand were killed on Laysan in 1909. It was estimated that altogether about five-sixths of the Laysan albatrosses *(Diomedea immutabilis)* were killed. A photograph taken in 1893 shows a large section of the island virtually covered with the birds—a far cry from the scattered nesting groups of today. In due course the rabbits of Laysan were killed off and the vegetation made a good recovery. Today the island is a carefully protected sanctuary.

Of the extinct land birds of Laysan, none was more characteristic of the low coral island than the little rail *(Porzanula palmeri),* a species that, in the absence of predators, had lost its powers of flight. Observers who visited the island about the turn of the century found them to be very active, fearless, and most inquisitive, the latter a characteristic of many island birds that have never known man. The rails moved rapidly through the long grass and were not averse to entering human dwelling places for food. When ornithologists, in the course of preparing albatross eggs as scientific specimens, let the yolk fall on the ground, the rails came out to feed on it.

The Laysan rail was introduced to Midway in 1891, where conditions similar to those on Laysan prevailed, and a sizable population built up from a single pair. Additional birds were introduced in 1913. Meanwhile, the destruction of the vegetation of Laysan by rabbits took its toll and the last rails died out there about 1923. They survived in good numbers on Midway until, with all the military activity in the early part of World War Two, rats came ashore. This was the end for the rails. The Midway rails became extinct in 1943.

The second Laysan bird to die out in modern times was the little grayish-brown warbler known as the miller bird *(Acrocephalus familiaris).* Like the rail, this species had relatives in the Pacific islands to the west. In the Carolines and Solomons such warblers live mainly in reed beds. They are readily recognizable by their beautiful songs; and hence the name "reed warblers." The Laysan miller birds spent the hotter hours of the day in the bushes and tall grass, but in the morning and afternoon they pursued moths and other insects in the open. They even entered houses in pursuit of insects, including those attracted by the lanterns at night. Some even alighted on test tubes in the laboratory. When Alexander Wetmore visited Laysan in 1923, virtually no vegetation remained and the miller birds had become extinct.

The Laysan honeyeater *(Himatione sanguinea fraithii)* was a distinctive local race of the common apapane of Hawaii referred to in the previous chapter. The scarlet birds

Right above: The foreshore of Rangiroa, largest island in the Tuamotu Archipelago, looking over the lagoon to islets along the reef rim. (Allen Keast) Right: Greater frigate or man-of-war bird (Fregata minor), *its inflated gular pouch showing that it is breeding, perches on a Scaevola bush. (Patricia Bailey Witherspoon)*

fed on insects in the bushes and on the blossoms of portulaca. Like the other birds, they were fearless and moved freely around human habitation. When Wetmore visited Laysan in 1923 only three honeyeaters remained on the island, and they died during a gale.

A second member of the Hawaiian Drepaniidae succeeded in reaching Laysan. It had a heavy, finchlike bill and so became known as the Laysan finch *(Psittirostra cantans cantans)*. Observers noted its omnivorous habits, which included the breaking and eating of tern eggs. Though reduced to a few dozen when the destruction of the vegetation was greatest, the finches were able to hold on until conditions improved. There are at present about five thousand of them, and they are safe from extinction.

Laysan has its unique duck, the Laysan teal *(Anas wyvilliana laysanensis)*. Even before the arrival of man it was obviously one of the rarest ducks in the world for, as noted, the island's lagoon measures only a mile by half a mile. In 1902 the Laysan teal population was estimated at one hundred and in 1911 at not much more than seven. Twenty were recorded in 1923, and thirty-nine in 1951, since which time the birds have been holding their own.

ALBATROSSES, BOOBIES, AND FRIGATE BIRDS

Albatrosses are basically inhabitants of the southern hemisphere. Three species, however, occur in the north Pacific, the black-and-white Laysan albatross *(Diomedea immutabilis)*, the dark-brown black-footed albatross *(D. nigripes)*, and the extremely rare short-tailed albatross *(D. albatrus)*. The first two nest on Laysan and Midway Islands and it is estimated that the first of these islands contains 46 per cent of the total breeding population of Laysan albatrosses and 61 per cent of the black-footed. The figures for Midway are 36 and 15 per cent, the remainder nesting on other islands in the group. It was estimated in 1957–1958 that 260,000 Laysan albatrosses were nesting on Laysan and about 200,000 on Midway, the figures for the other species being 67,000 and 17,000. The future of albatrosses on Midway is, however, uncertain since there have been many collisions between the birds and planes. Most of these have been of no moment, but it is always possible that an aircraft crash may result.

The albatrosses first appear on the breeding islands in late October and early November, most being present at the end of the latter month. The first nests are begun in early November, the black-footed albatrosses beginning a few weeks ahead of the Laysan albatrosses. By late November, many of the former and a few of the latter have eggs.

Left above: A fairy or white tern (Gygis alba) *brings a beakful of small fishes to its young. This tern balances its single egg on the knothole of a tree. (Thomas M. Blackman) Left: A pair of rare Laysan teal* (Anas wyvilliana laysanensis), *swim over a little freshwater pond on Laysan Island. The present world population of this teal, which is confined to Laysan Island, is about forty individuals. (Alfred M. Bailey) Right: Colony on Midway Island of sooty terns* (Sterna fuscata oahuensis), *a species common on many of the low sandy atolls. (Alfred M. Bailey and Robert J. Niedrach)*

Magnificent colony of Laysan albatrosses (Diomedea immutabilis) *on Laysan Island in 1893, before the slaughter of the birds by feather hunters. It is estimated that in the next sixteen years 500,000 of these and other sea birds were killed. (J. J. Williams, Courtesy George C. Munro)*

Incubation and tending of the young in the first days is carried out alternatively by the two parents. The young are fed by regurgitation. Until mid-May the young are covered with soft down, but then the adult body feathers start to appear. By late June they are very heavy for their size. Most of the young leave the islands in the first half of August, according to Alfred M. Bailey.

The albatrosses are a well-known feature of Midway Island today. They pay scant attention to vehicles and man. Home gardens and the old cemetery appear to be as suitable to them for nesting sites as the bare, open areas. People find the fluffy young and the dancing rituals of the adults amusing.

The northwestern islands of the Hawaiian chain support breeding colonies of many other sea bird species. At least five different kinds of petrels—some of the species are thousands strong—burrow into the soft coral sand. There are three different boobies, the red-footed *(Sula sula)* and brown *(S. leucogaster)* being the most common, but the somewhat heavier masked booby *(S. dactylatra)* is also widespread. There are two species of tropic birds, large white birds with long narrow tail streamers: the red-tailed tropic bird *(Phaëthon rubricauda)* occurs in moderate numbers but the white-tailed *(P. lepturus)* is rare as a breeding species. Large, with long, narrow wings, and a distinctly forked tail, the frigate bird or man-of-war bird *(Fregata minor)* is one of the most spectacular of all sea birds. It loves to hang motionless in the air, ready to swoop down on an incoming booby and relieve it of its fish. It builds its stick nest on top of bushes. In parts of Polynesia the natives train frigate birds as pets, and they are alleged to have carried messages between islands.

A 1949 photograph of colony of Laysan albatrosses among the ironwoods on Sand Island, Midway Atoll, shows how thin the colonies are today. But Alfred Bailey calculates the world population of Laysan albatrosses still at about 500,000. (Alfred M. Bailey)

The most numerous of the nesting sea birds on the Pacific islands are of course the terns. The commonest of them on the leeward Hawaiian chain is the sooty tern *(Sterna fusca),* a moderate-sized species with white undersurface and forehead, and black cap, back, wings and tail. Their number probably runs into the millions. Somewhat less common is the brown noddy *(Anous stolidus),* which prefers to nest on bushes. Most beautiful of the group, however, is the fairy or white tern *(Gygis alba);* it is pure white, with dark eyes and a black beak. It prefers to lay its egg in the knotholes of trees, but where these are not available it will then choose a piece of coral rock.

Jungles, Moss Forests, and Birds of Paradise

New Guinea and Melanesia

12

The islands that are considered continental remnants are found only in the southwest part of the Pacific, and the greatest of them all is tropical New Guinea. Covering 304,650 square miles, New Guinea is, after Greenland, the world's largest island. Near it on the north lie New Britain and New Ireland, collectively known as the Bismarcks. To the east are New Caledonia, the Solomons, New Hebrides, and Fiji. All have a backbone of high mountains and lowlands of dense, humid, tropical jungle, fetid sago, and mangrove swamps. These tropical islands constitute Melanesia, the home of some 2,500,000 dark-skinned, frizzy-haired, and traditionally war-like people.

Isolated in mid-ocean, some 350 miles to the east of Australia, is Lord Howe Island, a tiny speck of land dominated by two old volcanic peaks. It rests on a submarine ridge that extends from New Caledonia to New Zealand. Lord Howe, which was uninhabited until European times, contains several curious animals and plants that suggest that it is a continental cast-off. Far to the south, some twelve hundred miles southeast of Australia, are the delightful temperate islands of New Zealand. Despite their isolation, authorities agree in regarding them as true continental remnants. In their geology, climate and biology, the islands of New Zealand are quite different from the tropical islands north of Australia.

MOUNTAINS AND BLUE SEAS

New Guinea dominates Melanesia and displays all the aspects of the region in their most extreme form. Great ranges of brooding, mist-shrouded mountains rise above the coastline.

These, however, are only the foothills of the majestic ranges of the interior. New Guinea's backbone rises to heights of fifteen thousand feet and more, and the highest peak, Mount Carstensz, is 16,535 feet. The Snow Mountains, in the western half of the island, are permanently white-capped, the line of perpetual snow being 14,500 feet. The mountains of New Guinea give the island a remarkable diversity of climate and vegetation. Above the tropical jungles, at heights of five to ten thousand feet is a broad belt of montane forest, stunted trees adorned with dense, furry cascades of a pendant mosslike plant. On the broad mountain plateaus and in the highland valleys are wide grasslands and belts of coniferous (podocarp) forest. Above this are the alpine grasslands, and bare, rocky ridges where sparse shrubs are battered and flattened by ever-present winds.

The dominant theme of lowland New Guinea is dense rain forest, high humidity, and frequent rain. Men who served in this area in World War Two found themselves struggling through tangles of thorny lawyer vine, slipping and sliding on slushy trails and sinking knee-deep into mixtures of mud and rotting leaves. Their clothes were wet through for days on end, and the high, leafy canopy, though it held back the sun, served to intensify the oppressiveness and stickiness of the air. Malaria-carrying mosquitoes tortured them at night. Mountain campaigns, such as the fighting along the Owen Stanley Trail from Port Moresby to Buna, frequently entailed days of exhausting travel between ridgetops that were only a few miles apart. Pilots found the combination of frequent fog and jagged mountain spurs a greater danger than the enemy. They never knew, once in the air, whether or not they would be able to find their base again: many were the pilots who found the field fogged in and groped from landing strip to landing strip until, fuel gone, they either crashed or were forced to parachute. To servicemen, "a rotten, wretched hole" was an apt description of New Guinea.

At other times and under other circumstances, however, the island has been found beautiful in the extreme. Along much of the shoreline the jungle is broken up by white, palm-fringed beaches. Samarai, at the eastern tip of the island, is one of a series of picturesque green islets set in an azure sea. When the fog lifts from the mountain valleys their grandeur is breath-taking. Waterfalls cascade over the precipices and drop into glades where the limbs and trunks of the trees are heavy with hanging mosses, ferns, and orchids. The jungle is alive with multicolored parrots, and a great variety of fly-catchers, wrens, cuckoos, honeyeaters, kingfishers, and other small fry. One may be rewarded with the sight of a giant cassowary majestically stalking along a trail, a resplendent bird of paradise displaying high on a leafy perch, or a grotesque hornbill flapping lazily above the trees. The New Guinea coast seen from the air on a clear day is an arresting sight. Little patches of reef glow white in the deep blue sea. Inlets and bays, large and small, shallow and deep, carve their way into the land. In places, streams travel a winding course across broad coastal plains to stain the sea with their muddy waters. Outstanding among the great rivers of New

The precipitous Owen Stanley Range, about sixty miles from Port Moresby, New Guinea. It is still an untamed area despite the tiny native village on the slope. (Australian News and Information Bureau)

New Guinea is a lush tropical island with a backbone of high mountains, montane forests and grasslands, large rivers and, in the lowlands, steamy jungles and mangrove forests. It is the home of the magnificent birds of paradise and a great diversity of plants, birds, reptiles and insects.

Guinea are the Sepik in the north and the Fly in the south. The former, which winds through seven hundred miles to negotiate the two hundred miles from its source to the sea, resembles a gigantic snake. The Fly opens into a vast delta of tree-covered swamp.

Politically, New Guinea is divided into Papua and North-East New Guinea, both of which are administered by Australia, and a western section, West Irian, administrated by Indonesia. Very few scientists have a good knowledge of both sectors, which is not surprising for great areas of the interior still remain virtually unknown, only one or two parties having penetrated them. Many plants and animals, of course, are common to the whole of New Guinea, but a considerable number are confined to single regions or mountain blocks.

EUCALYPT-COVERED HILLSIDES AND MIST SCRUBS

The Portuguese navigator Antonio d'Abreu is credited with the discovery of New Guinea when, on a journey from Malacca in 1511, he touched on its north coast. In 1526–1527 a fellow countryman, Don Jorge de Menezes, saw signs of gold in one of the river mouths and optimistically gave the island its first name, Isla del Oro. The south coast remained unknown until 1707, when a Spaniard, Luis Vaez de Torres, sailed through the straits that now bear his name.

The approach to New Guinea today is made mostly by way of the south coast. Port Moresby, a thriving town and important airport, lies relatively close to the mainland of Australia, and was a vital base during the war: it was the point at which the Japanese southward advance was finally stopped. The coast here is really a segment of Australia: the climate is dry and the hilly terrain is covered with stunted eucalypts and coarse grasses. Only the observant naturalist, in fact, would detect the presence of some New Guinea animals and plants, and might thereby distinguish the savannas of Port Moresby from those of Cape York and the Northern Territory.

Like so many others, the writer made his first visit to Port Moresby during wartime service. In early 1944 the long war of attrition along the Owen Stanley Trail had been brought to a successful conclusion, and military activity was concentrated on the north side of the island. Where thousands of men had been camped a few months before, there were now abandoned camp sites, each marked with its clumps of papayas (known locally as pawpaws), bare patches of earth, and discarded paraphernalia. Little yellow sunbirds *(Cinnyris jugularis)* occasionally hovered around the pendant, bell-like flowers of the male pawpaws by day, inserting their long bills into the corollas of the blossoms, and the hummingbird hawk moths

Typical New Guinea highland country near Telefomin with jungle, grasslands and limestone outcrops. (H. W. Gill)

took over after dusk. Green tree ants had formed colonies in some of the trees, presenting a threat to anyone who climbed for the fruit. The luscious ripening fruits were now the property of fruit-eating birds like the friarbird *(Philemon novae-guineae)*. Where the tents had been, little lizards basked in the sun. Insect-catching birds used the old posts as perches from which to make sorties into the air after prey.

Southeastern New Guinea is deeply indented by bays and inlets, and the coastline near Port Moresby is no exception. The terrain is dry and open, for the rainfall is a mere forty inches a year here, and it is relatively easy to climb the rounded grassy hills and survey the environs. From high points here one can see far up and down the coast. The sea, as elsewhere in the tropics, is of the most vivid blue, its surface marked by occasional reefs and native fishing craft. Down below, the grassy slopes and stunted eucalypts fall away to a shoreline of rounded knolls and palm-fringed beaches, with thick clumps of mangroves in some of the sheltered inlets. Far down the coast, distant bays are shimmering mirrors in the strong tropical sunlight.

One of the interesting features of these coastal hills is the presence of strips of dark green vegetation just below their crests and in the steep creekbeds on their seaward sides. These are known as mist scrubs and are composed of a relatively few, hardy species of jungle trees and shrubs. They owe their existence to the mists that roll in from the sea and up the slopes. As these mists reach the top, they are rapidly dispersed by the hot air of the plateau. Hanging on the seaward side, they form a protective blanket and deposit moisture to supplement the rain squalls.

BUTCHERBIRDS, PIED WRENS, AND MANUCODES

A day's "bird walk" through the savanna-covered hillsides provides a most interesting introduction to this area where Australia and New Guinea meet. The first half-dozen species that one encounters here also occur along the northern fringe of Australia. Yellow-tinted honeyeaters *(Meliphaga flavescens)* hunt for scale insects around the outer leaves of the eucalypts. The raucous cries of a group of blue-winged kookaburras *(Dacelo leachi)* issue from a clump of trees. Periodically a black-and-white butcherbird *(Cracticus mentalis)* utters snatches of song from a treetop, or flashes past in hot pursuit of a small bird. Groups of white-breasted wood swallows *(Artamus leucopterus)* perch on an exposed limb, or hawk and flutter over an open clearing. Little doves *(Geopelia striata)* utter their familiar "doodle-doo" cries. There is an occasional wagtail *(Rhipidura leucophrys)*, rainbow lorikeet *(Trichoglossus moluccanus)*, and short-tailed parrot *(Geoffroyus geoffroyi)*.

Other species are quite distinctive, though they may be counterparts of familiar Australian species. The little flycatcher *(Microeca leucophaea)* behaves much like the familiar jacky winter, but it is grayer and more often silent. Crows *(Corvus macrorhynchus)*, common here as in most places, have quite different calls. The oriole *(Oriolus szayali)* is heavily striped ventrally but brown above—a very plain bird after the green-backed or yellow Australian species. The

Low-lying coastal plain of northern New Guinea near Alexishaven, west of Madang. (Derek Duparcq)

234

The blue bird-of-paradise (Paradisea rudolphi) *hangs head downward when displaying its feathers. (Alan Root: Okapia)*

Macleay kingfisher *(Halcyon macleayi),* a beautiful deep blue, differs in having a large white "panel" in the wing, a marking so prominent that in flight it looks a little like a large butterfly. Taxonomists consider it a separate race, *elizabethae.* But probably the most interesting New Guinea member of the savanna avifauna is the little pied wren *(Malurus alboscapulatus).* These wrens are an Australian group and are noteworthy for the brilliant and diverse coloring of the males. In some species they are liberally endowed with blue, in others turquoise, orange-red, or a combination of these colors. The females, by contrast, are brown. I had always wanted to see the New Guinea species because it brought a different color combination to the group, black-and-white, and the females were colored like the males. Only a small, insular derivative of the blue-and-white wren on Dirk Hartog Island off Western Australia, *Malurus leu-*

copterus, has a color pattern approaching that of the New Guinea birds, and "male-colored females" are otherwise unknown. The pied wrens were found to be quite common in areas of grassy thicket in the dry creekbeds about Port Moresby, as well as elsewhere in New Guinea. In behavior they proved to be quite like the Australian species, having the same twittering calls, and the habit of feeding in shrubbery and on the ground. Their tails, however, were noticeably shorter.

Up in the mist pockets and associated shrubbery of the hilltops adjacent to the sea, the swamp pheasant *(Centropus phasianinus),* a large, long-tailed brown cuckoo that has the "unusual" (for a cuckoo) habit of constructing its own nest and incubating its own eggs, was common. Its call is a succession of bubbling notes that resembles the water running out of a bottle. It fed in the thickets and in open places near to tall grass.

The fawn-breasted bowerbird *(Chlamydera cerviniventris)* also inhabited this area and built its double-walled bowers here. This brown-spotted species is the plainest of its tribe. There were also small flocks of brown-colored finches *(Lonchura caniceps)* with gray heads and yellow rumps, and sunbirds. Where the undergrowth gave way, as in the creekbeds, to dark-green mist forest, there proved to be a "mystery" bird; at least that was how I first thought of the owner of a piercing whistle that came echoing up the slopes. Despite much cautious stalking, several trips had to be made to the area before the bird was finally sighted; it proved to be a manucode *(Manucodia ater),* one of the less spectacular members of the bird-of-paradise family, a little smaller than a crow, sheeny black, with a bright red eye and somewhat long tail.

CRABS, MANGROVES, AND RAIN FORESTS

A few miles to the east of Port Moresby is an abandoned airfield, Jackson Strip, from which fighter planes used to operate. The field lay on a piece of level ground between a mist-scrub scarp and the mangrove-fringed shoreline. Within a few months of its closure the vegetation began to crowd its fringes, and rank grass pushed up through its runways. And so the bleating calls of the little yellowish-brown cisticolas *(Cisticola exilis)* replaced the whine of the plane engines, and the little tree martins *(Hylochelidon nigricans),* returning to their northern wintering grounds, found the air space over the drome the ideal place to hawk mosquitoes and other insects breeding in the nearby mangrove swamp.

The shoreline here was a mixture of sand and mud and it swarmed with small crabs. Interestingly, three very different kinds of birds had chosen the same spot to feed on the crabs: the migratory sacred kingfisher *(Halcyon sancta)* from Australia, the gray-tailed tattler *(Tringa brevipes),* a gray-bodied, long-billed, long-legged water bird that breeds in the Arctic, and the mangrove heron *(Butorides striata),* a resident species. The kingfishers, greenish-blue above and yellowish on the underside, chose dead stumps and exposed mangrove

A serpentine river valley in the rugged New Guinea highlands. Many of these streams are gold-bearing. (Paul Popper Ltd.)

branches as lookout points, dropping suddenly down onto the mud when an unwary crab exposed itself. The tattlers fed in a loose flock, the birds dispersed over the open places. They ran down their crabs, seized them by the nippers (chelae) or by the legs, and shook them until the body flew off. The maimed crabs were then grasped by another appendage and the operation repeated. The site was littered with the chelae and legs of crabs, the birds having removed most of the hard appendages before swallowing their prey. The somber-plumaged mangrove herons, too, had their special hunting pattern: they would crouch in the shade of a mangrove and make sudden forays among the crabs, seizing them with a stabbing action of the long, dagger-shaped bill.

The mangrove swamps of southern New Guinea closely resemble those of northern Australia and, as would be expected from their proximity, many of the animal species are the same. Near Port Moresby the mangroves are rather stunted and open, in contrast to other places where they form a dense forest. Nevertheless, two species of honeyeater, the varied honeyeater (Meliphaga versicolor), a medium-sized, brown species with a yellowish ear-patch and wash to the breast, and the smaller, dusky honeyeater, Myzomela obscura, kept strictly to them.

The Laloki River, a small, swift-flowing stream, bursts out of the mountains some twenty miles inland from Port Moresby, follows a turbulent course down a deeply notched valley and then plunges over the two-hundred-foot-high Rona Falls. The country here is precipitous and rugged. The near wall of the valley is a series of steep grassy slopes to which sundry undergrowth and twisted eucalypts cling; the far wall is Hombrom Bluff, a spur of the range. The road up to the rubber plantations at Koitaki follows the top of the ridge, providing a series of splendid vistas.

The bird life of the area is very rich. The most interesting spectacle by far was the erratic, batlike flights of the little glossy swiftlets (Collocalia esculenta) over the gorges. So brilliantly did the plumage of these birds shine in the sunlight that it often appeared more blue than black. Coucals and cisticolas called continuously from the undergrowth, and there seemed to be a continual progression of Papuan cuckoo shrikes (Coracina papuensis), butcherbirds, crows, blue-winged kookaburras, honeyeaters, and lemon-breasted flycatchers (Microeca flavigaster) up and down the slopes. From time to time a flock of white cockatoos (Cacatua galerita) flew over, screeching loudly.

Beyond Rona Falls the road climbs into the rain forest belt near Sogeri, in the foothills of the Astralobe Range. A series of rubber plantations have been carved out here by the Koitaki Rubber Company. The traveler now finds himself in the true New Guinea zone, and most of the Australian species among the birds drop out. The air rings with the loud, melodious calls of the Papuan mynahs (Mino dumontii), little green fruit pigeons (Ptilinopus) dash from treetop to treetop, and the large Papuan hornbill (Rhyticeros plicatus) flies over on loud wings. The kingfishers are quite different from those of the open savanna. There is a large chestnut-breasted species with a blue-and-black back (Sauromarptis gaudichaud) that squats on the shadowy branches near the ground, waiting for a lizard to show itself. From time to time the long-tailed kingfisher (Tanysiptera sylvia), a blue-backed, yellow-breasted, red-billed bird with long, streaming white tail feathers, comes floating through the forest. On a high treetop one sees a red-sided or eclectus parrot (Lorius roratus), a large, heavy-bodied, short-tailed species in which the male is brilliant green with a red patch on the side of the body, and the female is red and blue. Disturbed, it flies off, loudly protesting the intrusion. The dense jungle is not a good place to observe small birds, most of which appear only as silhouettes high in the foliage. A few cuckoos, like the little golden bronze species (Chalcites malayanus) and the brush cuckoo (Cacomantis variolosus), are identifiable from their distinctive calls; but most of the species go unrecognized. With its dense canopy, epiphytes, lianas, high humidity, brilliantly colored birds, the rain forest is a vastly different environment from the open savanna country.

GECKOS AND DEADLY TAIPANS

Reptiles abound in the tropics and New Guinea is no exception in this respect. A diversity of small lizards, mostly swift-running, shiny-skinned skinks, inhabit the savanna country, fleeing from under a visitor's feet as he walks along a path. If he remains still, they will come out of hiding and hunt for flies close by. In army days many a bored soldier took to killing flies for the small lizards that came around his tent; the reptiles learned to appreciate the service and even became quite tame. The most entertaining were the little nocturnal geckos. These took up their abode in the mess huts and other buildings and emerged from their hiding places at night to hunt the mosquitoes and moths that alighted on walls and ceilings. Geckos are able to move across the ceiling, hanging upside down. They would lose their footing only when they tried leaping for a moth that was too large for them; then both gecko and prey would land unceremoniously on the floor, a bed, or a writing table. Once during an army church service one evening in Port Moresby, I watched no fewer than eight small geckos stalking a large moth on the wooden ceiling with a skill that puts a cat to shame. After an initial rush, it is a step forward, a pause, a gentle swaying of the body in anticipation of the next move, another step, and so on. First one of the eight would draw a little closer than the others, then another would take the lead. Obviously the lizards were now aware of each other. Added to the strain of stalking was the desire to reach the prey first. Finally, three or four of the hunters drew to within a few feet of the moth, directly over the pulpit. The next move was too quick for the eye but suddenly geckos showered down over the padre. Sermons to troops were normally rather brief but this was the briefest of all; the minister uttered a few quick sentences and fled.

Snakes are common here but almost all are small, harmless species. Invariably they beat a hasty retreat to long grass or thick undergrowth. They are for the most part reminiscent of those that occur in Australia: for example, the brown tree snake (Boiga irreguloides), a five-foot-long species with large head and prominent eyes. This snake lives mainly in bushes and small trees, which it climbs with ease. Boiga is one of the back-fanged group and, though it has venom, it would have only a limited effect on a human being. The Colubridae also includes water snakes, and these are more numerous

Grasslands and cycads, with patches of rain forest in the background, at Murray Pass, Wharton. (H. G. Cogger)

in New Guinea than in Australia. The front-fanged poisonous snakes of Australia (Elapidae) are represented by two particularly dangerous species, the death adder *(Acanthophis antarcticum)* and the taipan *(Oxyuranus scutellatus).* The death adders, repulsive looking reptiles, have broad, flat heads, and narrow necks; the short, stumpy body narrows rapidly to a very thin and yellowish tail. They lie flat on the ground in open places where their blotched grayish or brownish coloring resembles dry leaves. Their method of hunting includes attracting prey within striking range by a wormlike wriggling of the tip of the tail. It is estimated that the contents of a death adder venom gland is sufficient to kill eighty-four sheep. The taipan is undoubtedly one of the truly deadly snakes, for it is large, reaching eleven feet in length, has fangs measuring half an inch, and has a venom content in its glands of up to four hundred milligrams. This is estimated to be equal to two hundred lethal doses for human beings. The death rate from taipans in Queensland, where most of the bites have been recorded, stands at about 50 per cent. Fortunately, an antivenin has now been developed. The taipan is rare and very timid and so is seldom seen. Unlike the death adder, which gives birth to live young, the taipan lays eggs, about twelve to fifteen at one time.

PYTHONS, TURTLES, AND CROCODILES

New Guinea has its share of pythons, especially in the rain forest. The largest is the amethystine python *(Python amethystinus),* which may exceed twenty feet in length and is capable of swallowing a wallaby or tree kangaroo. Most ground-dwelling jungle reptiles are blackish or brownish, colors that merge with the heavy shadows, though there are tree-dwelling skinks (Scincidae), dragon lizards (Agamidae), and goannas (Varanidae) that are green. The bright green python of New Guinea *(Chondropython viridis)* is common in many places. Juvenile specimens are bright yellow. The coloring of the jungle reptiles thus differs from the subdued reds and pale browns of those of the Australian desert.

The fresh-water tortoises of New Guinea belong, with one exception, to the same family as the Australian species, the Chelidae. They fall into short-necked species *(Emydura),* widely known from the south and north, and long-necked tortoises *(Chelodina).* The exception is a very curious turtle known as *Carettochelys insculpta,* or the pitted-shelled turtle. In this species, though a bony carapace and plastron are present, a leathery skin replaces the horny shields. The feet are paddle-shaped and the nose ends in a short trunk. These turtles, which can often be seen sunning themselves on the surface of rivers such as the Fly, are of particular interest because biologists regard them as a link between the soft-shelled and the hard-shelled turtles.

Crocodiles abound in New Guinea waters. There are two species, the sea-going estuarine crocodile *(Crocodilus porosus),* which reaches a length of twenty feet, and the fresh-water New Guinea crocodile *(C. novae-guineae),* reaching 12–14 feet. The estuarine crocodiles lurk in muddy rivers along the coast and seize a few human beings each year. Even along the Laloki River, close to Port Moresby, it has long been regarded as a hazard to try to raise cattle and horses because of them.

THE NORTH COAST

Most travelers today reach the north coast by air from Port Moresby. The plane climbs to perhaps twelve thousand feet to traverse the Owen Stanley Range in the vicinity of Kokoda. Nine days out of ten the mountains are covered with fog, but occasionally the clouds clear and reveal the majesty of the peaks, precipices, and steep, wooded hillsides below. Once across, the plane drops low over the coast to follow the green headlands and white, palm-fringed beaches to the seaside airport at Lae.

The rainy seasons at Port Moresby and Lae come at almost opposite periods of the year, the mountainous backbone of the island providing an effective barrier to the passage of rain-filled clouds. I had the experience of coming from the dry season at Port Moresby to the "wet" at Lae. Mud and slush lay inches deep everywhere, gutters were torrents of running water after each shower, and the little rivers draining the coastal lowlands were impassable. Lae has an oppressively humid climate and a tropical lushness. Rain forest crowds to the edges of the town. Bananas and papayas, red hibiscus, the introduced frangipani and other flowering shrubs grow riotously. All the birds at Lae are of the rain forest, and they include many species that do not occur near Koitaki, on the south side of the range. Most prominent are a beautiful little black sunbird with flashes of pale blue on the shoulder and cap *(Cinnyris sericea),* the little black-and-white, frill-necked flycatcher *(Arses telescopthalmus),* the little brown warbler *(Gerygone magnirostris),* which builds bulky nests in trees along the streams, and the lesser bird of paradise *(Paradisea minor).* The last-named, rare near the coast, has magnificent plumes ranging from creamy gold to daffodil yellow, and a yellow-green head and throat.

Twenty miles inland from Lae is a vast plain of kunai grass that resembles a dense rush and grows six feet high. The road out to Nadzab runs through the tall rain forests, an area very rich in colorful butterflies. Giant blue-winged insects dance their way along the edges of the forest canopy. Medium-sized yellow, brown, and white butterflies with great bull's-eyes on their wings flutter in and out of the shadows. There are black species with red flashes on the wings, green ones with black tips, orange-colored varieties, brilliant yellow ones, and others that, when they alight, look like fallen leaves. Some hover, others dart, or follow a swift, erratic path that seems to take them nowhere at all. The air is shrill with the stridulations of tree crickets, the chirruping of little green grasshoppers, and the loud buzz of cicadas. Flocks of shining starlings *(Aplonis metallica)* call melodiously as they sweep overhead. Papuan mynahs chortle, little warblers twitter, and parrots screech.

Right above: Where the Laloki River bursts from the Astralobe Range onto the coastal lowlands near Port Moresby it forms the spectacular Rouna Falls. Dense jungle crowds the valley floor but the tops and sides of hills are savanna. (H. G. Cogger) Right: The New Guinea crowned pigeon (Goura victoria), the size of a fowl, mounts a striking crest. It inhabits the mountain rain forest. (Alan Root: Okapia) Far right: The male lesser bird-of-paradise (Paradisea minor) flaunts its magnificent plumes during one of its frequent displays. (Alan Root: Okapia)

A spotted cuscus (Phalanger maculatus), *one of the commoner New Guinea species of this arboreal family. (Paul Popper Ltd.)*

The plane journey to Madang, the next important town to the west, is up the wide valley of the Markham River. This great muddy stream, which enters the sea near Lae, takes a twisted route through the kunai and swamplands. The plane flies so low that the precipitous mountains on both sides of the valley tower above it. In half an hour the plane sweeps into the valley of the Ramu and follows it almost to the sea before turning north to Madang. The low valleys of the Markham and the Ramu rivers are of considerable significance to plant and animal life of New Guinea, for they form an almost impassable barrier between the mountain blocks to the north and south.

SAGO SWAMPS, BLACK SANDS, AND SUGAR GLIDERS

Madang, set among coconut plantations, with a series of small scrub- and palm-covered islands offshore, is one of the more delightful parts of New Guinea. It is separated from Lae by the Huon Peninsula, whose backbone of peaks rises ten thousand feet or more. Running in an east-west line, the mountains are also a rainfall barrier so that here, too, the wet seasons are in part reversed. It is a joy to enter a dry area and be free of the overpowering humidity.

As along much of the north coast, there are areas of sago swamp close to Madang. Sago and nipa palms grow under conditions not unlike those that surround mangroves, except that the water must be fresh. They form a picture of complete disarray, with both large and small plants, fronds that are erect and others that fall back into the mud, and trunks that are straight, twisted, bowed, or toppled over. The air is completely still, so heavy that breathing seems difficult, and it is alive with the humming of clouds of mosquitoes. I tried using a mosquito net over my head but so many alighted on

it that my vision was cut off. Besides, it took maximum concentration to distinguish the birds in the deep shade. A few hours under these intolerable conditions revealed several ornithological gems: the shining flycatcher *(Monarcha alecto)*, of which the male is a shining blue-black and the female chestnut-brown above and white below, a large sooty-colored owl with distinctive facial disc *(Tyto tenebrosa)*, and a beautiful black-and-gold starling *(Melanopyrrhus anais)*.

At several points on Astrolabe Bay are beaches of black sand, relics of former volcanic activity. One of these is at the mouth of the Gum River and it proved to be the gathering place of small groups of common sandpipers *(Tringa hypoleucas)*, migratory visitors from the Arctic, and a few reef herons *(Demigretta sacra)*. One of the most beautiful islands along the New Guinea coast, Karkar, is just north of Madang. It is a perfect volcanic cone, six thousand feet high, but like the giant Finisterre Ranges that tower to the east, this peak is visible only on a mist-free day. Such days are rare, despite the almost continuous sunshine.

The coconut plantations of coastal New Guinea are the home of the attractive little gray gliding phalangers *(Petaurus breviceps)*. These emerge just at dusk to scamper up the palm trunks and undertake their long gliding flights. This species also ranges widely through the forests and woodlands of eastern and northern coastal Australia, indicating a versatility unusual for a phalanger.

These sugar gliders, as they are called, consume a wide variety of foods but prefer sweet substances, flower petals, and insects. Here they seemed to gain nourishment from the flowers of the coconuts. The gliding membrane is a flap of skin between the fore- and hindlimbs and is folded close to the body when the animal is scampering about the trees. In *Petaurus* the fourth finger of the forelimb extends somewhat beyond the others, apparently an adaptation for getting insects from crevices.

The heavy bombing that preceded the military occupation of Madang in 1944 was particularly devastating to the coconut palms, leaving acres of black, topless trunks riddled with shrapnel. The trunks were left standing, to decay in the course of time. With surprising promptness starlings *(Aplonis cantoroides)* appeared and commenced to nest in the shrapnel holes in the trunks. Some of the trunks soon had as many as eight pairs of birds occupying them, becoming veritable bird tenements. The starlings proved quite fearless, though they did take the precaution of nesting beyond human reach. This starling, which has dull black plumage and a relatively short tail, nests in hollow trees; as one walked through the area, the heads of the sitting birds would protrude from the holes to watch the observer. The beautiful glossy starlings *(A. metallica)* had a colony not far away, loading a huge tree with their bulky grass nests.

GREAT MOUNTAIN RANGES

New Guinea, fifteen hundred miles long and four hundred miles at the widest point, is dominated by its striking physiographic feature, the chain of mountain ranges called the central massif or cordillera. The chain runs the length of the island and reaches a height of fifteen thousand feet or more. One of the great mountain zones of the world, it is from 50 to 150 miles wide. The profile is irregular and jagged, with only a few passes as low as 5,500 feet. Precipices of 2,000 to 2,500 feet are common and on Mount Leonard Darwin, in western New Guinea, is the world's greatest precipice, with a drop estimated at 10,500 feet. The central massif dominates the watershed, dividing the island into northward and southward flowing patterns. At both the eastern and western ends of the island the cordillera dips into the sea, breaking into several series of high islands.

There are three other major physiographic features in New Guinea. These are the northern littoral or coastal region; the northern mountains; and a vast central intermontane trough, or central depression, occupied by the Markham, Ramu, Sepik, Idenburg, and Rauffer rivers. The trough isolates the northern mountains, with their plants and animals, from those in the center of the island. The main cordillera is a complex system of ranges, separated for the most part by broad, upland valleys. The result is that central New Guinea is made up of a series of isolated, or semi-isolated, "islands" of rain and montane forest, each with a number of unique botanical and zoological features. So many centers of evolution in a small mass are without parallel elsewhere in the world, which explains the spate of scientific expeditions to the New Guinea highlands in recent years.

As noted earlier, the highest mountains of New Guinea are permanently snow-capped, and there are a few small glaciers. At the height of Pleistocene glaciation, and probably until as recently as ten thousand years ago, glaciation was much more extensive. At that time the snow line was some 3,000 to 3,500 feet lower than at present and there is evidence that the glaciers reached down to 10,900 feet on Mount Wilhelm and 6,000 feet on Carstenz.

Physiographically New Guinea differs strikingly from Australia. The former is just as mountainous as the latter is flat. The reason for this is that stable Australia did not experience such a great Pliocene–Pleistocene era of mountain building. While the basement of both the northern mountains and the main cordillera of New Guinea is composed of relatively ancient, complex rocks, only in the western parts are there strata approaching the age of Australia's western shield. It is interesting to note, moreover, that parts of the New Guinea coastline represent seabed elevated as recently as one or two million years ago, some of the fossils being similar to those occurring offshore today.

A characteristic feature of all large mountainous areas is the layering or zonation of plants and animals with altitude. This has been the subject of much study in the case of the Rockies and Andes. Space here does not permit a detailed discussion of the subject in relation to New Guinea but, broadly speaking, major vegetation types and their distributions are as follows: rain forest, sea level to 7,900 feet; Antarctic beech *(Nothofagus)* forests, 2,800 to 10,200 feet; montane forests, in which the trunks of the trees are covered with bryophytes and hanging plants reminiscent of Spanish moss, 4,900 to 10,500 feet; subalpine forest, 9,800 to 13,300 feet; while there is a mid-mountain grassland zone between 3,000 and 6,000 feet, and alpine grasslands start at 10,000 feet. It is apparent that these vegetation zones are not strictly layered but overlap to a considerable extent.

The mountain forests of New Guinea are quite different from anything in Australia, for oaks *(Quercus)* and rhododendrons grow here, both predominantly northern-hemisphere plants, and giant pines like *Araucaria klinkii* and *A. cun-*

ninghamii occur. Rhododendrons are splendidly developed, no fewer than forty-eight species having been described, and included in them is a range of magnificent white-, orange-, and red-flowering shrubs. Only one rhododendron gets to Australia, occurring on Cape York.

Austin Rand of the Chicago Natural History Museum, E. Thomas Gilliard and others, have made a study of bird distribution relative to altitude in New Guinea. They found that there is a sharp changeover from lowland to mountain species at between 4,500 and 5,000 feet. Included in the new species that appear are birds of paradise, flycatchers and honeyeaters. A few kinds of New Guinea birds are confined to very high country, that is, eight thousand feet and over.

BIRDS OF PARADISE

New Guinea is the home of a group of forty species of birds that, in their beauty of color, ornate plumes, and bizarre displays, are without rival in the bird world. The first bird-of-paradise plumes to reach Europe were brought by El Cano, the captain who took command after Magellan had been killed in the Philippines in 1522; it was a gift from a Moluccan king to the King of Spain. Because many of the early skins were without feet and wings, fanciful accounts followed of how the birds flew continuously into the sun, and were found only when they fell to earth dead. Since their beauty surpassed that of all other birds, they came to be known as birds of paradise.

The group includes birds not much larger than a sparrow and others the size of a dove. The colors of the various species cover the full range of the spectrum. Many are black but the feathers are highly iridescent so that in bright light the plumage of parts of the body is shot with purple, green, and blue. Others are predominantly blue, red, orange, or yellow. The diversity of structure in the display plumes is amazing. In several of the best-known species *(Paradisea)* there is a long tuft of lacy plumes on the flanks. These are elevated during display. In others special breast and back feathers form aprons and capes, or else the special feathering drapes over the back in lacelike cascades. In the ribbontails *(Astrapia)*, long white feathers extend far beyond the limits of the body; in the little king bird *(Cincinnurus)* a pair of long, curved tail wires are tipped with iridescent medallions of intricately twisted feathers. The King of Saxony bird of paradise *(Pteridophora alberti)*, seven inches long, has crown plumes eighteen inches in length. In Wallace's standard-wing *(Semioptera wallacei)* of the Moluccas two sets of long, white, ribbonlike plumes grow from the bend in the wing. Other species still have colored fleshy caruncles or, during display, open their mouths to reveal jade- and opal-colored surfaces.

Among the most striking species is the blue bird of paradise *(Paradisea rudolphi)*, a black and bright-blue bird with a white eye-ring. When displaying, it hangs from a branch head down, with the pale-blue flank plumes flexed so that they fall in cascades. The lesser bird of paradise *(P. minor)* has a yellow crown, green throat, brown breast, and yellow and white flank plumes. In the Raggiana bird *(P. raggiana)* the flank plumes range from red to pale orange. The little king bird *(Cincinnurus regius)* is a vivid scarlet above, white below, with gray, green-tipped flank plumes that can be opened as fans. The ribbontail *(Astrapia mayeri)* is a very

Above: The colorful Rhododendron aurigeranum *extends down to about 3,500 feet in the New Guinea highlands. It is one of 48 species in New Guinea, whereas Australia has only one species, emphasizing the great botanical difference between the two landmasses. (L. J. Brass)   Below: The green tree-python (Chondropython viridis), widespread in jungle areas, is quite harmless. (Hobart Van Deusen)   Right: A clump of Dendrochilum. The New Guinea rain and mountain forests are particularly rich in orchids. (L. J. Brass)*

Above: Typical Fiji beach at Korolevu. (J. M. Taylor)
Left: Cuscuses resemble monkeys but are much more sluggish. New Guinea is their home but species reach the Celebes, New Britain, the Solomons, and northeastern Australia. (Alan Root: Okapia)

A *tree-kangaroo* (Dendrolagus matschiei), *inhabiting the Huon Peninsula; these arboreal species have longer forelimbs than other kangaroos. (Derek Duparcq)*

beautiful black-velvet color. Its white tail plumes are three feet long, three times the body length. It was originally given its name on the basis of the tail plumes only, an entire specimen not being known until 1939.

All the more brilliantly attired birds of paradise are polygamous and, as Thomas Gilliard has said, represent a new departure in evolution in that the emphasis is on polygamy and the development of ever more brilliant plumes and bizarre postures on the part of the males. The females, which remain plain-colored, are attracted to the displaying males and select the one with which they wish to mate. The successful male is, hence, the one that can achieve the maximum stimulation of the female. Thereafter the female retires to carry out all the reproductive duties on her own, the construction of the untidy stick nest, laying and incubation of the single egg, and the raising of the young. The replacement of the pair bond by this kind of social behavior has arisen independently in several groups of birds, including the South American cock of the rock *(Rupicola rupicola)* and the North American prairie chicken *(Tympanuchus cupido)*.

RELATIONSHIPS TO OTHER AREAS

A mixture of true endemic species and relatively recent colonizers from Australia characterizes the New Guinea mammal fauna. Thus, there are twelve small carnivores (Dasyuridae), nine bandicoots (Peramelidae), twenty-two phalangers (Phalangeridae), and fourteen kangaroos (Macropodidae), to give a total marsupial fauna of fifty-seven species. Of these the cuscuses and the tree kangaroos as well as the striped possums *(Dactylopsila* and *Dactylonax)* presumably evolved in New Guinea. Their occurrence in the rain forests of north Queensland is purely incidental. Of the carnivores one is a spotted native cat *(Satanellus albopunctatus),* which also occurs in northern Australia, and of the marsupial "mice," four belong to the continental genera *Planigale, Sminthopsis,* and *Antechinus.* The others are in general confined to New Guinea. The New Guinea mammal fauna also includes the short-beaked echidna *(Tachyglossus aculeatus)* and three species of long-billed echidna *(Zaglossus)* that are largely highland dwellers. The platypus does not reach New Guinea.

The indigenous placental mammals of New Guinea, like those of Australia, are all either bats or rodents, though there is also a feral pig and a small wild dog, descendants of animals introduced by early man. Giant fruit bats or flying foxes (Pteropidae) are a feature of the tropical lowlands, their large, flapping wings and harsh chatter enlivening evening in the jungle. The rat fauna includes some very interesting and distinctive giant species. A few of these, along with marsupials like the phalanger *Pseudocheirus cuprinus,* occur in the high montane forests and grasslands.

New Guinea presents several interesting problems to biologists. The plants, insects, and earthworms have strong affinities with the Oriental region, but the birds, tortoises, and mammals are distinctly Australian in character. In all groups, of course, there has been a tremendous development of new types on the island. One does not think of species or even of genera in making these generalizations, but rather of families or basic stocks. Broadly speaking, it may be said that it is the older groups (those that developed earlier on the planet) that have Asian affinities, and, at least in part, the newer ones, the birds and mammals, that have Australian affinities. Few authorities have attempted to explain this anomaly, but the plant geographer Ronald Good has offered the theory that Australia did not always lie so close to New Guinea as it does today. Dr. Good suggests that at some intermediate period the continent must have moved northward into the island archipelago.

In plant and animal life New Guinea is a phenomenally rich island. The number of land and fresh-water bird species, 568, is greater than that of Australia, which has only 531, despite the fact that the latter has ten times as much land mass. Included in this, as noted, are whole groups that occur nowhere else. Apart from the Paradiseidae, there are the cassowaries, incubator birds, giant crowned pigeons, the diminutive pigmy parrots, distinctive hawks, pigeons, and a tremendous diversity of small birds. The number of reptile and frog species is large. Insects are remarkably diverse and abundant. Apart from the natural richness of the tropical environment, New Guinea's biological splendor is undoubtedly explained by its great range of conditions and opportunities for life together with the many centers of evolution created by the numerous isolated mountain forest blocks.

MAN AS AN ECOLOGICAL FACTOR

Considering the island's size, the human population of New Guinea is not large. Its two million people occupy a land area six times the size of Java and twice that of the Japanese archipelago. The reason is, of course, the basic inhospitality of much of the island. Judging from the radio-carbon studies of cave remains in Borneo and elsewhere, man has probably been in New Guinea for twenty to thirty thousand years. The presence of several ethnic groups (pigmy Negritos occur in some of the remote areas) and a considerable number of languages and dialects indicates a long history of colonizations, incursions, and blendings by man. Viewed at any level, the impact of man on the New Guinea landscape has been prolonged.

As noted, man introduced the pig and the dog, and many of these are now feral. The greatest impact, however, is being felt in densely settled parts of the highlands. The Melanesian's characteristic method of agriculture is to fell virgin forest, grow crops—mostly sweet potatoes—for a few years, then abandon the worked-out plot and start afresh in a new area. Under normal conditions forest regeneration is relatively quick and effective, the secondary growth, over a period of perhaps seventy years, producing giant stands. Under conditions of dense settlement, the demand for firewood gives the forest no chance to recover. Hence, in places like the Wahgi valley in the central highlands the forest is being pressed back so resolutely that grasslands now extend to as high as seven thousand feet. These changes in habitat are undoubtedly having a drastic effect on plant and animal species that occur only in the middle altitudes.

The Melanesian is a hunter, and tree kangaroos, cuscuses, possums, cassowaries, snakes, and fish, form an additional part of his diet. He is also fond of bright colors and the making of elaborate ceremonial headdresses. The effort that goes into the hunting in this connection is only slightly if any less than that expended on food. Chief items of importance are the feathers of the birds of paradise and parrots, and the skins and tails of small mammals such as the striped possum. Hunters will spend days at a time stalking these animals. No species is in imminent danger of extinction. The introduction of money, however, now makes it possible for the natives of settled areas to buy birds of paradise from the inhabitants of remote areas where the birds, hitherto, have been protected. Authorities are worried about the long-term effect of this. Only half a century ago birds of paradise were slaughtered in thousands for the European millinery trade, and it was not until 1921 that this wanton killing was outlawed.

The elaborately decorated bower of the short-crested Gardener bowerbird (Amblyornis subalaris) *at two thousand feet in the tropical jungle of the Owen Stanley Range. The ornaments include red and green flowers and fruits, blue beetles, yellow star-shaped flowers, and bluish snail shells. (Heinz Sielmann)*

The long-beaked echidna (Zaglossus), a large species in which the spines are largely hidden in fur, mainly inhabits the mountain areas. (Christa Armstrong: Rapho-Guillumette)

THE BISMARCK ARCHIPELAGO AND THE SOLOMONS

Northward from New Guinea is the narrow crescent-shaped island of New Britain, 370 miles long and 50 miles broad, and beyond, at right angles to it, two hundred miles long and an average of seven miles wide, is New Ireland. The land areas of the two are 14,600 and 3,600 square miles respectively. Together with the Admiralty Islands to the east (eight hundred square miles), these make up the Bismarck Archipelago, a northern extension of Melanesia. New Britain has a backbone of high and rugged mountains, the highest peak being The Father, an active volcano 7,500 feet high.

Earthquakes and volcanic eruptions are very much a feature of New Britain. The town of Rebaul, at the northern end of the island, is surrounded by active craters. On May 28,

1937, two eruptions occurred at once, on Matupi Island and Vulcan Island, the latter an island that appeared in the bay in 1878 during an earlier upheaval. Rabaul was all but destroyed by the pumice and ash, and two hundred people were killed. At the end of the eruption Vulcan Island, formerly flat, was a cone five hundred feet high.

Its vast areas of rain forest between the sea and the foothills give New Britain a superficial resemblance to the lowlands of New Guinea. It has, however, a much poorer fauna. The only marsupials are a bandicoot, a phalanger, and a scrub wallaby; five species of large fruit bat, some fourteen smaller species, and nine rodents have also been recorded on the island. Birds of paradise have been unable to cross the ocean gap between New Guinea and New Britain. The island backbone has always been difficult of access. That it can still reveal new animal species was shown a few years ago when Dr. Thomas Gilliard discovered two unrecorded birds there.

The writer spent ten months on New Britain in 1945–1946, much of it around Jacquinot Bay on the east coast. The area is one of coconut plantations, with small, delightful coral reefs offshore and dense tropical rain forests inland. A series of small but attractive streams enter the bay, some clear and swift-running, others sluggish, muddy, and the haunts of crocodiles. Road-building excavation of the low hills on the south side of the bay have shown them to be composed of coral fragments, indicating that this whole section was, in the not too remote past, uplifted from the sea.

At the time of our arrival, the plantations had been abandoned for some years and were overgrown with saplings, creepers, and rank grass. They were a haven for a wide range of insect and reptile life. Attracted by the light, hundreds of insects would come flying into the tents at night; large moths, cicadas, grasshoppers, stick insects, lacewings, and myriads of beetles, midges, and mosquitoes. Outside, the air was shrill with the piping of the tree crickets, punctuated by the periodic "chop-chop-chop" of the large-tailed nightjar. When it became known that the writer was collecting material for the Australian Museum of Sydney, he found himself deluged with "gifts" of all kinds. Many of these were snakes in various stages of dismemberment, but one batch included a blind snake *(Typhlops)* that proved to be an undescribed species. The most primitive of their tribe, blind snakes resemble overgrown worms, are subterranean, and apparently subsist largely on termites and other forms of life. In due course I found that the museum's herpetologist, Roy Kinghorn, had named the snake *T. keasti*. Not everybody can claim to have had one of the "lowest" snakes in the world named after him.

The rain forests of Jacquinot Bay yielded a total of about ninety bird species: cassowaries, incubator birds, shining starlings, crested hawks, coconut lories, red-sided parrots, pigmy parrots, cuckoo shrikes, cuckoos, hornbills, flycatchers, and some six species of pigeon. The streams were frequented by two very delightful little kingfishers, both with azure backs. One had a white breast *(Alcyone pusilla)* and the other an orange-colored breast *(A. azurea).*

The Solomon Islands, two hundred miles east of New Britain, are a chain of a dozen large islands that extend over nine hundred miles of ocean. The largest of them, Guadalcanal, has an area of two thousand five hundred square miles. In their high rainfall, mountains, and dense jungles, they resemble New Guinea and the Bismarcks. Though richly endowed with birds, it is apparent that mammals have had difficulty in reaching them, for only thirty species occur: seventeen bats, twelve rodents, and a phalanger.

NEW CALEDONIA AND THE NEW HEBRIDES

New Caledonia, seven hundred miles off the Queensland coast, 248 miles long by 31 wide, is one of the largest islands in the Pacific, having an area of 6,223 square miles. It bears a close resemblance to Australia, large areas being covered by green hills of grass, stunted shrubbery, and white-trunked paperbarks or melaleucas *(Melaleuca leucadendron),* known locally as gum trees. There are, however, no native eucalypts. Ranges rising to a maximum of something over

five thousand feet lend a backbone to the island and provide the conditions for extensive rain forest. *Nothofagus,* the Antarctic beech, occurs in the higher regions, and among the shrubs are several with large red flowerheads similar to those of the Australian grevilleas and callistemons.

Sixty-eight native land and fresh-water birds occur on New Caledonia. Several of these, such as a yellow robin, an owlet nightjar, a bustard quail, the little scarlet honeyeater *(Myzomela dibapha),* and the white-eye *(Zosterops lateralis),* must have colonized the island directly from Australia, since they do not occur in New Guinea. The bird life is fairly well balanced, including several herons, ducks, hawks, rails, pigeons and doves, parrots, cuckoos, warblers, flycatchers, and honeyeaters. Two of the pigeons impressed me particularly, the bright-green cloven-feathered dove *(Drepanoptila holosericea),* which is eleven inches long, and the large, long-tailed giant pigeon *(Ducula goliath).* The latter, twenty inches long, is slate gray on the back, chestnut on the abdomen, red on the bill and feet.

The most interesting bird of New Caledonia is the kagu *(Rhynochetos jubatus),* a forest-dwelling, bitternlike bird so distinct that a special family has been created for it, the Rhynochetidae. Kagus are twenty-two to twenty-three inches long and are ash-gray above, washed with brownish on the back and wings. The underparts are pale buff. The beak and feet are orange-red and the iris red. When the bird is annoyed or harassed it spreads its wings, which reveals that they are strikingly marked with broad black, white, and chestnut bars, a pattern reminiscent of the South American sun bitterns. Kagus keep to the dense forest; their soft, barking cries are heard mostly at dusk or dawn. They feed on snails and worms, mainly at night. They lay a single egg on the ground. The opening up of the forest is the greatest danger faced by the kagus, for they are then exposed to the native dogs.

The New Hebrides, to the east of New Caledonia, consist of about eighty islands, some of them containing volcanoes, in a double chain. The largest island is Santo, with an area of fifteen hundred square miles. Fifty-four species of native land and fresh-water birds have been described from the group. Like New Caledonia, however, these islands lack mammals and frogs.

THE FIJI ISLANDS

Fiji lies about 1,500 miles northeast of Australia and 1,100 from New Zealand. There are two major islands, Viti Levu, 4,011 square miles, and Vanua Levu, 2,137 square miles, plus about 320 small ones, some of them atolls. The larger islands are true continental remnants, with cores of red sandstone and quartzite, shale, and granular limestone. Viti Levu has a maximum elevation of 4,400 feet, and Vanua Levu, 3,500 feet. There are many old volcanoes on these islands. The coastline is deeply indented in places, and many small rivers run down to the sea. Renowned for their scenic diversity and the blueness of the surrounding seas, the islands are among the most beautiful in the south Pacific.

The vertebrate fauna of Fiji consists of two species of frog—this is the most remote point reached by amphibians in the Pacific; four snakes (a blind snake, two boas, and a poisonous member of the Elapidae); and various lizards, including a little dragon lizard (Agamidae) and many small,

shiny-bodied, swift-running skinks. The most interesting of the lizards is an iguanid *(Brachylophus)* that has relatives in the West Indies and the Galapagos.

Just how an iguanid lizard got to Fiji is a major enigma. We do know, of course, that the group formerly had a much wider range, since fossils of it are found in Eocene rocks, thirty-five million years old, in Europe. Outside of the Americas, where they are extremely common, iguanid lizards survive on Madagascar.

Sixty-seven species of land and fresh-water birds have been recorded from Fiji. The islands have developed their own species of goshawk, incubator bird, and rail, several doves, a few species of parrot, and several flycatchers and honey-eaters. One of the little fruit doves has a beautiful orange color, and one of the most fascinating birds is the little silktail *(Lamprolia victoriae),* which resembles a miniature bird of paradise, with black coloring, the top of the head a glossy green blue, the tail white, and the back and wings a velvety texture. Little is known of its habits beyond that it is an inhabitant of the undergrowth of the mountain forests, feeding small insects among the vines and on the ground.

THE PUZZLE OF LORD HOWE ISLAND

Although only a speck of land three hundred miles from Australia, Lord Howe merits attention because of its very interesting plant and animal life. The island is only seven miles long and half a mile across, and it has a lowland section of coral rock; its two great rounded mountains of lava reach heights of 2,500 and 2,800 feet. Normally it would simply be regarded as a volcanic island, but it has several forms of life that could hardly have been transported over the sea; hence certain biologists postulate that at some time in the past it must have had connections with New Zealand to the south and New Caledonia to the north. Broadly speaking, the plant and animal life of the island are a blend of elements from these two sources, together with Australia to the west. There are four species of palms peculiar to the island but no mammals, except for two bat species, no amphibians, and in the reptile category only three kinds of lizard. The number of native plant species is 209, about one-third of which are peculiar to the island. There are no gums or acacias. The indigenous land birds number fifteen species and include two pigeons, a woodhen, a gallinule, an owl, a parakeet, a kingfisher, three flycatchers, a robin, a crow shrike, and a shining starling. The gallinule was particularly interesting, being white. At least half of these species are now extinct, the result of predation by the descendants of rats that came ashore in 1918 when a vessel sank just off the coast. Rats now swarm over much of the island, so that conditions are very different from those described by early voyagers, who found the pigeons so tame that they could be knocked over with sticks. Apart from the endemic species of land birds, some fifteen other land species visit the island from time to time as wanderers. Lord Howe, and its offshore islands, have large colonies of sea birds.

On the top of Mount Gower, one of the twin peaks, is a plateau several acres in extent. It is usually shrouded in cloud and is very moist. Here is a dense "moss forest" of tree ferns, terrestrial ferns, rare palms, sedges, and mosses, a wonderful world of soft, green luxuriance. Its safeguard is its isolation: to visit this plateau one has to scale the high precipices from the sea. Here live the small animals whose distribution is such a puzzle: a little fresh-water crab, *Halicarcinus lacustris,* known elsewhere only from fresh-water streams on Norfolk Island and lakes in New Zealand and Victoria, and a little sand flea or amphipod, *Talitrus sylvaticus,* an inhabitant of moist debris. The latter occurs elsewhere only in Australia. In 1959, Dr. John Evans, Director of the Australian Museum, visited the site and collected some primitive bugs (Peloridiidae) that live in damp moss and are incapable of flight: these were sufficiently distinct from other known species to form a new genus, *Howeria.* This constituted a third case of a bewildering distribution. Such insects require very special conditions; their ancestors must certainly have been on Lord Howe for a very long period of time. When, however, it comes to explaining how they and the two crustaceans managed to reach isolated oceanic Lord Howe, the authorities can offer no other explanation than that either the tiny islet was once part of a continent or it lay close to one.

The overhanging cliffs at Ouvea on the southern extremity of the Loyalty Islands, adjacent to New Caledonia. (Noel Calé)

Land of the High Mists

New Zealand: The North Island

13

In his book, *The Coming of the Maori,* the famous Maori anthropologist Te Rani Hiroa, known to the outside world as Sir Peter Buck, gives a vivid account of the Polynesian myth of the origin of New Zealand. In it, Maui, the famed culture hero who snared the sun and forced it into its regular daily movement across the sky, decided, while lost in southern waters with his brothers, to try to catch fish for food, but he lacked a hook and bait. He produced the lower jaw of his grandmother, Murirangawhenua, smeared it with his own blood to add to its supernatural powers, tied it to the end of a line, and threw it overboard. Almost immediately he hooked a giant sting ray, so large that it stretched from horizon to horizon. It carried the canoe high into the air when it broke the surface. Thus did the four-cornered North Island of New Zealand, with its long tail of land extending to the northeast, come into existence. Maui directed his brothers not to eat the creature until he could bring some priests from Hawaiki, legendary home of the Polynesians, to divide it properly. The brothers, however, commenced to hack at the sting ray with their knives: this is why the island's surface today is so marked with valleys and mountain ranges.

The South Island, a long, rounded rectangle, is not explained in such a clear-cut way. Many tribes believe, however, that it had its origin as Maui's canoe, which drifted away to the south. Traditions hold that its original name was Te Waki o Maui, the Canoe of Maui.

LAND OF FIORDS, GLACIERS, AND FLIGHTLESS BIRDS

New Zealand, twelve hundred miles southeast of Australia, is made up of the North Island and the South Island, each

Some 2,700 birds occupy this colony of gannets (Sula serrator) *on Cape Kidnappers at the southern end of Hawke's Bay. Birds ringed here have been recovered in Australian waters, 1,500 miles away. (K. and J. Bigwood)*

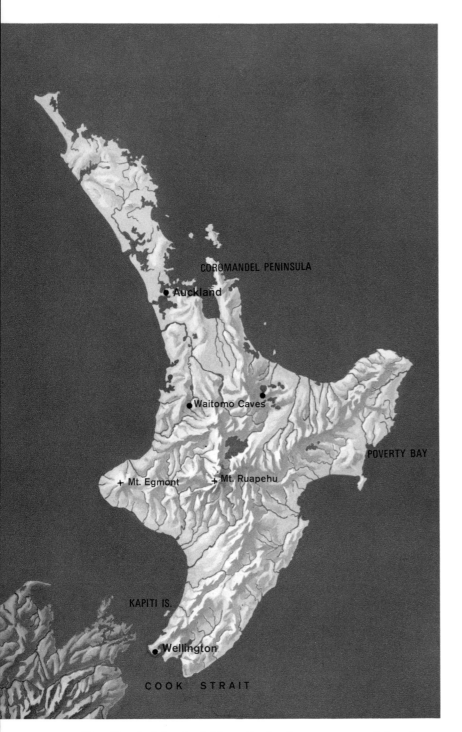

The North Island of New Zealand, once covered by dense bush and forest, has been largely cleared. Part of the volcanic zone fringing the Pacific, it has hot springs and geysers.

fauna has numerous gaps. There are no furred animals, save two species of bat, and birds have taken over many of the mammal niches in the ecology, or ways of life. In the process some have lost the powers of flight. The grazers and browsers of the grasslands and bush were the flightless moas, now extinct, one species of which was twelve feet tall. Other avian curiosities include the kiwi, with its hairlike feathering and long bill, flightless rails, and a flightless parrot (the kakapo). These still survive.

Scenically, New Zealand gives a whole new dimension to the Pacific. The North Island, subtropical and with many fine harbors and inlets, is a land of ferny plateaus, thick bush, volcanic cones, hot springs, and geysers. The South Island is dominated by huge, jagged mountain chains, precipices, waterfalls, glaciers, breath-taking highland lakes, and deep coastal fiords. More than five-sixths of the entire surface of New Zealand is above 650 feet in elevation. On the South Island there are sixteen peaks over ten thousand feet in height, and 220 above the snow line. The highest peak is Mount Cook (12,349 feet), called Aorangi, "the cloud piercer," by the Maoris. Also on the South Island are the highest waterfall, the Sutherland, 1,904 feet, and the longest glacier, the Tasman, measuring eighteen miles and with an average width of one-and-one-quarter miles. These features are among the most striking of their type in the southern hemisphere.

New Zealand rivers are short and swift-flowing. The longest stream in the north is the Waikato, which runs for two hundred seventy miles, draining Lake Taupo, and in the south the Clutha, two hundred ten miles. The latter, which drains large snowfields, has a formidable flow—two million cubic feet per minute. Taupo, the largest lake, has a surface area of 234 square miles and a depth of 522 feet. The numerous southern lakes, occupying as they do old glacial valleys, are mostly long and narrow, and sometimes very deep.

All in all, New Zealand combines the fiords of Norway, the mountain lakes and snow-capped peaks of Switzerland, the geysers of Iceland, the old volcanic cones of Hawaii, the moors of Scotland, and the soft green countryside of England, while maintaining an individuality of its own. Scenically, as well as in flora and fauna, it is very different from Australia. There is none of the spaciousness, the open woodlands and the dry plains of the latter. And, despite the proximity of the two, there are no eucalypts or wattles in New Zealand, except for those introduced in recent years.

Today one can land in Auckland or Wellington after a few hours' air travel from Australia. New Zealand, however, was one of the last major habitable areas of the globe to be settled by man. Kupe, the great Polynesian explorer, is credited with being its first visitor, possibly in about A.D. 900. Knowledge of the voyage is largely legendary since no written record is available. But, on the basis of the voyage the people of Hawaiki (generally believed to be the Society Islands) knew about "the great land with the high mists" to the southwest that was inhabited only by the weka (wood hen), kokako (bellbird) and tiwaiwaka (fantail). The origin and status of the first inhabitants of New Zealand are virtually unknown.

about five hundred miles long, and small Stewart Island. Cook Strait, separating the major islands, ranges from about fifteen to as much as fifty-eight miles across. Several groups of subantarctic islands on the New Zealand Shelf are included in the region, notably the Chathams (372 square miles) and Aucklands (234 square miles).

New Zealand is a continental remnant, the greater part of its rocks being sedimentary. As such it is perhaps the most isolated relic in the world. This explains the distinctive nature of the flora and fauna, and the high proportion of forms that occur nowhere else. Compared with those of a continent, the

The kauri pines (Agathis australis) *in Waipoua Forest may reach a height of one hundred feet and have a girth of thirty-five feet. So great has been the demand for their timber that only a few good stands remain. (John H. Johns)*

Despite Maori legends that they were an inferior people, archaeological studies have shown that they were Polynesian. At one time referred to as the Moriori, these people have now been given the collective name Moa-Hunters, since their ancient camp sites abound with the remains of these extinct birds. Roger Duff, the archaeologist, has given A. D. 950 as the earliest Carbon 14 date for one of these sites.

In about A. D. 1350, due to great population build-up in the major Polynesian islands of the eastern Pacific, and the attendant warfare and harsh laws, a fleet of seven canoes, according to Maori legend, set out from Hawaiki to colonize the legendary land of the high mists to the west. The canoes were great double-hulled boats with supporting platforms, and each carried up to sixty people, as well as sweet potato, taro, dogs, and the migrants' personal possessions. Progress was by sail and paddle. Finally, with great joy, the mariners saw the irregular skyline of their new home on the horizon. As they approached their destination they could make out the long Pacific rollers sweeping up to its shores and the red-blossoming *Metrosideros* trees (pohutukawa) on the cliffs. A landing was made on the gravelly beaches of the Bay of Plenty, the North Island, and then the canoes dispersed around the coast to found separate settlements.

And so it was that long before the first Europeans, Abel Tasman in 1642 and James Cook in 1769, approached the coasts of New Zealand, man had already modified the landscape and its flora and fauna. The early Moa-Hunters all but exterminated the great moas, and were in turn overrun and absorbed by the Maori, except on the remote Chatham Islands. Beginning at least five hundred years ago, fires were leveling forests that probably covered seven-eighths of the land. The Maoris soon discovered the edible qualities of fern root, which was to become their major item of sustenance, and wandered far in search of it. They trapped and snared the wild birds in great numbers, and fished the offshore waters. Yet, in eight hundred years they brought about only the merest fraction of the change made by European man in a century of settlement.

HEADLANDS, DENSE BUSH, AND TALL FORESTS

That part of the North Island where the seven canoes landed and where Cook, four hundred years later, made contact with the Maori, is scenically diverse and beautiful. It is a land of bays and small offshore islands, where rounded green headlands alternate with sandy and pebbly beaches, rocky foreshore and little clumps of mangroves. The long Coromandel Peninsula thrusts into the sea far to the east. At the end of the long Northland Peninsula is Cape Reinga, marked by a steep cliff where, according to Maori legend, the spirits of the dead set out on their final journey across the waters back to Hawaiki. The long rollers of the Pacific crowd the land in

never-ending succession, their white crests topping the green inshore waters and the deeper blue sea beyond. Gulls and gannets ride the air currents. On shore the coastal shrubbery sways with the breeze and the slender golden toetoe plumes, dried flowerheads of a species of rush, wave and toss in graceful accompaniment. Here and there are spindly *Pandanus* or screw pine. Clumps of nikau palms rise here and there. And visible from afar are the red *Metrosideros* shrubs, called the Christmas tree in New Zealand since its flowering is at its height in December. This same plant is equally prominent along the cliffs and headlands of the Hawaiian Islands, thousands of miles to the northeast.

In former times, the North Island of New Zealand was covered with a lush undergrowth or scrub, and tall forests of kauri pine and tree fern. The kauri is one of the principal timber trees of the southern hemisphere, reaching a height of one hundred feet and more, and commonly having a girth of thirty-five feet. Some kauris are centuries old and one on the Coromandel Peninsula is estimated to be two thousand years old. Because they are straight and strong, the trunks of the kauri came into demand at an early period for the spars of sailing ships. In 1794, a Captain Dell made a trip from Sydney especially to obtain kauri timber. It was not long before a vigorous trade developed and virtually whole tribes of Maoris were employed to fell and trim the trees, and to float them to the coast. Fire, carelessly used by settlers to clear the land, quickly added to the devastation. Today, only twenty-five thousand acres remain of the kauri forests that once occupied two million acres of the North Island.

Here and there, remaining small tracts of kauri give a vivid impression of what primordial New Zealand must have been like. One of these is the Waipoua Kauri Forest north of Auckland. Many of the giants here, trees of great majesty, bear individual Maori names. They rise above the dense subtropical jungle, their coarse trunks festooned with epiphytes, vines, and lianas. Ferns grow riotously, the smaller species clustering in the clearings and along the small creeks, the larger plants, twenty to thirty feet high, competing with the trees for a place in the sun. This kind of vegetation is called

Left: The New Zealand morepork (so named from its call) or boobook owl (Ninox novaeseelandiae) is a nocturnal hunter of rodents, small birds and moths. (G. J. H. Moon) Right: The white-eye (Zosterops lateralis), a small bird that apparently colonized New Zealand from Australia in the 1850's and soon became very common. It eats insects and berries. (Robin Smith)

lowland mixed forest because of the diversity of plant species. Among the trees here is the rimu, a pine with graceful, pendulous branchlets. It provides about a quarter of New Zealand's timber. Another tree, the kowhai, a member of the pea family, is seasonally adorned with large, hanging, golden blossoms, and is the delight of the nectar-feeding birds. The rata, one of the species of *Metrosideros,* with brilliant crimson flowers, is parasitic in its early stages, its seed lodging in the branches of another tree and progressively strangling it as it grows. The nikau palm also grows in these forests.

This original forest flora of New Zealand shows its closest relationships with the mountain floras of New Guinea and New Caledonia. Affinities with Australia are fewer, although orchids, ferns, and other plants with minute seeds or spores, which are readily transported by wind, are common to the two countries. As one moves from north to south in New Zealand one sees a steady change in species. Again, as elsewhere, some species prefer wetter areas, others drier ones, some sea level, and others the higher altitudes. The Antarctic beech, *Nothofagus,* dominant in the South Island, occurs only sporadically in the North Island; there is a considerable patch of it on the Coromandel Peninsula.

FROGS WITHOUT TADPOLES

The Northland and Coromandel peninsulas are the home of two of the world's most primitive frogs, both members of the genus *Leiopelma.* They differ from other frogs in many ways. For example, their vertebrae are hollowed at both ends, and their tail-wagging muscles—but not, of course, the tail itself— are retained in the adult. Their nearest living relative is a North American frog, *Ascaphus,* and they are quite unlike any Australian or New Guinea species. The presence of frogs in New Zealand is one of the many pieces of biological evidence that the islands were once joined with a continental mass, since neither frogs nor tadpoles can stand immersion in salt water or prolonged exposure to dry air.

Biologically *Leiopelma* has an interesting peculiarity. The tadpole stage occurs in the egg so that, on hatching, it is already a small-tailed frog. It does not need to return to water to breed. The eggs, laid in moist soil beneath logs and rocks high up on scrubby hillsides, take about six weeks to hatch.

Leiopelma was found by a group of prospectors who were screening the soil of a mountain stream on the Coromandel Peninsula in 1852. It greatly surprised even the Maoris, who had never seen one before; they regarded it with awe as a small spirit or god. But little more was learned of the New Zealand frogs until recently, when Drs. Pat and Neville Stephenson completed a study of their biology. One of the two mainland species is found both on the hills and in streams, the other only on the hills. The latter species takes shelter beneath large boulders, in crevices of decaying logs and among the sedges and grasses. Small snails, insects, and crayfish form the food; in captivity they thrive on houseflies and blowflies. No two individuals are alike in color, every shade between predominantly green and predominantly brown

A bush forest with numerous tree ferns above Bridal Veil Falls, Kawhia, Auckland Province. (New Zealand National Publicity Studios)

occurring. They make only shrill, chirping sounds, and they move in a series of leaps rarely more than a foot long.

BIRDS

Among New Zealand's exciting bird fauna are several families that occur nowhere else, having evolved in the isolation of these islands. These include the kiwis (Apterygidae), the so-called New Zealand wrens (Acanthisittidae), the wattle crows (Callaeidae), the saddlebacks (Philesturnidae), the pio-pios, a group of thrushlike birds (Turnagridae), and a few distinctive groups of parrots (Nestoridae and Strigopidae). The extinct moas have been placed in an order by themselves, the Dinornithiformes. Interestingly enough, the last century has seen a steady colonization of New Zealand by Australian birds. The very common little white-eye *(Zosterops lateralis)* first appeared in the 1850's. The spoonbill, egret, and spur-winged plover *(Lobibyx novae-hollandiae)* are recent arrivals. The last, common today in paddocks and fields of the South Island, was first seen in 1886 and was recorded breeding, presumably after larger numbers had arrived, in 1932. One of the newest is the Australian swallow *(Hirundo neoxena)*; a nesting pair was observed for the first time a few years ago.

It is probable that Australian birds, singly and in flocks, have been blown across the sea to New Zealand throughout the ages. A strong wind blows from west to east across the Tasman Strait for part of the year, sometimes discoloring the skies of New Zealand with red dust from the Australian interior and smoke from its coastal bush fires. The establishment of Australian birds in New Zealand in recent times has undoubtedly been made possible by extensive clearing and other changes in the countryside that have produced an open environment not unlike that of their homeland. Several species introduced by man are now highly successful also, including the magpie *(Gymnorhina hypoleuca)* and the black swan *(Cygnus atratus).*

To get a glimpse of what life was once like in the forests of the North Island one has to go back to the journals of the pioneers, or venture to one of the offshore-island sanctuaries that have escaped the change. One of the best books on life in the bush is *Pioneering in Poverty Bay,* by Philip Kenway, who settled there in the 1880's. Kenway built a little home-stead on a bracken-covered flat among "steep hills of fern and bush, and bounded by a little river of rapids and clear deep pools." From the forest canopy beginning twenty or thirty feet up, came a continuous variety of musical calls and chatterings. An outstanding bird was the kaka *(Nestor meridionalis),* a large brownish parrot, which feasted on berries and, by means of a long upper mandible, dug big white grubs out of the trunks of trees. The tui or parson bird *(Prosthemadera novaeseelandiae),* a honeyeater, shin-ing metallic green, with purplish reflections on the shoulders and two tufts of white curled feathers on the throat (hence the name), was the most numerous, as well as the most melodious, of the birds. It has several calls and a repertoire of submusical conversation. It is a close relative of the bell-bird *(Anthornis melanura)* that so delighted Sir Joseph Banks when the *Endeavour* anchored in Queen Charlotte Sound in 1770. Banks wrote:

> I was awakened by the singing of the birds ashore, from whence we are distant not a quarter of a mile. Their

numbers were certainly not very great. They seemed to strain their throats with emulation, and made, perhaps, the most melodious wild music I have ever heard, almost imitating small bells, but with the most tunable silver sound imaginable, to which, may be, the distance was no small addition.

In his book Kenway writes lovingly of the occasional, long-drawn-out note of the kokako or wattle crow *(Callaeas cine-rea),* which he describes as a "well-mannered little crow, coal black save for two purple cheeks." The call had an enchantment all its own in the silent woods. Periodically, a wanderer in the bush would disturb the big New Zealand pigeon *(Hemiphaga novae seelandiae),* which would take flight with loudly beating wings. The pigeon is a striking sight when it is perched in the foliage in full sunlight. The head and breast are golden green with coppery reflections, the back chestnut-purple, the breast white, and the bill crimson. Need-less to say the early settlers relished pigeon pie. Native quail *(Coturnix novae seelandiae)* flew up from the forest floor. Duck and teal abounded in the river, and the red-billed, blue-breasted swamp hen or pukeko *(Porphyrio mela-notis)* came out from the marshes to feed in the clear patches.

Today the beautiful wood pigeon has been greatly reduced in numbers because of the clearing of the forest, but it still survives on Kapiti Island and in little pockets of suitable habitat on the mainland. Like most pigeons, it moves around widely so that some are occasionally seen even near towns in the north. The same can be said of the kaka. In Waipoa, and elsewhere, small flocks frequent the upper tier of the foliage, one always remaining in a position of vantage, ready to fly around the others to warn of impending danger. They utter harsh screeching notes continuously. Like most parrots the kaka lays its eggs in hollow limbs, three or four making up the clutch. The little New Zealand quail is extinct, but the wattled crow continues to thrive in scattered localities. The tui, however, has adapted completely to settlement, becoming a common inhabitant of gardens, where it visits nectar-bearing plants. The swamp hens and ducks are holding their own over the greater part of New Zealand.

Kapiti Island, some three and one half miles off the south-west corner of the North Island, is as good a place as any to see native forest birds at the present time. Wekas *(Gallirallus australis),* large flightless rails, come stalking from heavy cover into the open glades to view the observer. They may even become quite tame around houses. In some areas wood pigeons feed on garden lawns. The swift-flying green parakeets, *Cyano-ramphus novaezelandiae,* with crimson forehead and crown, screech as they fly from treetop to treetop. This bird was formerly killed in great numbers because of its destruction of crops. Kakas, tuis, and bellbirds all abound on the island.

Right above: The pukeko or swamp hen (Porphyrio mela-notus) *is a common inhabitant of marshlands both in New Zealand and Australia. (Robin Smith) Right: The red-fronted parakeet* (Cyanoramphus novaezelandiae), *mainly an inhabi-tant of treetops, is sometimes killed because it destroys crops. (New Zealand National Publicity) Far right: The North Island kiwi* (Apteryx australis). *These curiously shaped, flightless, hairy-feathered nocturnal birds, formerly wide-spread in forest and scrub, are in some places still holding their own. (New Zealand National Publicity)*

THE KIWI

The national bird of New Zealand is one of the real curiosities of its clan. A forest dweller, strictly nocturnal in habits, it has survived very well in the scattered areas of bush in both islands. Kiwis have short, powerful legs, stumpy bodies covered with curious hairlike feathers, only rudiments of wings, long necks, very long bills, and no tails. Their size is about that of a domestic hen and the coloring is gray or brown, and sometimes blackish on the back. By day they sleep in hollow logs or under banks; at night they emerge to hunt for worms, insects, and berries. Their senses of hearing and smell are well developed but their sight is poor. When alarmed they can run off quickly through the undergrowth.

The North Island kiwi *(Apteryx australis)* was first discovered at Tolaga Bay in the East Cape district in 1827 by the French commander, Admiral Dumont d'Urville. It was probably once widely distributed in forest areas of soft ground and rotting leaves and logs, where its long, sensitive bill could operate most effectively. Today the Manawatu Gorge is one of the best areas for them, but their nocturnal habits make them difficult to see.

Some years ago, A. D. Haeusler published an interesting account of the feeding of the kiwi:

> In searching for earth worms they showed a considerable degree of ingenuity. The hunt opened with the usual tapping. When by this means the bird discovered the burrow of one of these worms it set to work at once enlarging the opening, using its bill as a workman uses a crowbar. When it had formed a funnel-like depression, it inserted its bill and took a good hold of the worm. With a steady pull it often succeeded in bringing its victim to the surface. When it was not able to do so, it ceased pulling, as continuing to do so would have resulted in tearing the worm and losing the greater part, and leaning well back remained in the same position, waiting, without the faintest movement of any part of its body, until the worm, tired out by its exertion, momentarily relaxed its hold. Then with another steady pull it gently drew it out of its burrow.

The kiwi nests in holes underneath the roots of trees, beneath logs, or where the bank of a watercourse has fallen away. Usually one egg is laid any time between July and February. As with all flightless birds, the male does the incubating. The Maoris used the kiwi for food and valued its feathers for making cloaks. They generally caught the birds at night by imitating its cry, a short, high-pitched whistle, or with the aid of dogs.

CURIOSITIES: THE TUATARA AND THE STEPHEN ISLAND WREN

A few of the small, offshore islands of New Zealand are the home of a most interesting reptile, the tuatara or *Sphenodon*. This single species is the only surviving member of the Order Rhynchocephalia, a contemporary of the dinosaurs. They are thus survivors of a line that apparently became extinct everywhere else at least fifty million years ago. The tuatara is about eighteen inches long and superficially resembles a big iguanid lizard. It is dark gray and a crest of spines extends along the back of the head and down the back. A pineal eye

is present on the top of the head. Though this is covered with skin it is possibly capable of registering light. Tuataras live mostly on the grassy and rocky slopes of the islands where they often share burrows with petrels and other burrowing sea birds.

Tiny Stephen Island, in Cook Strait, the site of a lighthouse for nearly a century, is zoologically of great interest because of the unique occurrence there of a third species of the frog *Leiopelma* and of a small genus of flightless wren, *Traversia lyalli*. The bird belonged to the endemic family Acanthisittidae, referred to earlier. *Traversia* represents a sad saga in the annals of conservation: it was discovered and exterminated by a cat. In 1894 the lighthouse keeper's cat brought in eleven specimens of a distinctive little bird, olive-brown above, olive-yellow on the throat and breast, and with a little yellowish streak over the eye. It was said to be seminocturnal, never to fly, and to live among the rocks, running about and hiding. Attempts to locate *Traversia* subsequently were unsuccessful. It is likely that the cat eliminated the last few members of a species that was dying out—a demonstration of the danger of introducing predatory animals to islands.

FRAGMENT OF A CONTINENT

The primitive living relics of New Zealand, the tuatara and the leiopelmid frogs, the total absence of native mammals save for two bats, the very distinctive native avifauna, and the unique development of flightless birds, require explanation on the basis of geological history.

New Zealand lies at the meeting point of three great submarine ridges, one coming from the south and two from the north. Along these swellings, the depth of the ocean is less than 3,300 feet, and the ridges break the surface as Lord Howe Island and New Caledonia. Between Australia and New Zealand, however, the sea depths exceed 6,600 feet.

It is obvious on various grounds that New Zealand is a continental remnant. Basically, New Zealand is composed of a sedimentary rock called greywacke, a kind of dirty sandstone, whose deposition is believed to require fine volcanic dust, fast rivers, and subsiding marine trenches. It is of Triassic and Jurassic age, that is, from 150 to 190 million years old. The sheer volume of this rock in New Zealand is much too great for it to have developed from sediments arising within the islands. It must have come from a much larger continental mass. The older geologists postulated the existence of a sunken continent, so-called Tasmantis, between New Zealand and Australia. A decision on this had to await a study of the bottom of the Tasman Sea. This was made in 1955 by C. B. Officer, who found that the crustal thickness of the basin is only three to six miles, the same as that for the Pacific east of New Zealand, indicating that there is no sunken continent. Accordingly, the alternative hypothesis that Australia and New Zealand once were one, and have since drifted apart, has been advanced.

Be that as it may, the isolation of New Zealand must have occurred at a time when reptiles like the tuatara and frogs

A New Zealand kingfisher (Halcyon sanctus) *approaching its nest in a hollow limb. (G. J. H. Moon)*

The tui (Prosthemadera novaeseelandiae), one of the finest songsters in the New Zealand bush, seen in a flowering kowhai. (M. F. Soper)

like *Leiopelma* ranged more widely on the earth. In the protective insularity of New Zealand alone they have survived. Birds evolved in the Jurassic period, and presumably the forerunners of the large flightless birds reached the islands before the land separated—although one can never be sure that these were not flying forms. The passerines, or song birds, evolved rather late and hence probably flew to New Zealand. The absence of mammals other than bats is interesting. Their absence is probably explained by their having appeared in adjacent Australia only after New Zealand had become separated. Alternatively, mammals could have reached New Zealand and died out.

In its isolation New Zealand has undergone great geological change, which must have had a drastic effect on whatever forms of life it inherited from the larger land mass. Throughout the Tertiary period, extending from perhaps sixty million down to a few million years ago, great sections of both major islands were at some time beneath the sea, as shown by the age and structure of the sedimentary rocks over much of the terrain. Parts of the islands, of course, were never submerged: some areas, however, much reduced, remained as suitable habitat for land animals. The area of New Zealand today is probably greater than it has been for much of the history of the islands.

THE VOLCANIC UPLANDS

The central topographical feature of the North Island of New Zealand is a series of unbroken mountain chains, three to six thousand feet high. They represent a northward extension of the great massives of the South Island. To the west of these ranges, in the center of the island, is a volcanic plateau dominated by two large mountains, Ruapehu (9,175 feet high) and Ngauruhoe (7,515 feet), which periodically exudes vapor and steam. The land is one of peaks and plateaus.

The active volcanoes of New Zealand are in a line that strikes directly across the ocean to those in the Kermadec Islands to the north. This volcanic activity has apparently continued unabated for at least a million years, for in the central part of this belt, lava and other volcanic deposits are estimated to be several thousand feet thick. None of the peaks today, however, have the activity of those of Hawaii. Rather, underground forces express themselves in the form of geysers, hot springs, and periodic earthquakes.

The thermal area of New Zealand extends from Wairakei to Rotorua, the well-known tourist area, and beyond. Here are found geysers, blowholes, boiling mud pools, and ponds that are hot on one side and cold on the other. The air is strong with the smell of sulphur and shrill with the sound of jets of geothermal steam. At the old Maori village of Whakarewarewa the inhabitants calmly wash their clothes in the conveniently boiling waters.

Geysers occur in two other parts of the world, Iceland and in Wyoming in the United States. In all cases their eruptive action is believed to result from the existence of an underground body of very hot rock, the relic of a body of magma. The neck of a geyser is an irregular tube into which water seeps from outside. At its base the heat of the water increases constantly until it changes into steam, and blows the column of water high out of the hole. At first the water overflows gently but as the column becomes lighter a larger quantity of the hot water changes into steam and produces an explosive effect. The greatest of all New Zealand geysers, Waimangu, occasionally spouted jets of water to fifteen hundred feet, but in 1904 the draining of nearby Lake Tarawa caused Waimangu's water level to drop about thirty-five feet, whereupon it became quiescent. The crater of Waimangu, four hundred feet across, has stepped walls and slopes caked with silica and mud. Pohutu, the best-known geyser today, reaches only ninety feet, but is nevertheless spectacular.

Earthquakes occur periodically along a line from Whakatane to Hawera. Eighty-two major quakes have occurred since 1835. The most destructive in recent times destroyed much of the city of Napier in 1931. Land was elevated six feet, and docks along the waterfront could no longer be reached by incoming ships.

A SUBTERRANEAN GALAXY

Among the zoological curiosities of New Zealand are the glowworms of the caves of Waitomo, located at the center of the North Island. The grotto is a high cave, pitch dark, that has to be entered by boat. Once inside, the whole of the roof appears to be illuminated by a hundred thousand tiny lanterns. The effect is like that of a dark starry night, except that the tiny blinking points of light are so much closer together

The harrier (Circus approximans) *flies slowly over tussock grassland, swamps and sea coast in its hunt for rodents, frogs and large insects. (G. J. H. Moon)*

than in the sky. The reflection of the blue-green light in the black river water produces a magnificent but eerie sensation.

The glowworm of Waitomo *(Arachnocampa luminosa)* is about half an inch long and less than one-tenth of an inch across. It is really the larva of a small fly. The worms live in a tangle of webs, from which hang fine, sticky threads that are the fishing lines of the insects. Whereas the light of fireflies of the northern hemisphere is largely associated with the species' courtships, here it serves to attract tiny midges emerging from the water. The midges fly up toward the light and are entangled in the webs. The chemistry of light production by insects is not fully understood. It differs, however, from an ordinary flame in that less than 5 per cent of the energy created is liberated as heat.

The Waitomo caves were first explored in 1887 by a young surveyor, Fred Mace, and a Maori chief, Tane Tinorau. The surveyor had been fascinated by the way the Waitomo River disappeared under a hill. The two men floated through the caverns on a raft, forced at times to lie down to avoid stalactites and low sections of roof. The explorers, understandably dazzled by the beauties of the limestone formations and of the glowworms, named the first cave the banqueting chamber, the second the organ loft, the third the cathedral, and so on. Soon the fame of the caves spread. Today Waitomo, and nearby Ruakuri, are visited by tourists from everywhere.

THE GANNETS OF CAPE KIDNAPPERS

Thrusting out into Hawke's Bay on the east coast is a long promontory called Cape Kidnappers. It is the home of a huge gannet colony, possibly the largest in the southern hemisphere. The approach entails a long journey along a beach at low tide. The colony occupies the great triangular plateau of the cape. There are some two thousand seven hundred of the solemn white birds perched on their six-inch-high mounds of earth and guano, about two feet apart.

The gannets of Cape Kidnappers are the same species as those nesting in Bass Strait, and are quite similar to those of the northern hemisphere. The general body color is white, with the crown of the head and back of the neck golden buff. The outer wing feathers and central tail feathers are black, providing a conspicuous identification feature in flight. The birds remain in the vicinity of the nesting colonies, of which there are some eighteen in New Zealand waters, for about seven months of the year; at other times they disperse through the surrounding seas, often as far away as the Australian

Overleaf: Sulphur springs in a thermal region; chemicals in the running waters have marked the rocks in curious fashion. (New Zealand National Publicity)

265

coast. Their food consists mainly of small surface-living fishes such as garfish, herrings, young mullet, and some squids. The feeding dives of the gannets are spectacular: the bird suddenly drops vertically, with head outstretched and wings partly folded, from a height of twenty to thirty feet. When a shoal of fishes is located a whole flock of the birds may gather over them, with individuals constantly dropping to the water and taking to the air again.

Most of the gannets arrive at Cape Kidnappers in August. The eggs are laid from mid-September to the end of October. Both parents take part in the incubation. Unlike most birds, which press the egg close to the body, the gannets spread the webbed feet over the egg. The incubation period is forty-three to forty-seven days, so that most of the young hatch in November and December.

MOUNT EGMONT AND THE LIMESTONE COASTS

At the southwest corner of North Island the land jets out into the ocean as a broad-based promontory. Its chief feature is magnificent Mount Egmont (8,260 feet high); so perfect is the symmetry of the cone and so white is its cap that it is known as New Zealand's Fujiyama. Egmont, or as it is called by the Maoris, Taranaki, is an isolated volcano whose activity ceased two thousand years ago. Cook likened it to the peak of Teneriffe in the Canary Islands, stating that it is "of a prodigious height and its Top is cover'd with Everlasting Snow."

Today much of the country around the mountain has been cleared and one approaches its greenish-purple foothills over rich green pasture lands. The most beautiful view of all is the peak seen across the serene waters and densely bushed foreshores of Lake Mangamahoe. Egmont's atmosphere varies with the season. In summer, storms mount here and the dark clouds come rolling up from behind the mountain. Often the peak is obscured by low clouds, at other times mists swirl around the base so that only the white cone is seen, shimmering in the sunlight. With the coming of winter, the whiteness of snows creeps down the sides. Fingers of snow and ice linger on in crevices long after the advent of spring.

The Maoris had a charming legend to account for the isolation of Egmont from the other volcanic peaks on the central plateau. Tongariro was a beautiful maiden who was loved by two neighbors, Ruapehu and Taranaki (Egmont). Taranaki was the favored one, so Ruapehu asked another mountain, Karangahape, to spy on the lady. Tongariro carried on so scandalously with Taranaki that, finally, Ruapehu could stand it no longer, and gave Taranaki a violent kick. The kick sent Taranaki off the edge of the plateau—but not before he was able to pass a similar treatment on to Karangahape, breaking him into a scattered range. Taranaki, hurt and furious, traveled until he reached the coast, there to settle down to think of a way of avenging himself. He is still there today, his beautiful snow-capped head sticking up high in the sky, master of the coast and plains as far as the eye can see.

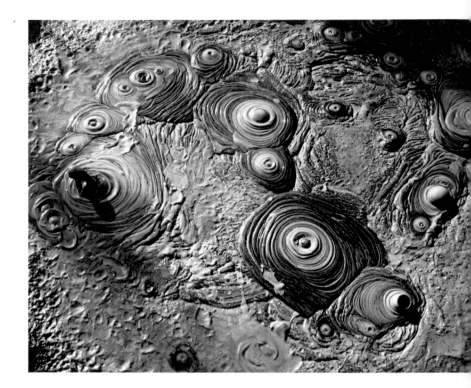

Boiling mud, Rotorua, in the thermal area of the North Island of New Zealand. (Robin Smith)

The coastal area commanded by Taranaki is indeed a beautiful one. There are wide sweeps of white limestone cliffs, with black volcanic sands below them. The cliffs near Tongaporutu, some distance away, are spectacularly colored, the browns of the soil on their crests forming a harmony in pastels with the greenish-blue of the hills, the white wave crests rolling in at their base, and the blues of ocean and sky.

FROM FORESTS TO FARMS

The southern parts of the North Island form today some of the prime grazing and agricultural land of New Zealand. Plains and hills form a vast rolling carpet of greens and browns, interrupted here and there by patches of bush and scrub, and by gravelly river courses. The climate is mild, and the abundance and regularity of the rain maintains the greenness for which the area is famous.

In these farmlands, as well as in the densely settled area of Wellington and other cities, one soon becomes aware of another aspect of New Zealand wildlife today, the prominence of introduced European birds. English settlers tried to recreate as many features of their homeland as possible, and in the early days acclimatization societies flourished. Accordingly, the shrubbery of garden and farm is filled with the melodious calls of such species as blackbird, song thrush, goldfinch, greenfinch, chaffinch and redpoll, and with the chattering of sparrows and dunnocks. And, in spring, the paddocks and fields ring with the flight song of the skylark.

The snow-covered cone of Mount Ngauruhoe, an active volcano in the Tongariro National Park. (Robin Smith)

269

Fiords, Glaciers, and Antarctic Beeches

New Zealand: The South Island

The magnificent mountains of the South Island have earned it the name of the "Switzerland of the South Pacific." Where only 18 per cent of the North Island is mountainous, fully 70 per cent of the South Island is highland. The very ruggedness and inaccessibility of the South Island has protected it from man.

14

Left: Rugged western coast of the South Island between Punakaiki and Westport. (K. and J. Bigwood) Below: The southern crested grebe (Podiceps cristatus), *an inhabitant of New Zealand lakes, is a widely distributed species, occurring also in Australia, Asia, and Europe. (M. F. Soper)*

Because of the cold it was not favored by the Maoris, and even today by far the greatest part of the Maori population is in the North Island. Europeans with their sheep have made inroads in the west and elsewhere. Introduced deer, stoats, and possums have invaded the forests in great numbers. Nevertheless, considerable areas of the west coast, and especially Fiordland, are as Cook saw them in 1770.

The climatic differences between the two main islands of New Zealand are marked. The North Island's climate is mild: summer heat is not excessive, thanks to the nearness of the sea, and only at high altitudes is the winter severe. A benevolent rainfall of forty to eighty inches a year keeps the country green and fertile. But the South Island, especially its west coast, is exposed to the full force of the bitterly cold winds off the southern ocean. The snow line creeps down to within three thousand feet of the sea in the west, and three thousand five hundred feet in the east. Rainfall and snowfall exceed one hundred inches a year; Milford Sound has even more—the average there is two hundred fifty inches per year, with three hundred recorded on one occasion. Twenty-four inches of rain once fell in a day. Usually the rain falls in a continuous drizzle, but the area has the distinction of having more thunderstorms than any other part of New Zealand.

Such marked contrasts in climate express themselves in distinct differences in vegetation. The indigenous forest of the north is a mixed evergreen forest with a considerable diversity of species. Great areas of the south, however, especially on the higher mountains and in parts of the drier lowlands, are covered with forests that are almost pure stands of the Antarctic beech (Nothofagus). The five main species of beech are known as silver, mountain, black, red, and hard.

THE SOUTHERN ALPS

The Alps extend from one end of the South Island to the other; there is range upon range of jagged peaks and precipitous terrain. Along the west coast the rocks range in age from pre-Cambrian to Devonian; the oldest was laid down five hundred million years ago. In the Ordovician period, four hundred million years ago, vast thicknesses of sandstones and limestones were deposited; these stones are characterized by abundant graptolites, tiny colonial animals with a coral-like skeleton. Subsequently, these rocks were changed by crustal stresses, pressures, and heat, into schists—characterized by their sparkle and a tendency to cleave into flaggy slabs, and gneisses—characterized by a coarse-grained and foliated appearance. Schists and gneisses today form two of the dominant rock types of the Southern Alps. They rank in importance with a gray sandstone called greywacke that forms a girdle around the island.

The basic differences between the schists and gneisses and the sedimentary greywackes have had a marked influence on the evolution of land forms and scenery. Because schists weather directly into clay, mountains formed of them usually have smooth sides, and lack talus and shingle slides at the

The wrybill plover (Anarhynchus frontalis), *inhabits the mudflats of the estuaries. The unique twist of its bill is believed to be an adaptation for getting prey from under stones. (M. F. Soper)*

The Royal albatross (Diomedea epomophora) *has a small nesting colony on Taiaroa Head, at the entrance to Otago Harbor. (William W. Dunmire)*

base. Greywacke, by contrast, breaks up into angular blocks when exposed to wind, rain, and frost. These fragments form deep piles in the valley floors and stream bottoms.

The striking physiographic features of the Alps developed largely during the last million or two years. Height and jaggedness are indicative of youth. Mountain building began a long time ago, but the great earth forces that thrust the backbone ridge of the island high into the air are recent. During this period of instability and torment, whole blocks of country were contorted and overthrust. In other places extensive sections dropped downward: the so-called Alpine Fault in the west of the island is an example of this. The rugged hilltops, jagged precipices, and tumbled slopes are largely the results of erosion. Lastly, glaciers, formerly more extensive than they are today, carved majestic paths down toward the sea. Often the ice scoured the valley floors so deeply that they are now below sea level. Some, high up on the slopes, produced hanging valleys, for they terminated in precipices. Gradually, as the climate warmed, the glaciers dropped great masses of rock and rubble, called moraines, on the valley floors. The rivers, blocked off, welled up into the magnificent mountain lakes that are such a feature of the Alps today. Where the glaciers reached the sea, and the sea level subsequently rose, fiords were formed. Characteristically, these are shallower at the mouth, where the snout of the glacier dropped its debris, and deeper in their upper reaches.

The Alps today effectively divide the South Island of New Zealand into distinct eastern and western sections. The rain from the west is trapped by the high peaks, so that the lush forests of the west coast are moist and dripping. Waterfalls, like so many little pencils of water, adorn the precipices, and fogs are forever rolling up over the mountain peaks. The mountains shield the eastern part of the island from the winds and snow, and only a fraction of the rain gets through to the east of the ranges. Hence, the climate in the east is much milder and drier and there are vast areas of grassland.

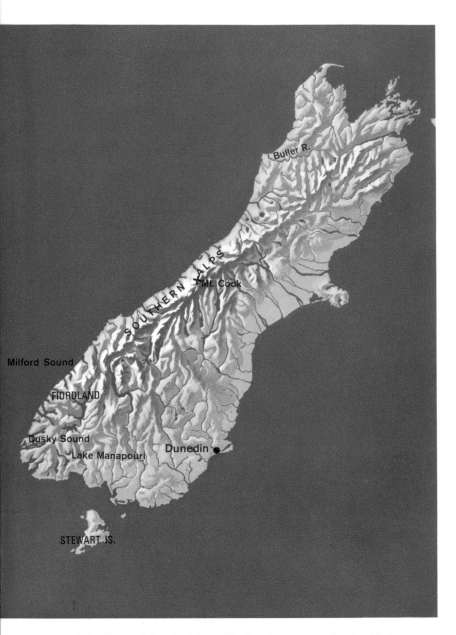

The South Island of New Zealand is known for its high, snow-capped peaks, montane grasslands, picturesque mountain lakes, deep fiords and dense forests.

Scottish Lakes; deep and blue, its somber green headlands and hills cast long shadows on the surface. Tree ferns and dense shrubbery grow right to the water's edge. This sound is an old valley, drowned by the rising of the sea. Today the section is known for its sunniness and for the excellent cultivated fruits it produces. Back from the ocean the gaunt ranges rise, their tussock grassland and tangled beech forests providing a striking contrast. To the south along the coast is the beautiful Buller River, with its mossy boulders, dense scrub, and clear water. The limestone headland of Punakaiki, where the sea thunders into a series of blowholes, caves, and chasms, is covered with bush and nikau palms.

The rivers of this section of the coast are famous for the grandeur of their gorges about which, in wet weather, the mountain mists swirl. On a little stream near Okarito is New Zealand's only known breeding colony of the white egret *(Egretta alba),* an Australian species that has become established here in the last hundred years or two. The community, containing only a dozen pairs of birds, inhabits an old kowhai tree. The birds in their kowhai, against a background of tree ferns and dense shrubbery, would seem a strange sight to anyone accustomed to seeing them in a bare tree on a broad Australian marsh.

The shallows, gravelly beds, and flats near the river mouths are the summer home of various migrants from the Arctic, including the bar-tailed godwits *(Limosa lapponica),* characterized by their long, upturned bills. Pied stilts *(Himantopus leucocephalus)* yelp like so many small pups as they fly from one feeding ground to another. Here, too, may be seen the two species of oyster catcher, *Haematopus ostralegus* and *H. unicolor,* pied and sooty black respectively, but sharing long red bills, red irises, and feet.

Mount Cook, halfway down the coast, towers above its surroundings. Seen on a clear day, its jagged tops and sharp ridges stand out against the sky, and the vivid snow-white cap contrasts with the grays and blacks of its precipices. On closer view the 12,349-foot mammoth is seen to be part of a jostling cluster of peaks, a jumble of spurs, each partly hiding the other. The mountain reflects the moods of the weather; in a matter of hours it can be obscured by snow, sleet, or mist, shimmer in the midday sun, or serenely reflect the golds of the sunset.

MOUNT COOK AND ITS SATELLITES

The first European to visit New Zealand, Abel Tasman, sighted the west coast of the South Island in 1642. Though black clouds hid the summits of the mountains, the great height of the land was apparent. His ships sailed north along the coast and anchored in a bay near Cape Farewell at the northwest tip of the island. There they had an encounter with a large group of Maoris in canoes, and lost four men. Prevented from entering Cook Strait by unfavorable winds, he turned for home. Tasman's experience of New Zealand was thus tragic and brief. A hundred years later, Captain James Cook in the course of two voyages sailed the length of South Island, fully charting it and recording a vivid description of its ruggedness, grandeur, and wild beauty.

The most impressive body of water in the north of the South Island is Queen Charlotte Sound, reminiscent of the

GLACIERS

Cook is only one of many mountains here, and each has its individuality. Thus, the 10,359-foot-high Mount Sefton has flanks that climb straight from valley floor to sky. Mount Tasman, 11,475 feet, is a perfect cone. On one of its sides, the great Fox Glacier descends eight thousand feet in an eight-mile course, until it melts at about seven hundred feet to form the dainty Peters Pool and the Waiho River. Another glacier in this area is the Franz Josef, which descends from 8,800 to 750 feet; its base is an ice cliff, one hundred feet high and half a mile wide, among thick forest. The Tasman glacier is

Spotted shags (Phalacrocorax punctatus), *one of the interesting New Zealand cormorants, nesting on cliffs in Cook Strait. (M. F. Soper)*

274

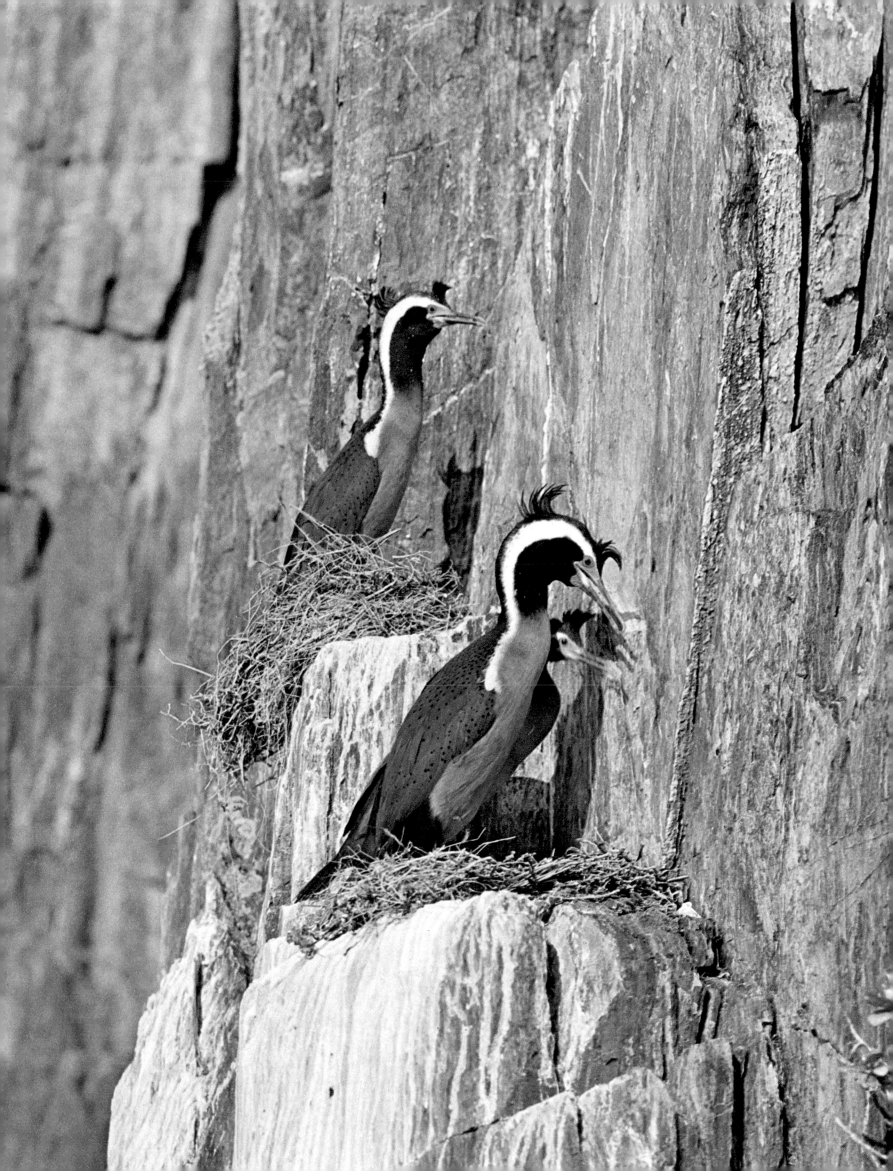

eighteen miles long and over a mile wide. Its rate of movement has been estimated at nine to seventeen inches per day, groaning, thundering, and squealing with its burden of millions of tons of ice.

Glaciers occur today in Alaska, Switzerland, Norway, Sweden, Peru, Patagonia, Kenya, and New Zealand. They represent, however, only 4 per cent of the waters of the world that are tied up as ice, the great ice sheets of Antarctica and Greenland accounting for the rest. All in all, some 10 per cent of the earth's land area is covered by ice, much less than during the ice ages, when the volume is believed to have been 300 to 400 per cent greater. The great ice sheets that moved down over northern Europe and the northern parts of North America during the Pleistocene have no counterpart in the southern hemisphere, where the land masses lie closer to the Equator. Each cold period has, however, served to increase the extent of the glaciers. In New Zealand they were considerably deeper and more extensive during the Pleistocene period, covering part of the Canterbury Plains to the east and much of Otago province. The many deep U-shaped valleys, as well as lakes Te Anau, Wakitipu, Hawea, and hundreds of others, are their aftermath.

Ice action as a molding force has been very protracted and there have been a whole series of temperature fluctuations up to modern times. With the waning of the ice age ten thousand years ago there followed a warm period of five thousand years (the "thermal maximum"). Subsequently, from about 500 B.C. to A.D. 1, the world climate became cold again. There was a warming between the fifth and seventh centuries, the mild climate persisting to the fourteenth century when the Norsemen settled in Greenland. At the fifteenth century there followed the so-called little ice age, which culminated in the eighteenth and nineteenth centuries. Each of these changes must have had its effects in New Zealand.

THE KEAS OF THE HIGH COUNTRY

Here and there, passes cut through the high country to the plains of the east. In former times they were used by Maoris on their journeys to Westland in search of the ceremonial greenstone or pounamu that they carved. The passes follow the river valleys, often necessitating successive crossings of a swift-flowing stream between high canyon walls, and through dense, dark beech forests. Such a place is Lewis Pass, from Reefton to Christchurch. The view from the exposed "tops" is spectacular. Below, great jumbled hills recede toward the horizon. Immediately below one are gnarled old beeches, their foliage torn by high winds; tufts of moss wave from dead branches like miniature flags. Here, above the forest line, stunted scrub and tussock grass alternate with great bare rocks and areas of shingle.

This bleak, wind-swept plateau country is the home of one of the world's most interesting parrots—the kea (Nestor notabilis)—the most skilled prankster of its tribe and the only one that will occasionally take meat. It is the notorious "sheep-killing" parrot.

The kea is likely to introduce himself quite informally and familiarly; one will appear from nowhere and soon there will be a dozen, flying or hopping after the observer. Close inspection, which is not difficult for they are invariably tame, shows the general coloring to be olive-green, the underwings

orange—the color is striking in flight—and the bill long and relatively straight for a parrot.

Keas live in the high country throughout the South Island. They have extended their range since European settlement— one of the few native birds to do so. Their natural food includes various fruits, roots, nectar, and other vegetable substances, along with insects and larvae found on the ground and under stones. Their cry is a plaintive "kee-e-ah." The nesting site is a deep crevice in a mountain crag; the four white eggs are laid on wood chips or on a small platform of grass between five and ten feet from the entrance. They apparently breed any time from July to January.

The sheep-attacking habit of the kea was first noted in 1867 when various sheep were found with flesh wounds on the loins. Investigation showed that where a herd of sheep had been snowed in they were attacked by the birds. These alighted on the animal's back, pecked through its wool, then tore off pieces of skin, taking them to the rocks to eat. Some sheep became so terrified that they dashed to their death over the rocks. Soon a bounty was placed on the head of the kea and shooting parties organized. In one period of eight years twenty-nine thousand were killed, but without producing any apparent reduction in numbers. Actual figures for the number of sheep killed by these birds are difficult to obtain, though in one area it was alleged to be five hundred a year!

Later studies show that only a small minority of keas attack sheep, and that they develop the habit when decaying carcasses are left lying about. Ornithologists have suggested that the birds' desire for maggots led them to the carcasses in the first place, and that the step from eating flesh to attacking live sheep was a logical one. It is significant that when carcasses of dead sheep are buried promptly, the attacks on live sheep cease.

Campers in high places are often visited by groups of keas that amuse themselves by sliding down the tent covers or trying to undo the guy ropes of the tents. The birds will also fly off with objects that amuse them, and one is alleged to have acquired the habit of letting the air out of automobile tires.

FIORDLAND AND ITS LAKES

Alpine lakes are found throughout the high country. Just south of Mount Cook are three very attractive ones, Ohau, Pukaki, and Tekapo. Set among yellowish tussock grassland, with a backdrop of low snow-covered peaks, their bright, clear waters mirror the surroundings in perfect detail. At some seasons eels glide over the shingly beds of these lakes. Waterfowl, such as the beautiful paradise duck (Casarca variegata), the male of which has a black head and back and a rufous abdomen, find the lakes a natural home.

Fiordland, the name given to the southern end of the Alps, has the most striking lakes on the island. Lake Wakatipu, on whose shore Queenstown is located, is fifty miles long. It is flanked by the Remarkables, a rugged and jagged range with precipices of brown rock and a crown of snow, around which

The precipitous peak of Mount Aspiring (9,957 feet high) in New Zealand's Southern Alps. (Robin Smith)

the morning mists float. Grassy promontories jut out into the lake. Water birds are numerous, red-billed and black-billed gulls *(Larus novaehollandiae* and *L. bulleri)* competing with scaup ducks *(Aythya novaeseelandiae)* for scraps thrown into the water. An impression of the terrain can be gained from the fact that the road from Queenstown to the old mine workings called Skippers has four hundred eighty bends in an ascent of three thousand feet over fourteen miles. Wakatipu, which has a depth of nearly fifteen hundred feet, was dug out, according to legend, by an ancient Maori chief.

In a world of lakes, Te Anau, forty miles long, and Manapouri, eighteen miles long, both toward the southern end of the island, reign supreme. They are fiordlike, with deep arms stretching back into the gorges and thick bush. High mountains tower overhead, with hanging valleys that fill with snow in winter. Beech forests extend along the shoreline. Swift streams come bursting out of the heights to feed the lakes. Manapouri, regarded by many as the most beautiful of all New Zealand lakes, has a depth of 1,455 feet. It lies six hundred feet above the sea.

Matching these mountain lakes on the seaward side of Fiordland is a series of deep inlets whose beauty rivals that of the Norwegian fiords. Best known of these is Milford Sound. First to be recorded, however, was Dusky Sound, which Cook discovered and charted in 1773. He anchored beneath precipitous rock walls so near the shore that he was able to reach it with a hawser, yet the depth of the water was fifty fathoms. Rain and sandflies annoyed the mariners, but they were able to kill some of the abundant seals for meat and to make friendly contact with the Maoris.

The tourist today can reach Milford Sound by way of a road down the Hollyford and Eglinton valleys, and through the Homer Tunnel, but a much more rewarding trip is by foot down the Milford Track from Lake Te Anau. Milford Sound, with its deep, clear water is dominated by Mitre Peak, a giant triangle five thousand feet high. The flanks of the peak make up part of the sound's wall. In summer the upper slopes above the sound stand out as bare rock against the blue sky and scattered clouds, but in winter snows cling to the cap and upper slopes. The foreshore is gravelly, or adorned with ferns and beeches. The awesome majesty of the jagged skyline is faithfully reproduced in the still waters at one's feet. The distance by water from the upper reaches of the sound to the sea is fourteen miles.

BIRD LIFE IN THE BEECH FORESTS

Fiordland provides better opportunities for seeing the native birds of New Zealand than any other area. Three different species of kiwi are present. The weka freely visits camping areas along the Milford Track. The wood pigeon gazes fearlessly from the top of a kowhai or a fuchsia. The brown kaka occurs in various parts of the forest. The long-tailed cuckoo

Left: The rare white egret (Egretta alba) *was highly prized for its plumes by the Maoris. (Robin Smith)   Right: Snow-covered Mount Cook, New Zealand's highest peak (12,349 feet high) viewed from the bed of the Hooker River. (K. and J. Bigwood)*

(*Eudynamys taitensis*), recognizable by its screeching call, inhabits the treetops. The plump little gray bush or wood robins *(Miro australis)* come down to picnic spots to collect crumbs, as does the smaller tomtit *(Petroica macrocephala)*. Pied fantails *(Rhipidura flabellifera)*, called gray fantails in Australia, vivacious little birds with wide spreading tails that permit them to tumble in the air after insects, keep up a ceaseless chatter from the edge of the track. There is also a black form, *R. fuliginosa*, present in smaller numbers. Melanism, that is, the occurrence of dark forms, occurs in various New Zealand birds; conceivably it is associated with life in dense, wet forests where predators might find a pale-colored bird easier to detect.

Many other birds may be seen in Fiordland. The gray warbler *(Gerygone igata)*, a small plain-colored insect-eater, does most of its hunting in the foliage. The yellowhead *(Mohua ochrocephala)* is a brownish bird with bright yellow head that keeps to the interior of the gloomy beech forests, frequenting the upper parts of the trees, and is therefore usually difficult to find. Sometimes heard chattering high overhead are yellow-crowned parakeets *(Cyanoramphus auriceps)*. Tuis and bellbirds are conspicuous where trees are flowering. The tiny rifleman *(Acanthisitta chloris)*, with its long, pointed bill and foreshortened tail, may be seen climbing the trunks of trees, hopping through the shrubbery or over the ground. A mere three inches long, it is nevertheless the commonest native bird in the bush, found at all levels from valley floor to tree line. The males are mostly green, the females streaked olive and brown. They are dainty birds and are ceaselessly on the move.

The number of predatory birds in the New Zealand forests is much less than in an equivalent area in Australia. The New Zealand falcon or bush hawk, like all members of its tribe, is fierce, fearless, and swift on the wing. In the forest it is known to take tuis, pigeons, and kakas, and in open areas, pipits, ducks, and pukekos. In the forest it hunts by flying swiftly through the trees, and coming up on the prey from beneath. Until their numbers were reduced bush hawks were very destructive to poultry. There are two native owls in New Zealand, the morepork or boobook *(Ninox novaeseelandiae)*, whose call, "morepork," is such a part of still nights in the bush, and the little laughing owl, *Sceloglaux albifacies*, which is now exceedingly rare.

THE TAKAHE AND THE KAKAPO

Up to 1898 only four specimens were known of a large, heavy-bodied, rail-like bird, greenish above, with blue breast and head, a short, heavy, red bill, and thick red legs. The sealers who caught the first specimen in the snow at Dusky Bay in 1849 had said it was able to run swiftly, and struggled violently when caught. Little more was learned of the bird thereafter. After 1900 it was believed extinct. Then, in 1948, to the amazement of the scientific world, the takahe *(Notornis hochstetteri)* was rediscovered in a glaciated valley two thousand two hundred feet above Lake Te Anau. The small valley, high up on the plateau of the Alps, is isolated by walls, the stream that drains it disappearing underground.

Studies of the takahe since 1948 suggest that perhaps one hundred adults survive. At nesting time the bird builds a nest in a grass tussock, lining it with leaves. Two eggs are laid, very few for a rail-like bird. After the first few weeks of life the young feed entirely on the seeds and soft parts of plants. Banding operations have shown that they may breed twice in a season. There is, however, no evidence of any increase in numbers, the species barely holding its own against introduced predators and such factors in its inhospitable home. In 1958 four chicks were brought out of the mountains and were installed at a farm near Masterton in the hope that it might be possible to form a breeding colony in another part of the former range. They did not survive and the project has not been pursued further.

Equally interesting, and also rediscovered only in recent years, is the flightless parrot *Strigops habroptilus*, known as the kakapo, a Maori name that means "green parrot." This species is also confined to the high beeches and grasslands of Fiordland. It is very beautifully patterned, with light green above, and yellowish-green below. The kakapo formerly had a wide range throughout New Zealand. It hides in the forest by day, its den being a hole among the rocks or beneath the trees. Truly nocturnal, it travels along well-marked paths to feed in the tussock grasslands by night. It can climb trees for fruit and nectar, gliding as much as ninety yards to the ground. It is unable to fly, however. In the grasslands it feeds on shoots and tender grass sprouts. The eggs are laid in a hole or tunnel in the ground. The rarity of the bird today is due to the progressive destruction of its habitat and the predatory action of cats, pigs, and stoats. So far, however, they have failed to survive in captivity.

Left: The mountain buttercup (Ranunculus lyalli), *largest of all buttercups, with waxy flowers two inches across, is found in the high meadows. (New Zealand Information Service) Right: A kea* (Nestor notabilis) *in the Te Haihi River Valley, South Westland. Keas sometimes become sheep killers, a habit they apparently acquire when carcases are left lying about. (John H. Johns)*

PLANT LIFE IN THE SNOW COUNTRY

As one climbs above the beeches and tree ferns into the sub-alpine and alpine zones, a new world of plants appears. The curious grass tree or *Dracophyllum,* its slim, twisted trunk surmounted by a tuft of foliage that reminds one of a pine-apple, appears. If it is autumn the coloring is reddish-bronze. Low-growing conifers like the snow totara and mountain toatoa crowd into depressions. The mountain toatoa has a fine resinous odor after rain. The great mountain buttercup, *Ranunculus lyalli,* the plants over two feet across, is the most famous of the flowers. The blooms are at their best in early summer. The celmisias, large white daisies, are an eye-catching feature. The alpine harebells, pale bluish in color, hide among the grasses, and white violets cling to the moist banks.

Flowers and their accompanying insect life are very much a feature of mid and late summer, after the snow has shrunk back from the cliff edges. At this time carpets of flowers line the damp spots and edges of the little creeks. One sees the jet-black high-mountain butterfly *Erebia,* coppers, blues, the red admiral, the giant noctuid moth, moving over the slopes. About the flowers buzz many different kinds of flies, beetles, and wasps.

THE INTRODUCED DEER

Ever since the time of Captain Cook, New Zealand has been subject to introductions of domestic and other animals. Cook was responsible for the introduction of the first pigs, partly to give the Maoris a new domestic animal and partly to help voyagers who might be stranded in the future. By 1840 pigs were established throughout both main islands, as well as on a number of outlying ones. Cook also brought the first goats, and these early arrivals have been joined in the wild by some domesticated escapees. Today, feral goats are found in many of the drier parts of the North Island. Dr. K. Wodzicki has recently published a detailed review of the status of deer in New Zealand.

The alpine regions of the South Island now support a number of different species of deer. No fewer than ten are established in the islands as a whole. Most of these were brought in for sport. The European red deer *(Cervus elaphus)* was introduced from the English parks in 1851, being released near Nelson. Successive introductions by acclimatization societies, interested in fees for licenses and an extension of hunting, led to the spreading of these adaptable animals throughout South Island, including Fiordland. In 1905, fifteen American wapiti from the United States were set free near George Sound; but the species has spread rather slowly. The moose,

Left above: The curious kakapo (Strigops habroptilus), *a large, flightless, ground-dwelling green parrot. Formerly widely-ranging, the last few survive in the high mountain valleys of Fiordland. (M. F. Soper) Left: Mountain daisies* (Celmissia coriacea) *in the Mount Cook National Park flower when the snow has retreated from the mountain tops. (New Zealand National Publicity) Right: A flowering rata (Metro-sideros scandens) glows a dull red in the forests of the Waiho Valley, Westland. (John H. Johns)*

which stems from ten animals introduced in 1910 to Dusky Sound, has also not built up in numbers to any extent. The American white-tailed deer occurs today near Lake Wakatipu and on Stewart Island. High areas of the Southern Alps are today occupied by chamois from Austria and tahr from northern India. On the North Island occur fallow deer from the Spanish Pyrenees, Japanese deer, sambas from Ceylon, and rusa from Java.

Until about 1930 these various exotics were given full protection and could be shot only under license. Then, as they increased and spread several of the species began to impinge on a variety of human activities, destroying the vegetation in some areas, and in other places competing with stock for pasture. The government engaged professional hunters to try to reduce their numbers. By 1955 field poisoning with sodium fluoracetate was initiated, with only limited effect. The number of full-time shooters was then increased to seventy-five. The animals killed in the South Island reached a total of forty per day, or two thousand per man during one summer season. Between 1932 and 1954 it is estimated that the total number of deer shot in New Zealand was no less than 2,400,000!

Despite this, it is freely admitted today that there is no chance of clearing the deer from the forests of New Zealand. Continued alarm is expressed at their destructiveness. The hunting fraternity is provided with shooting unrivalled anywhere in the native range of these animals. And New Zealand continues to pay for its indiscriminate introductions.

WRYBILLS AND ROYAL ALBATROSSES

Eastward from the Southern Alps is a belt of grassland measuring two hundred by forty miles. These are the Canterbury Plains. They are made up of a great thickness of gravel, believed to have been dropped by old rivers coming down from the mountaintops. Many small streams drain them today and these are the habitat of a very curious little plover, the wrybill *(Anarhynchus frontalis),* named for its bill, which is twisted sideways. Other shorebirds may have a downcurved beak, or one with an upturned tip, but that of the wrybill looks more like a mistake than a purposeful adaptation. Biologists are at a loss for an explanation, and can only suggest that it is advantageous for getting insect life from beneath stones. The little wrybill is bluish-gray above and white below, with a black chest-band. After breeding they disperse northward to spend the winter on the estuaries. They feed on the sand at low tide, then gather in little groups above the high-tide line to await the next feeding period. In September they return to their gravelly riverbed home. The two eggs are laid among the stones and are almost invisible.

It is almost axiomatic that albatrosses nest on remote islands. There are no fewer than eight species breeding on the outer subantarctic islands of New Zealand. There is, however, a small colony of the royal albatross *(Diomedea epomophora)* on Taiaroa Head, on the east coast of the South Island. The three or four pairs, protected by barbed wire from would-be visitors, have been the subject of a classical study by L. E. Richdale.

The royal albatross is white, with blackish-brown wings, and a flesh-pink bill. It is only slightly smaller in size than the wandering albatross *(D. exulans)* having a wingspan of ten feet. The males appear on Taiaroa Head in October and a few days later some females arrive. The egg is laid in early November in a basin-shaped nest of grass, soil, and guano. The breeding season of eleven months is among the longest known in birds. During incubation the two adults change places at intervals of five to fourteen days, the eggs taking seventy-eight to eighty days to hatch. Although an attempt to found the Taiaroa colony had been repeated annually since 1920, the first chick was not reared on Taiaroa Head until 1937–1938, after full protection was given the birds.

PREHISTORIC MOAS AND MOA-HUNTERS

In 1937 a farmer, seeking a burial place for a horse on his property in Pyramid Valley, fifty miles to the northwest of

Left: The rare takahe (Notornus hochstetteri), *only four specimens of which were known until it was rediscovered in 1948 in a glacial valley above Lake Te Anau. Its total population is about one hundred. Right: The Spencer Mountains in the north central part of the South Island are covered with open tussock grassland. (Both by Robin Smith)*

Christchurch, unearthed several huge bones. Science thereby learned of a unique graveyard of moas, the giant flightless birds that inhabited New Zealand in bygone ages. Excavations brought to light the giant *Dinornis maximus,* which must have stood ten to twelve feet high, the tallest bird of all time. Three other species of moas, *Pachyornis,* standing five and a half feet to seven feet high, and *Euryapteryx* and *Emeus,* four and a half feet to five feet high, were also present in good numbers. Many of the skeletons were excellently preserved. The remains of an egg measuring seven by five inches were also found. Further study revealed the existence of gizzard stones, which certain herbivorous birds swallow in order to help them grind their food. Among these were recognizable seeds, twigs, and coarse grasses, the remains of the last meals of the birds. Also present were the bones of an extinct eagle, *Harpagornis,* somewhat larger than the golden eagle of Europe and North America. The deposits thus yielded not only a more satisfactory series of skeletons of moas than were known up to that time, but also information on their food and on the predator that attacked them.

The Pyramid Valley swamp today has an eighteen-inch layer of surface peat above a soft, jellylike sediment. It is thought that this treacherous sediment may have trapped the birds, and that they sank to a point where they could not struggle free. They were perhaps then attacked by the eagle, which itself became bogged down.

Up to thirty species of moas are believed to have existed in New Zealand, though not all at the same time. Their remains have been found from sea level up to mountain heights of seven thousand feet.

That early man was the cause of the final extinction of the moa is now proved beyond doubt. As early as 1850 moa bones were recorded in refuse adjacent to old fires. What is more, egg fragments, when reassembled, were found to have a single hole in one end—sure evidence that they had been used as water containers.

For nearly a hundred years the identity of the moa-hunters remained obscure. The Maoris had some legends about giant birds, but the stories were conflicting; and most tribes had never even heard of them. The aborigines were equally obscure about their predecessors in New Zealand, the inhabitants of the islands before the arrival of the Great Fleet in 1350. It was inferred by some that they were darker-skinned people, and this led anthropologists to suspect that they may actually have been Melanesians who somehow had found their way south from New Caledonia or Fiji.

Then, in 1939, a chance discovery by a thirteen-year-old boy revealed the grave of an ancient chief who lived before the Great Fleet. His skull was found facing the setting sun and this, along with his possessions, proved him to be Polynesian. Subsequent researches by Dr. Roger Duff brought out clearly that there were two distinct cultures in ancient New Zealand, an ancient one associated with moa bones, and a more modern one. To these earlier Polynesians, who must also have drifted down from the north, the name Moa-Hunters was given. Their camps are characterized by an abundance of moa bones, eggs, and necklaces of moa vertebrae.

The consensus now is that the moas as a group died out about the time of the arrival of the fleet of 1350. Nevertheless, in parts of the South Island early settlers came upon Maori chiefs wearing moa-skin cloaks with feathers still adhering to them. And in 1949, biologists who entered Takahe Valley to make a study of the bird life discovered an old camp of a Maori hunting party in a shelter in a cliff. Among the remains on the floor were the bones of *Megalapteryx,* the "big kiwi" moa. Some of the bones contained deep gouges that could have been made with a metal knife. If so, it would mean that the moa had been killed subsequent to the arrival of the first Europeans. At any event, the excellent preservation of the remains suggested that moas may have survived until a couple of hundred years ago.

GALAXIAS AND THE ANCIENT ANTARCTIC

In a small inland lake adjacent to Dusky Bay, New Zealand, one of the naturalists with Cook collected "a small species of fish, without scales, resembling a little trout; its colour was brown, and mottled with yellowish spots in the shape of some ancient Asiatic characters." Thus did *Galaxias* become known to science.

In later decades *Galaxias* was to become the subject of much controversy, for as biological knowledge increased, it was realized that these little fishes occurred in all the southern continents, but not north of the Equator. This, to some biologists, was additional proof that the southern continents had at some former time been directly connected with each other.

There is a surprising similarity between some of the plants and insects of Australia, New Zealand and South America. As a result, the German geographer, Alfred Wegener, advanced the theory of continental drift. Others maintained that it was impossible for giant land masses to move in this way. Is it not reasonable, they argued, that the plants and animals now confined to the southern hemisphere once ranged more widely, and have secondarily become extinct north of the Equator? The question is unresolved, but more scientists are against continental drift than are for it.

Recent studies of fossil pollens have shown that *Nothofagus,* now confined to Australia, New Guinea, New Zealand, and South America, once occurred in Antarctica. This is striking evidence that the antarctic has not always been covered with ice and snow, but once supported forests.

In sum, the plants and animals of New Zealand show all the signs of prolonged isolation. There are ancient forms that have become extinct elsewhere and others whose nearest relatives are a matter of speculation. The way in which these forms reached the islands is unknown. A notable number of plants and animals are absent simply because they have been unable to cross the ocean barrier. That there have been vacant niches for new species to fit into is shown by the success of the deer and other animals that have been introduced.

Some of the most interesting forms of life in New Zealand

Milford Sound, finest of all New Zealand's fiords, mirrors the precipices and peaks that tower overhead. (Robin Smith)

Overleaf: Beautiful Lake Manapouri in Fiordland, 600 feet above the sea and 1,455 feet deep, is surrounded by dense forest. (Robin Smith)

are the direct result, so to speak, of the absence of others. The prehistoric moas, those giant flightless birds, for example, lasted only until the arrival of hunting man. The evolution of the smaller flightless birds was made possible by the absence of ground-dwelling mammalian predators; they persisted into late European times. Now the last little Stephens Island wren is gone, killed by a lighthouse keeper's cat, and the kakapoe and tahake are virtually extinct. The bizarre kiwi, however, persits as a relict from other days, moving silently through the forests and bush at night to prod the soil for earthworms.

Hawaii has not developed anything approaching the strange birds of New Zealand probably because, as a volcanic island group, it is geologically too recent and has a relatively small surface area. There is nothing as fascinating as the ancient tuatara and frogs. As in New Zealand, mammals have never arrived to dominate the animal world.

At the other end of the scale from the large islands of the Pacific are the innumerable tiny ones that dot its surface. These do not appear on the maps and there are no planes or tourist boats making regular trips to them. For man many are still, as romantic writers describe them, earthly paradises. They are among the few places in which man can still feel completely a part of nature, alone in a world of land and water. He can sense what it is like to live as the occasional birds, the fish, the creatures of the shore live. He may even be able to identify with the island itself, that steadfast agglomeration of sand and stubborn vegetation that has defied the sea for untold ages and that will probably continue to do so unless other men come and destroy it.

Tree ferns in the Lake Manapouri–Doubtful Sound area. A rainfall of two hundred inches a year produces lush vegetation around the sound. (John H. Johns)

Supplementary Reading

Most of the literature consulted in the writing of this book appeared in scientific journals that are not readily available. Standard works that are of great value include the following:

AUSTRALIA

Cayley, N. W. (1963). *What Bird is That* (3rd Edit.)? Angus and Robertson, Sydney.

Chisholm, A. H. (1958). *Bird Wonders of Australia.* Angus and Robertson, Sydney.

Commonwealth Scientific and Industrial Res. Organ., Melbourne (1960). *The Australian Environment.*

Darlington, P. J. (1957). *Zoogeography. The Geographical Distribution of Animals.* John Wiley & Sons, New York.

David, T. W. E. (1950). *The Geology of the Commonwealth of Australia,* 2 vols. Edward Arnold & Co., London.

Elkin, A. P. (1938). *The Australian Aborigines.* Angus and Robertson, Sydney.

Finlayson, H. H. (1952). *The Red Centre.* Angus and Robertson, Sydney.

Frith, H. J. (1962). *The Mallee-Fowl.* Angus and Robertson, Sydney.

Gillett, K. and McNeill F. (1959). *The Great Barrier Reef and Adjacent Isles.* Coral Press Pty. Ltd., Sydney.

Harris, Thistle Y. (1962). *Wild Flowers of Australia* (5th Edit.). Angus and Robertson, Sydney.

Jacaranda Press Pocket Guides (1959–1966). Brisbane:
  Marlow, B. *Marsupials of Australia*
  Common, I. F. B. *Australian Moths*
  Keast, A. *Some Bush Birds of Australia*
  McMichael, D. *Shells of the Sea Shore*
  McPhee, D. R. *Snakes and Lizards of Australia*
  Oakman, H. *Some Trees of Australia*
  Riek, E. *Insects of Australia*
  Whitley, G. *Marine Fishes of Australia* (2 vols.)
  Whitley, G. *Native Freshwater Fishes of Australia.*

Keast, A., Crocker, R. L. and Christian, C. S. eds. (1959). *Biogeography and Ecology in Australia.* Dr. W. Junk, The Hague.

Kinghorn, J. R. (1957). *The Snakes of Australia.* Angus and Robertson, Sydney.

Leach, J. A. (1961). *An Australian Bird Book.* Whitcombe & Tombs, Melbourne.

Life Nature Library (1964). *The Land and Wildlife of Australia.* Time Inc., New York.

McKeown, K. C. (1952). *Australian Spiders* (2nd Edit.). Angus and Robertson, Sydney.

Marshall, A. J. (1954). *Bower Birds.* Oxford University Press, Inc., New York.

Mountford, C. P. (1951). *Brown Men and Red Sand: Wanderings in Wild Australia.* Phoenix House Ltd.

Serventy, D. L. and Whittell, H. M. (1962). *Birds of Western Australia.* Paterson Brokensha Pty. Ltd., Perth.

Sharland, M. S. (1945). *Tasmanian Birds, How to Identify Them.* Oldham, Beddome, and Meredith, Hobart.

Tillyard, R. J. (1926). *The Insects of Australia and New Zealand.* Angus and Robertson, Sydney.

Tindale, N. B. and Lindsay, H. A. (1963). *Aboriginal Australians.* Jacaranda Press, Brisbane.

Troughton, E. (1948). *Furred Animals of Australia.* Angus and Robertson, Sydney.

Waterhouse, G. A. (1932). *What Butterfly is That?* Angus and Robertson, Sydney.

NEW ZEALAND AND THE PACIFIC

Amadon, D. (1950). *The Hawaiian Honeycreepers (Aves, Drepaniidae).* American Museum of Natural History, New York.

Bailey, A. M. (1952). *Laysan and Black-footed Albatrosses.* Denver Museum of Natural History.

Bailey, A. M. (1956). *Birds of Midway and Laysan Islands.* Denver Museum of Natural History.

Cumberland, K. B. and Fox, J. W. (1957). *New Zealand: A Regional View.* Whitcombe & Tombs, Wellington.

Dunmire, W. W. (1961). *Birds of the National Parks in Hawaii.* Hawaii Natural History Association.

Gilliard, E. T. (1958). *Living Birds of the World.* Doubleday & Co., New York.

Gilliard, E. T. (1966). *Birds of Paradise and Bowerbirds.* American Museum of Natural History, New York. (In press.)

Gressitt, J. Linsley ed. (1963). *Pacific Basin Biogeography.* Bishop Museum Press, Honolulu.

Hawaii Audubon Society (1959). *Hawaiian Birds.* Hawaii Audubon Society.

Hiroa, Te Rangi (1962). *The Coming of the Maori.* Whitcombe & Tombs, Wellington.

Hubbard, D. H. (1952). *Ferns of Hawaii National Park.* Hawaii Natural History Association.

Hubbard, D. H. and Bender, V. R. (1960). *Trailside Plants of Hawaii National Park.* Hawaii National Park and Hawaii Natural History Association.

Iredale, T. (1956). *Birds of New Guinea* (2 vols.). Georgian House, Melbourne.

Macdonald, G. A. and Hubbard, D. H. (1961). *Volcanoes of the National Parks in Hawaii.* Hawaii Natural History Association.

Mayr, E. (1945). *Birds of the Southwest Pacific.* Macmillan Co., New York.

Murphy, R. I., Niedrach, R. J. and Bailey, A. M. (1954). *Canton Island.* Denver Museum of Natural History.

Oliver, W. R. B. (1955). *New Zealand Birds.* A. H. and A. W. Reed, Wellington.

Powell, A. W. B. (1961). *Native Animals of New Zealand.* The United Press, Wellington.

Ruhle, G. C. (1959). *A Guide for the Haleakala Section, Island of Maui, Hawaii.* Hawaii Natural History Association.

Williams, G. R. (1963). *Birds of New Zealand.* A. H. and A. W. Reed, Wellington.

Zimmerman, E. C. (1948). *Insects of Hawaii, Vol. 1.* University of Hawaii Press, Honolulu.

Index

Asterisks indicate pages
containing illustration captions

THE AUTHOR

Professor Allen Keast is an Australian biologist who holds a Master of Science degree from the University of Sydney. In 1953 he was awarded the Peter Brooks Saltonstall Scholarship at Harvard and took his Ph. D. there. From 1955 to 1961 he was Curator of Birds, Reptiles and Amphibians at the Australian Museum, Sydney. Since then he has held a professorship at Queen's University, Kingston, Ontario. He is a former President of the Royal Australasian Ornithologists' Union and a Corresponding Fellow of the American Ornithologists' Union. He became a Research Fellow of the American Museum of Natural History, New York, in 1964. He is the author of several books and one of the editors of *Biogeography and Ecology in Australia* (1959). Dr. Keast has spent twenty years in the areas about which he writes and has traveled widely in the Pacafic in the course of his research.

ENGRAVED AND PRINTED BY CONZETT & HUBER OF ZURICH — DESIGNED BY ULRICH RUCHTI

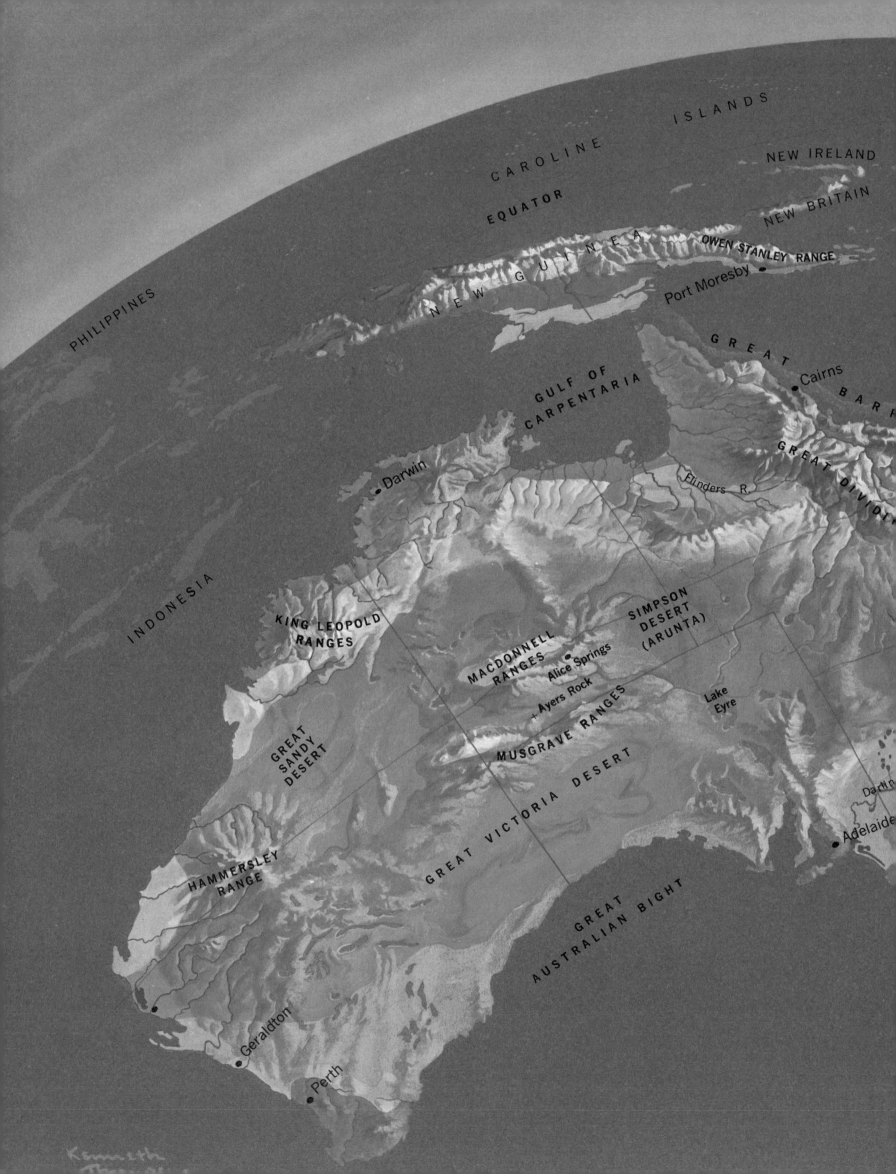

CAROLINE   ISLANDS

NEW IRELAND

EQUATOR

NEW BRITAIN

OWEN STANLEY RANGE

N E W   G U I N E A

PHILIPPINES

Port Moresby

G R E A T

GULF OF
CARPENTARIA

Cairns

B A R R

Darwin

GREAT DIVIDI

Flinders R.

INDONESIA

KING LEOPOLD
RANGES

SIMPSON
DESERT
(ARUNTA)

MACDONNELL
RANGES

Alice Springs

Lake
Eyre

+ Ayers Rock

GREAT
SANDY
DESERT

MUSGRAVE RANGES

GREAT VICTORIA DESERT

Darlin

Adelaide

HAMMERSLEY
RANGE

GREAT
AUSTRALIAN BIGHT

Geraldton

Perth